W9-CZB-806

DATE DUE

AUG 1 4 1987			
FEB 2 0 2000			
1/31/24			

HIGHSMITH 45-220

Thermal Comfort

Thermal Comfort

Analysis and Applications in Environmental Engineering

by P. O. Fanger

Professor, D. Sc.
Technical University of Denmark
Laboratory of Heating and Air Conditioning

ROBERT E. KRIEGER PUBLISHING COMPANY
MALABAR, FLORIDA
1982

Original Edition   1970
Reprint Edition   1982

Printed and Published by
ROBERT E. KRIEGER PUBLISHING COMPANY, INC.
KRIEGER DRIVE
MALABAR, FLORIDA 32950

Printed in the United States of America

Library of Congress Cataloging in Publication Data

Fanger, P.O.
   Thermal comfort.

   Originally presented as the author's thesis
(doctoral—Danmarks Tekniske Hojskole, 1970)
      Bibliography: p. 225
      Includes index.
      1. Buildings—Environmental engineering.
2. Heating. I. Title.
TH7222.F35   1982   697.9'315   81-20935
ISBN 0-89874-446-6   AACR2

PREFACE

The present book is based on research undertaken during the last five years at the Laboratory of Heating and Air Conditioning, Technical University of Denmark, and at the Institute for Environmental Research, Kansas State University, where the author worked for a period in 1966/67.

The author initiated this research work recognizing that the existing knowledge of thermal comfort was quite inadequate and unsuitable for practical applications. This lack in basic knowledge appeared particularly striking in view of the fact that the creation of thermal comfort for man is one of the principal aims in environmental engineering and in the entire heating and air-conditioning industry. A distinct need was felt for extensive research work.

The results of this comprehensive research program are contained in the present book. A rational basis is set up for the establishment of thermal comfort conditions, for the evaluation of thermal environments and for the carrying out of environmental analyses. An underlying idea is that it is the combined thermal effect of all physical factors which is of prime importance for man's thermal state and comfort. It is impossible to consider the effect of any of the physical factors influencing thermal comfort independently, as the effect of each of them depends on the level of the other factors. Therefore, emphasis has been placed on the combined influence and the interactions between the effects of the various factors.

The study of thermal comfort touches on many disciplines, including heat and mass transfer, thermal physiology, psychophysics, ergonomics, biometeorology, architecture, textile engineering. The present work attempts to bridge the gap between artificial professional boundaries and to integrate these various disciplines. A special effort is made to present the results in such a way that they are directly applicable in environmental engineering, and the book thus contains numerous examples showing their use in practice. The new data presented and methods recommended may be used without prior detailed study of the theoretical background.

5

It is with great indebtedness that I wish to thank colleagues and students at the Laboratory of Heating and Air Conditioning for their assistance in this research work. Special thanks are due to Dr. N. F. Bisgaard, Professor and Director of the Laboratory, for his devoted interest and support to the present work. Thanks are due also to Mr. P. Kjerulf-Jensen, Asst. Professor, for his excellent leadership in designing and equipping the environmental chamber and other facilities. Messrs. O. Bjørn Rasmussen, O. Smith-Hansen, O. Angelius and B. Lund have, as graduate students, participated in various phases of the present work.

I express my gratitude also to Mrs. Hanne Dalgas Christiansen and Mr. Karsten Schmidt, both Associate Professors at the Institute of Mathematical Statistics and Operations Research, Technical University of Denmark for their assistance with the experimental planning and the statistical calculations described in chapter three.

Members of the Indoor Climate Committee of the Danish Academy of Technical Sciences (ATV's indeklimaudvalg), in particular the Chairman, Professor Vagn Korsgaard, have been very encouraging in the interest they have shown in the present work.

My stay in 1966/67 at the Institute for Environmental Research, Kansas State University, was very fruitful and I wish to express my heartfelt thanks for the collaboration and hospitality given me by Dr. Ralph G. Nevins, Director of the Institute and Dean of the College of Engineering, and Dr. P. E. McNall, Professor and Head of the Department of Mechanical Engineering. Dr. McNall has commented upon the manuscript and edited the text in great detail. Dr. F. H. Rohles, Professor of Psychology and Mechanical Engineering, has kindly provided experimental data which have been valuable in the development of the proposed new method for rating the quality of thermal environments (chapter four).

I wish to acknowledge my thanks also to Dr. A. P. Gagge, Professor of Environmental Physiology, Yale University, and Fellow, Pierce Foundation Laboratory, for his devoted interest in the present work and for the encouraging and helpful advice I have received from him during our many discussions during the past four years. I have benefited greatly from his wide experience in comfort research.

I am also grateful to the following persons who have rendered me services of various kinds: Mr. James M. Waligora, Manned Spacecraft Center, NASA, Houston; Mr. George Rapp, Pierce Foundation Lab., New Haven; Dr. David Wyon, Swedish Building Research Institute, Lund; Dr. Bodil Nielsen, University of Copenhagen, and Dr. K. Lustinec, Charles University, Prague, during his stay at the Technical University of Denmark.

The English text has been revised by Mrs. Judith Ørting, WHO, Copenhagen, and I thank her for her instructive cooperation.

The present study has been generously supported by the Danish Government Fund for Scientific and Industrial Research (Statens teknisk-videnskabelige Fond) and by the Copenhagen General Housing Corporation (Københavns almindelige Boligselskab).

P. O. FANGER

Technical University of Denmark
Building 402, 2800 Lyngby
Copenhagen

Preface to the American edition
The present edition contains a number of corrections and minor changes, but the content is otherwise the same as in the original edition, published in November 1970 by Danish Technical Press.

September 1972

P. O. Fanger

CONTENTS

10

11

Chapter 1.
INTRODUCTION

The present study will deal with the conditions necessary for optimal thermal environments for human beings, the methods of evaluating a given thermal environment, and the principles for the establishment of a detailed thermal analysis of any environment.

The growing mechanization and industrialization of society has resulted in most people spending by far the greater part of their lives (often more than 95%) in an artificial climate. This fact has caused an increased interest in the environmental conditions which should be set, i.e. which climates should be aimed at. With the techniques at our disposal today we have the possibility of creating almost any indoor climate. For the sake of the rational calculation and operation of existing forms of environmental systems, and also of the development of completely new systems, reliable quantitative conditions for the desired indoor climate are necessary.

Indoor climate is often defined as the collective whole of all the physical properties in a room which influence a person via his heat loss and respiration. This definition includes also non-thermal factors, such as the composition of the air, its content of dust, odours, electric particles, microorganisms, etc., which may be of importance in evaluating a given indoor climate. These non-thermal quantities can be estimated, and specifications can be drawn up independent of the thermal climate, but these will not be treated in the present study.

Wherever artificial climates are created for human occupation, the aim is that the thermal environment be adapted so that each individual is in thermal comfort. In agreement with ASHRAE standard 55–66 (4), thermal comfort for a person is here defined as "that condition of mind which expresses satisfaction with the thermal environment". If a group of people is subject to the same room climate, it will not be possible, due to biological variance, to satisfy everyone at the same time. One must then aim at creating optimal thermal comfort for the group, i.e., a condition in which the highest possible percentage of the group is in thermal comfort.

13

Thermal neutrality for a person is defined as the condition in which the subject would prefer neither warmer nor cooler surroundings. Thus thermal neutrality is a necessary condition for thermal comfort, but it need not be a sufficient condition. For instance, a person who is exposed to an extremely asymmetric radiant field can very well be in thermal neutrality without being comfortable. In most cases, however, thermal neutrality will be the same as thermal comfort and the two concepts will therefore be treated synonymously hereafter, except for certain sections in which cases where they differ will be discussed.

The reason for creating thermal comfort is first and foremost to satisfy man's desire to feel thermally comfortable, in line with his desire for comfort in other directions. Moreover, thermal comfort can be justified from the point of view of human performance. In this connection, a considerable number of investigations have been carried out in the laboratory, as well as in the field, to determine the influence of thermal surroundings on performance. Even though the results of these investigations are not conclusive, due to methodical difficulties, they nevertheless seem to show a clear tendency for hot or cold discomfort to reduce a person's performance (258). Man's intellectual, manual and perceptual performance is in general highest when he is in thermal comfort.

Whether thermal comfort is also a necessary condition for optimal human health in general, is difficult to say with certainty. Extreme hot or cold discomfort over a long period would obviously be unfavourable. Naturally, this does not necessarily mean that constant thermal comfort is worth striving for in relation to human health in general, even though this does seem probable. However, as the problem regarding a connection between health and comfort is unsolved, only the two above-mentioned reasons for creating thermal comfort will be referred to.

Creating thermal comfort for man is a primary purpose of the heating and air conditioning industry, and this has had a radical influence on the construction of buildings, the choice of materials, etc., and thus on the whole building industry. Viewed in a wider perspective, it can perhaps even be maintained that man's dependence on thermal surroundings is the main reason for building houses at all, at least in the form in which we know them today.

The enclosures where artificial climates are created today comprise various types of rooms in houses, offices, factories, shops, hospitals, schools, theatres, cinemas, meeting rooms, restaurants, hotels, athletic halls, museums, churches, libraries, etc.; also in many forms of vehicles: cars, buses, trams, trains, ships, aeroplanes and space craft. In the not too distant future

14

we may perhaps add the completely covered cities which already today are a subject of feasibility studies. If one moves outside the closed room into the natural climate, it cannot be excluded that some time in the future it will be possible to influence this to a greater or lesser degree, so that also outdoors it may be possible to create local artificial climates.

In all the above-named instances where it is desired to produce artificial climates where people congregate, one will normally endeavour to create thermal comfort, and it is therefore of the greatest importance to have a thorough quantitative knowledge of the conditions establishing thermal comfort.

The most important variables which influence the condition of thermal comfort are:

activity level (heat production in the body),
thermal resistance of the clothing (clo-value),
air temperature,
mean radiant temperature,
relative air velocity,
water vapour pressure in ambient air.

Thermal comfort can be achieved by many different combinations of the above variables and therefore also by the use of many fundamentally different technical systems. In all cases thermal comfort is the "product" which is produced and sold to the customer by the heating and air-conditioning industry. It is therefore obvious that quantitatively expressed comfort conditions are of great importance. These conditions are dealt with in chapter two.

In many earlier comfort studies all the above-mentioned six variables have not been controlled, measured or reported. In other studies the variables have been controlled and the effect of one or two variables has been determined, with no attempt to generalize the results beyond the actual test conditions.

In the present work an underlying idea is that it is impossible to consider the effect of any of the physical factors influencing thermal comfort independently, as the effect of each of them and the necessary requirements depend on the level and conditions of the other factors. It is the combined thermal effect of the variables on the human body which is important. This idea forms the background for the derivation of a general comfort equation which defines all combinations of the variables which will create thermal comfort.

To this end, experimental investigations involving a group of college-age subjects have shown that mean skin temperature and sweat secretion at a given activity level are closely connected with the sensation of thermal comfort. The values for mean skin temperature and sweat secretion – both as functions of the activity level – can therefore be used as basic conditions for thermal comfort. These two functions, combined with a heat balance for the human body utilizing general heat transfer theory, form the basis for the deduction of the general comfort equation which contains the above-mentioned six basic variables. By means of the comfort equation it is possible, for any activity level and any clothing, to calculate all combinations of air temperature, mean radiant temperature, relative velocity and air humidity, which will create optimal thermal comfort for man.

The equation, which gives the relative and absolute influence of the different variables, has been solved on a digital computer and represented in numerous diagrams which are designed for direct practical use in engineering. The comfort equation is of importance for engineering calculations and the operation of all existing forms of thermal comfort installations, and it will also be of importance in the development of completely new systems. Moreover, the equation forms the mathematical basis for analysis and optimization in the comparison of different types of systems. The application of the equation in environmental engineering is shown by numerous practical examples.

The comfort equation is deduced on the basis of experiments with American college-age subjects under steady-state conditions. It cannot, however, be taken for granted that the equation can be used for other groups without corrections. This is investigated in chapter three, which also discusses the influence of a series of other special factors on the application of the comfort equation. The chapter deals first with observations made on Danish college-age subjects and elderly subjects, the purpose of which has been to determine a possible national-geographic influence and a possible age influence on the preferred thermal surroundings. From the same experimental data an assessment of the influence of the sex, body build and menstrual cycle on comfort conditions was possible. Chapter three discusses furthermore a number of other special factors which might influence thermal comfort: ethnic differences, food, circadian rhythm, thermal transients, unilateral heating or cooling of the body (including asymmetric radiant fields, draught, and warm and cold floors), colour, crowding, and finally the influence of air pressure.

The comfort equation is not so applicable for the assessment of a given room climate, since it only indicates how the climatic parameters should be combined in order to create optimal thermal comfort. It does not give direct information on man's thermal sensation in a climate which deviates from the optimum.

In chapter four, a new thermal sensation index is deduced which meets this requirement. This index is the basis for the introduction of a rational method of rating the quality of thermal environments. Up till now, such a method has not been available. With the aid of the index, which combines the same six variables as the comfort equation, it is possible, quantitatively, to evaluate how any thermal climate influences the thermal sensation of persons in the room. While the comfort equation only indicates how the variables should be combined in order to obtain optimal thermal comfort, the index gives, on a psycho-physical scale, the "Predicted Mean Vote" (PMV) of a large group of persons exposed to the actual environment. It thus provides information on the deviation from the comfort equation, i.e. the degree of discomfort.

As the index, from a mathematical point of view, is rather complicated, a comprehensive table has been made from which the value of the thermal sensation index can be determined in practice, after measuring the environmental variables. From this value one can further determine the predicted percentage of dissatisfied occupants, using a diagram constructed from an analysis of experimental data including one thousand three hundred subjects. Since it is actually the dissatisfied persons who in practice will be inclined to complain about the thermal environment, the magnitude of the "Predicted Percentage of Dissatisfied" (PPD) would seem to be meaningful in rating the thermal quality of a given indoor climate.

The more non-uniform a thermal field in a room, the greater the number of dissatisfied persons to be expected. On the basis of measurements taken in practice, one can calculate the "Lowest Possible Percentage of Dissatisfied" (LPPD) which it is possible to obtain in the actual room by altering the temperature level. The magnitude of LPPD is an expression for the non-uniformity of the thermal field and is therefore suitable for characterizing the heating or air-conditioning system in the actual room.

The method thus makes possible partly a prediction of how many dissatisfied can be expected for the conditions under which the measurements are taken, and partly an estimation of how low it is at all possible to bring the percentage of dissatisfied in the given room by using the actual heating or air-conditioning system.

After going through the practical procedure for the use of the new method for evaluating thermal environments, chapter four gives, finally, a short summary of suitable methods for measuring the four physical environmental variables which are important in practice.

A detailed thermal analysis of a controlled space, based on comfort criteria, will often be necessary as a basis for rational calculation and selection of the practical systems which will create a desired thermal room climate. An important part of this analysis, the determination of the mean radiant temperature, is considered in chapter five. This often presents special difficulties, particularly in rooms possessing heating and cooling panels, high-intensity IR-heaters, lighting installations with high illumination power, or large, cold wall or window surfaces. In connection with the determination of mean radiant temperature for persons irradiated by high-intensity radiant sources, a new and rational procedure for calculating this type of heating system is put forth.

The calculation of the mean radiant temperature presupposes a detailed knowledge of man's radiant geometrical data, which so far have not been thoroughly examined. Chapter six gives an account of a comprehensive experimental determination of effective radiation areas, projected areas of the body as a function of the direction, and angle factors between the body and any horizontal or vertical rectangle. Twenty male and female subjects, standing and seated, clothed and unclothed, were evaluated in the experiments. The results are given in diagrams which can be directly applied in engineering.

Thereafter, in chapter seven, a general method is put forward for a detailed theoretical thermal analysis of a controlled space, based on the comfort criteria. The idea is here to consider man and his environment as a whole and perform the analysis for the total system, the aim being thermal comfort. Heat balance equations for room surfaces and for air and the comfort equation are then solved simultaneously. Depending upon the environmental system chosen, one can, using this analysis, for example determine the necessary temperatures or areas of possible heating or cooling panels, the heat to be produced by convective heaters in the space, the temperature or flow rate of supply air, and the temperature of, and heat flow through, all surfaces. The analysis is based on demands for thermal comfort at a particular point in the room, after which values for the mean radiant temperature and the predicted mean vote can be calculated and plotted for the entire occupational zone. Moreover, the LPPD can be calculated as an expression of the non-uniformity of the room.

Chapter 2.
CONDITIONS
FOR THERMAL COMFORT

In the present chapter, quantitative conditions for optimal thermal comfort for human beings will be set up. A general comfort equation will be derived which makes it possible, for any activity level and any clothing, to calculate all combinations of the environmental variables (air temperature, air humidity, mean radiant temperature and relative air velocity) which will create optimal thermal comfort. The equation, originally published by the author in 1967 (79), will be presented here in a slightly revised version, including a detailed analysis of the influence of the individual variables and including a large number of comfort diagrams, their application in environmental engineering being demonstrated by a series of practical examples.

As thermal comfort is the primary aim of most heating and air-conditioning systems, it is not surprising that over the years a considerable number of studies have been made with the purpose of investigating comfort conditions. A number of studies have been carried out as field experiments, where the surrounding variables have been measured under practical conditions, and at the same time people have been asked to vote on their thermal sensation on suitable psycho-physical scales. Subsequently, the results were treated statistically and most often the optimal ambient temperature has been determined for the actual group. Field studies of this nature are relatively simple to carry out, and there are thus a large number of investigations from all parts of the world, in the literature: Yaglou and Drinker (345), Partridge and McLean (252), Bedford (21), Houghten et al. (140, 141, 145, 147, 148, 239), Tasker (310), Rummel et al. (286), McConnell and Spiegelman (203), Chester (55), Rowley et al. (283), Goromosov (110, 111), Rao (265), Ellis (74, 75), Webb (324, 325), Black (33, 34), Ambler (3), Hickish (136), Angus and Brown (8), Hindmarsh and MacPherson (139), Snellen (300), Wyndham (339), Sevryukova (297), Rudeiko (285), Andersen and Lundquist (6), Grandjean (113), Ballantyne et al. (12), Wyon et al. (340). In many of the investigations, some of the environmental variables have often not been measured and activity level and especially clothing, have often not been specified. Even though the results have no doubt been of importance in the actual conditions under which they were measured, it is difficult, however, to generalize these results to apply to other conditions. For example, in many of the earlier field studies, the persons were no doubt clad in heavy, but unspecified clothing of the day, and as accurate clothing specification is impossible now, these studies are of limited value today.

Another group of studies comprises laboratory experiments, normally involving relatively few subjects, where the influence on comfort of one or more of the variables has been studied, physiological parameters in some cases also being measured (Houghten and Yaglou (142, 143, 342, 343, 348), Drysdale (67), Mom et al. (222, 223), Nielsen (241), Koch et al. (163), Fahnestock et al. (76, 77). Recently comprehensive investigations of this character have been performed at Pierce Foundation Laboratory, Yale University, where especially the influence of high-intensity radiant sources, thermal transients and metabolic rate has been studied (Gagge et al. (93, 94, 96, 97, 98, 101, 102), Hardy (128)). These, and a number of other studies dealing with the influence on comfort of a series of special factors, will be discussed in chapter three. Quite recently, theoretical models have been set up by Morse and Kowalczewski (226), by Lustinec (196), by Nishi and Ibamoto (245, 153) and by Gagge et al. (100).

Extensive experiments of a somewhat similar nature as the previously mentioned field studies, but under carefully controlled laboratory conditions, have been performed in recent years at Kansas State University by Nevins et al. (234), and McNall et al. (206, 207, 205). The method employed has been to expose many hundreds of subjects, clothed in a standard clothing ensemble, to different combinations of two environmental variables (e.g. air temperature and relative humidity) while keeping constant, insofar as practically possible all other factors which influence thermal comfort. Large numbers of subjects have been asked to vote upon their thermal sensation according to special scales. From a statistical analysis a comfort line has then been determined, i.e. a line representing all combinations of the two variables which give optimal thermal comfort.

Due to the large number of subjects (comprising a fair statistical sample, representative of a large population) and the carefully controlled experimental conditions, this method has given particularly valuable results. Nevertheless, the practical application of the results found must be said to be relatively limited, as they are valid only for the invariant conditions, i.e., for the constant values of the other four parameters, under which the experiments have been performed. For instance, the comfort line found in ref. (234) (air temperature versus relative humidity) is strictly valid for only one activity (sedentary), for one clothing (0.6 clo), for one relative air velocity (0.1 m/s) and for the mean radiant temperature equal to the air temperature. With so many parameters, each interdependently having an effect on the human body, there will be an enormous number of combinations necessary to cover the range adequately, and thus the method will be slow and expensive. Existing data cover, therefore, only certain special cases, and do not provide information for an overall assessment and calculation of the relative and absolute influence of all the individual variables.

In the present study a different method of approach is presented. It is based on the establishment of three basic conditions for optimal thermal comfort.

The first condition necessary for thermal comfort for a person under long exposure to a given environment is the existence of a heat balance, a condition which is naturally far from sufficient. Man's thermoregulatory system is quite effective and will therefore create heat balance within wide limits of the environmental variables, even if comfort does not exist.

With the establishment of a double heat balance an equation of the following form can be obtained (only the main variables have been taken into consideration):

$$f\left(\frac{H}{A_{Du}}, I_{cl}, t_a, t_{mrt}, p_a, v, t_s, \frac{E_{sw}}{A_{Du}}\right) = 0 \qquad (1)$$

where $\dfrac{H}{A_{Du}}$ = Internal heat production per unit body surface area (A_{Du} = DuBois area)

I_{cl} = thermal resistance of the clothing

t_a = air temperature

t_{mrt} = mean radiant temperature

p_a = pressure of water vapour in ambient air

v = relative air velocity

t_s = mean skin temperature

$\dfrac{E_{sw}}{A_{Du}}$ = heat loss per unit body surface area by evaporation of sweat secretion

The derivation and form of eq. (1) is dealt with in the first part of this chapter.

For a given activity level, the skin temperature, t_s, and the sweat secretion, E_{sw}, are seen to be the only physiological variables influencing the heat balance in eq. (1). The sensation of thermal comfort has been related to the magnitude of these two variables. Experiments involving a group of subjects at different activity levels have been performed to determine mean values of skin temperature and sweat secretion, as functions of the activity level, for persons in thermal comfort. The results have the following form:

$$t_s = f\left(\frac{H}{A_{Du}}\right) \tag{2}$$

$$E_{sw} = A_{Du}\, f\left(\frac{H}{A_{Du}}\right) \tag{3}$$

Equations (2) and (3) are presented as the second and third basic conditions for thermal comfort.

The quantitative evaluation of eqs. (2) and (3) and the theoretical foundation for relating the sensation of thermal comfort with skin temperature and sweat secretion are set out in the second part of this chapter.

By substituting conditions (2) and (3) in (1), the desired comfort equation takes the following form:

$$f\left(\frac{H}{A_{Du}},\ I_{cl},\ t_a,\ t_{mrt},\ p_a,\ v\right) = 0 \tag{4}$$

Using the comfort equation (4), it is possible for any activity level (H/A_{Du}) and any clothing (I_{cl}) to calculate all combinations of air temperature (t_a), mean radiant temperature (t_{mrt}), air humidity (p_a) and relative air velocity (v) which will create optimal thermal comfort.

The third part of the present chapter contains the derivation of the general comfort equation, its solution by digital computer, the construction of comfort diagrams, practical applications illustrated by numerous examples, the derivation of the relative influence of the single variables by partial differentiation of the comfort equation, and finally a comparison with earlier investigations.

HEAT BALANCE

Since the purpose of the thermoregulatory system of the body is to maintain an essentially constant internal body temperature, it can be assumed that for long exposures to a constant (moderate) thermal environment with a constant metabolic rate a heat balance will exist for the human body, i.e., the heat production will equal the heat dissipation, and there will be no significant heat storage within the body. The heat balance for this condition is

$$H - E_d - E_{sw} - E_{re} - L = K = R + C \tag{5}$$

where H $\quad=$ the internal heat production in the human body
$E_d \quad=$ the heat loss by water vapour diffusion through the skin
$E_{sw} =$ the heat loss by evaporation of sweat from the surface of the skin
$E_{re} =$ the latent respiration heat loss
L $\quad=$ the dry respiration heat loss
K $\quad=$ the heat transfer from the skin to the outer surface of the clothed body (conduction through the clothing)
R $\quad=$ the heat loss by radiation from the outer surface of the clothed body
C $\quad=$ the heat loss by convection from the outer surface of the clothed body

The double eq. (5) expresses that the internal heat production H minus the heat loss by evaporation from the skin ($E_d + E_{sw}$) and by respiration ($E_{re} + L$) is equal to the heat conducted through the clothing (K) and dissipated at the outer surface of the clothing by radiation and convection (R + C). It is assumed that the evaporation corresponding to E_{sw} and E_d takes place at (or underneath) the skin surface.

In the following sections each of the terms in eq. (5) will be discussed and quantified.

Internal Heat Production

The energy released by the oxidation processes in the human body per unit time (metabolic rate M) is sometimes partly converted to external mechanical power W, but is mainly converted to internal body heat, H, so that

$$M = H + W \qquad (kcal/hr) \qquad (6)$$

Introducing the following definition of external mechanical efficiency

$$\eta = \frac{W}{M} \qquad (7)$$

into eq. (6) gives

$$H = M (1 - \eta) \qquad (kcal/hr) \qquad (8)$$

or, expressed per unit body surface area:

$$\frac{H}{A_{Du}} = \frac{M}{A_{Du}} (1-\eta) \qquad (kcal/hr\ m^2) \qquad (8a)$$

Table 1. *Metabolic Rate at Different Typical Acitivities*[1]

Activity		Metabolic Rate M/A_{Du} kcal/hr m²	Mechanical Efficiency η	Relative Velocity in Still Air m/s
Resting				
Sleeping.....................		35	0	0
Reclining...................		40	0	0
Seated, quiet................		50	0	0
Standing, relaxed............		60	0	0
Walking				
On the level	km/hr			
	3.2..........	100	0	0.9
	4.0..........	120	0	1.1
	4.8..........	130	0	1.3
	5.6..........	160	0	1.6
	6.4..........	190	0	1.8
	8.0..........	290	0	2.2
Up a Grade				
% Grade	km/hr			
5............. 1.6..........		120	0.07	0.6
5............. 3.2..........		150	0.10	0.9
5............. 4.8..........		200	0.11	1.3
5............. 6.4..........		305	0.10	1.8
15............. 1.6..........		145	0.15	0.4
15............. 3.2..........		230	0.19	0.9
15............. 4.8..........		350	0.19	1.3
25............. 1.6..........		180	0.20	0.4
25............. 3.2..........		335	0.21	0.9
Miscellaneous occupations				
Bakery (e.g. cleaning tins, packing boxes).................		70–100	0 – 0.1	0 – 0.2
Brewery (e.g. filling bottles, loading beer boxes onto belt).....		60–120	0 – 0.2	0 – 0.2
Carpentry				
Machine sawing............		90	0	0 – 0.1
Sawing by hand.............		200–240	0.1 – 0.2	0.1 – 0.2
Planing by hand............		280–320	0.1 – 0.2	0.1 – 0.2
Foundry Work				
Fettling (pneumatic hammer).		160	0 – 0.1	0.1 – 0.2
Tipping the moulds..........		200	0 – 0.1	0.1 – 0.2
Roughing (i.e. carrying 60 kg).		270	0 – 0.2	0.1 – 0.2

[1] Compiled from refs. 326, 253, 314, 225, 185.

Table 1. *Metabolic Rate at Different Typical Activities* (cont.)

Activity	Metabolic Rate M/A_{Du} kcal/hr m²	Mechanical Efficiency η	Relative Velocity in Still Air m/s
Tending the furnaces........	340	0 – 0.1	0.1 – 0.2
Slag removal..............	380	0 – 0.1	0.1 – 0.2
Garage Work (e.g. replacing tyres, raising cars by jack)....	110–150	0 – 0.1	0.2
Laboratory Work			
Examining slides...........	70	0	0
General laboratory work.....	80	0	0 – 0.2
Setting up apparatus........	110	0	0 – 0.2
Locksmith..................	110	0 – 0.1	0.1 – 0.2
Machine Work			
Light (e.g. electrical industry).	100–120	0 – 0.1	0 – 0.2
Machine fitter.............	140	0 – 0.1	0 – 0.9
Heavy (e.g. paint industry)...	200	0 – 0.1	0 – 0.2
Manufacture of tins (e.g. filling, labelling and despatch)....	100–200	0 – 0.1	0 – 0.2
Seated, heavy limb movements (e.g. metal worker)........	110	0 – 0.2	0.1 – 0.4
Shoemaker..................	100	0 – 0.1	0 – 0.1
Shop assistant...............	100	0 – 0.1	0.2 – 0.5
Teacher.....................	80	0	0
Watch repairer..............	55	0	0
Vehicle driving			
Car (light traffic)...........	50	0	0
Car (heavy traffic)..........	100	0	0
Heavy vehicle (e.g. power truck)..................	160	0 – 0.1	0.05
Night flying...............	60	0	0
Instrument landing.........	90	0	0
Combat flying.............	120	0	0
Heavy Work			
Pushing Wheelbarrow (57 kg at 4.5 km/hr)........	125	0.2	1.4
Handling 50 kg bags..........	200	0.2	0.5
Pick & shovel work..........	200–240	0.1 – 0.2	0.5
Digging trenches.............	300	0.2	0.5
Domestic Work			
House cleaning..............	100–170	0 – 0.1	0.1 – 0.3
Cooking....................	80–100	0	
Washing dishes, standing......	80	0	0 – 0.2
Washing by hand and ironing...	100–180	0 – 0.1	0 – 0.2
Shaving, washing and dressing..	85	0	0 – 0.2

Table 1. *Metabolic Rate at Different Typical Activities* (cont.)

Activity	Metabolic Rate M/A_{Du} kcal/hr m²	Mechanical Efficiency η	Relative Velocity in Still Air m/s
Shopping...................	80	0	0.2 – 1
Office Work wpm			
Typing (electrical).... 30......	45	0	0.05
40......	50	0	0.05
Typing (mechanical).. 30......	55	0	0.05
40......	60	0	0.05
Adding machine..............	60	0	0
Miscellaneous office work (e.g. filing, checking ledgers)......	50– 60	0	0 – 0.1
Draughtsman................	60	0	0 – 0.1
Leisure activities			
Gymnastics..................	150–200	0 – 0.1	0.5 – 2
Dancing....................	120–220	0	0.2 – 2
Tennis.....................	230	0 – 0.1	0.5 – 2
Fencing....................	350	0	0.5 – 2
Squash....................	360	0 – 0.1	0.5 – 2
Basketball..................	380	0 – 0.1	1 – 3
Wrestling..................	435	0 – 0.1	0.2 – 0.3

It should be noted that the external mechanical efficiency η is often defined somewhat differently from the above, namely as the relation between the external mechanical power and the difference between the actual metabolic rate and the basal metabolic rate. The definition of η given in eq. (7) seems, however, more reasonable from an engineering point of view and therefore will be used in the following.

The magnitude of M/A_{Du} is a function of the activity of the person. In table 1, values of M/A_{Du} are given for various characteristic activities, types of work, etc. In a number of cases the activities given are not very well defined, e.g. "shoemaker work", "pick and shovel work". The figures given are mean values, and it is clear that considerable deviations can occur. However, if the activity or the type of work is known, the value of M/A_{Du} can be estimated from table 1 with reasonable accuracy for most environmental design purposes.

Estimated values of η are also given in table 1. For most activities, $\eta = 0$, corresponding physically to no external mechanical work being performed. For example, the external mechanical efficiency for a person who walks on the level will be equal to zero since he is performing no work from a physical point of view. For special types of activity, however, η can take on values up to 0.20–0.25. This applies, for example, to walking uphill (or upstairs), ditch-digging, lifting sacks to a higher level, and cycling on an ergometer. In special cases, η can also take on values which are less than zero, when external work is transferred into heat in the human body (negative work) (240). This is the case, for example, when a person walks downhill. The potential energy of the person is then transformed into heat, which is released in the joints and muscles of the legs.

Heat Loss by Skin Diffusion

Water vapour diffusion through the skin is one part of the insensible perspiration, a process not subject to thermoregulatory control. The magnitude of the diffusion per unit area is assumed to be proportional to the difference between the saturated water vapour pressure p_s at the skin temperature and the partial pressure of water vapour p_a in the ambient air (40). The equation for the heat loss by water vapour diffusion through the skin, is:

$$E_d = \lambda \, m \, A_{Du} \, (p_s - p_a) \qquad \text{(kcal/hr)} \qquad (9)$$

where E_d = heat loss by vapour diffusion through the skin (kcal/hr)
λ = 575 kcal/kg = heat of vaporization of water (at 35°C)
m = permeance coefficient of the skin (kg/hr m² mmHg)
p_s = saturated vapour pressure at skin temperature (mmHg)
p_a = vapour pressure in ambient air (mmHg).

The main vapour barrier is provided by the deeper layers of the horny layer of the epidermis (47). The diffusion resistance of this barrier is large in relation to the diffusion resistance of normal types of clothing. The magnitude of the permeance coefficient for the skin has been determined by analysing data of Inouye et al. (155), concerning evaporation loss for sedentary subjects under comfort conditions. From the analysis m was found to be $6.1 \cdot 10^{-4}$ kg/hr m² mmHg.

From steam tables p_s can be found as a function of t_s. For $27°C < t_s < 37°C$ the following linear expression will give an approximation with less than 3% error:

$$p_s = 1.92\, t_s - 25.3 \qquad \text{(mmHg)} \qquad (10)$$

Substituting λ, m and p_s into eq. (9) gives:

$$E_d = 0.35\, A_{Du}\, (1.92\, t_s - 25.3 - p_a) \qquad \text{(kcal/hr)} \qquad (9a)$$

Heat Loss by Evaporation of Sweat Secretion

For the moderate sweat secretion and air temperatures, and thus moderate vapour pressures, which apply to persons in thermal comfort, it would seem reasonable to assume that all secreted sweat evaporates. The magnitude of the sweat secretion as a function of the activity level, for persons in thermal comfort, will be dealt with later.

Latent Respiration Heat Loss

Heat and water vapour are transferred to inspired air by convection and evaporation from the mucosal lining of the respiratory tract. On reaching the alveoli the air is at deep body temperature and saturated with water vapour. As the air moves outward through the respiratory tract some heat is transferred back to the body and water is condensed but the expired air emerging from the nose still contains more heat and water than the inspired air in comfortable environments. Breathing therefore results in a latent heat loss and a dry heat loss from the body.

The latent respiration heat loss is a function of the pulmonary ventilation and the difference in water content between expired and inspired air:

$$E_{re} = \dot{V}\, (W_{ex} - W_a)\, \lambda \qquad \text{(kcal/hr)} \qquad (11)$$

where E_{re} = latent respiration heat loss (kcal/hr)
$\dot{V}$ = pulmonary ventilation (kg/hr)
W_{ex} = humidity ratio of the expiration air (kg water/kg dry air)
W_a = humidity ratio of the inspiration air (kg water/kg dry air)
λ = 575 kcal/kg = heat of vaporization of water (at 35°C).

Pulmonary ventilation is mainly a function of the metabolic rate, though minor differences have been observed between working tasks where arm and leg movements respectively are dominant. Based on an analysis of data by Asmussen and Nielsen (10), and a review by Liddel (187), the following linear expression has been found as a practical approximation for the mean pulmonary ventilation for different types of work:

$$\dot{V} = 0.0060 \ M \qquad (kg/hr) \qquad (12)$$

Formula (12) is also in excellent agreement with data recently published by Datta and Ramanathan (61).

Although the "air-conditioning system" of the respiratory tract is quite effective, the condition of the expired air will still depend to a certain degree upon the condition of the inspired air. According to McCutchan and Taylor (204) the difference in humidity ratio between expired and inspired air can be expressed by the following equation:

$$W_{ex} - W_a = 0.0277 + 0.000065 \ t_a - 0.80 \ W_a$$
$$\cong 0.029 - 0.80 \ W_a \qquad (kg \ water/kg \ dry \ air) \qquad (13)$$

Substituting $W_a = 0.622 \ \dfrac{p_a}{P - p_a} \cong 0.00083 \ p_a$ in eq. (13) gives

$$W_{ex} - W_a = 0.029 - 0.00066 \ p_a \ (kg \ water/kg \ dry \ air) \qquad (13a)$$

where p_a == the partial pressure of water vapour in inspired air (ambient air) (mmHg)

P = 760 mmHg (sea level barometric pressure)

Substituting the expressions for $\dot{V}$ and $W_{ex} - W_a$ in eq. (11), one obtains the following formula for the latent respiration heat loss:

$$E_{re} = 0.0023 \ M \ (44 - p_a) \qquad (kcal/hr) \qquad (11a)$$

Dry Respiration Heat Loss

The heat loss from the body due to the difference in temperature between expired and inspired air can be expressed by

$$L = \dot{V} \ c_p(t_{ex} - t_a) = 0.0014 \ M(t_{ex} - t_a) \qquad (kcal/hr) \qquad (14)$$

where c_p = 0.24 kcal/kg°C, i.e. the specific heat of dry air at constant pressure.

For strict accuracy, McCutchan and Taylor (204) have derived the following formula for the temperature of the expired air as a function of the condition of the inspired air:

$$t_{ex} = 32.6 + 0.066\, t_a + 32\, W_a \qquad (°C) \qquad (15)$$

However, since the dry respiration heat loss is relatively small compared to other terms, it will be sufficiently accurate to use the constant average value 34°C for t_{ex}.

Eq. (14) can hereafter be written

$$L = 0.0014\, M(34 - t_a) \qquad (kcal/hr) \qquad (14a)$$

Heat Conduction Through the Clothing

Transfer of dry heat between the skin and the outer surface of the clothed body is quite complicated, involving internal convection and radiation processes in intervening air spaces, and the conduction through the cloth itself. To simplify calculations, Gagge et al. (92) introduced the term I_{cl} as a dimensionless expression for the total thermal resistance from the skin to the outer surface of the clothed body. I_{cl} is defined by

$$I_{cl} = \frac{R_{cl}}{0.18} \qquad (clo) \qquad (16)$$

where R_{cl} = the total heat transfer resistance from skin to outer surface of the clothed body (m² hr °C/kcal).

The clo-unit has been generally accepted and today is used in most parts of the world. Especially in England, however, the term "tog" is also used, introduced by Peirce and Rees (257):

$$1\ tog = 0.100°C\ m^2/W = 0.116°C\ m^2hr/kcal = 0.645\ clo$$

In the literature, clo-values and tog-values are occasionally given which include the surface resistance, and this can very well give rise to misunderstandings. In the following, however, the clo-unit referring to the clothing itself will be used exclusively.

The dry heat transfer from skin to the outer surface of the clothed body can hereafter be expressed by the following formula:

$$K = A_{Du} \cdot \frac{t_s - t_{cl}}{0.18\, I_{cl}} \qquad (kcal/hr) \qquad (17)$$

The magnitude of I_{cl} for a certain clothing ensemble is rather difficult to measure. For example, it is not sufficient to measure the conductive resistance of each textile layer, analogous to the measuring of conductive resistances for building materials. In order to obtain reasonably accurate measurements it is necessary to use a heated manikin in life size (237), which is garbed in the whole actual clothing ensemble (textile system). As heated manikins including the necessary electronic equipment are expensive to produce, only very few examples are to be found in operation, most of them being in connection with military and aeronautical applications. Unfortunately, therefore, there exist in the literature, clo-values for relatively few clothing ensembles. Some of these clo-values are listed in table 2, which furthermore comprises values for the f_{cl} factor (ratio of the surface area of the clothed body to the nude body), which will be mentioned in the following sections concerning heat loss by radiation and convection. Even though it must be said that table 2 at the moment is rather incomplete, it should be possible, by interpolation, to make estimates of the clo-value of a given clothing ensemble with reasonable accuracy.

However, extensive experimental investigations are being undertaken at the moment at Kansas State University (Institute for Environmental Research and Department of Clothing and Textiles) with the aim of determining clo-values for a large number of typical clothing ensembles for both males and females, chosen on the basis of a statistical analysis of people's clothing habits. When these measurements are available, table 2 can then be up-dated and expanded, the desired aim being to gain information on clo-values to an extent analogous with existing tables for coefficients of heat transmission for various types of building construction.

The thermal resistance of a given textile system depends first and foremost on the thickness and porosity of the individual textile layers (210). For all ordinary textile materials intended for clothing, the variation in porosity is, however, so moderate that the thickness is the most important property which determines the conductive resistance of the individual textile layer (329). The type of textile fibre (wool, cotton, silk, rayon, nylon, glass) does not seem to be of great significance (162, 268, 269). Changes in the humidity content of the textile caused by variations in the air humidity, have only a small influence on the conductive resistance (268, 179). On the other hand, if the textile becomes really "wet", i.e., if the air between the fibre and the yarn is replaced by water, the conductive resistance will of course be reduced considerably.

Apart from the conductive resistance of the textile itself, the layers of air between the textile layers are also of importance, and it thus follows that the tailoring and fit have a certain influence on the clo-value. For very loosely hanging clothing, a certain ventilation of the air layers can occur, arising from a "chimney effect". The same thing can occur with vigorous body movements with a "bellows effect".

For high air velocities the dynamic pressure of the air current can create an air stream through the clothing, depending on the permeability of the clothing material. This ventilation heat loss could be treated together with I_{cl}, i.e., the I_{cl} values could be measured for different clothing ensembles as a function of the velocity. However, for the low velocities usually encountered in indoor environments, it may normally be assumed that this ventilation heat loss is negligible.

The clo-values given in table 2 refer to the clothing ensemble itself. If a person sits in an upholstered chair or lies on a divan, the effective clo-value will be greater than the clo-value for a standing person in the same clothing ensemble, and therefore allowances must be made for certain additions to the values given in the table.

The vapour diffusion resistance of ordinary clothing is mostly relatively low, and all the sweat secreted by persons in thermal comfort will therefore normally evaporate. However, the magnitude of the diffusion resistance of the clothing will have an influence on the "wetted area" of the body (89). As a large wetted area in itself can give rise to non-thermal discomfort, it will perhaps be reasonable to fix an upper limit for wettedness, as suggested by Gagge et al. (100). In order to perform calculations of this nature, it would be desirable to carry out measurements of the diffusion resistance of a series of typical clothing ensembles. Some investigations of water vapour movement through clothing systems have been performed (337, 338, 198, 181, 246), but the processes involved are complicated and more research is needed.

Heat Loss by Radiation

Radiant heat exchange takes place between the human body and its surroundings, just as between any two physical objects. The heat loss by radiation from the outer surface of the clothed body can therefore be expressed by Stefan-Boltzmann's law:

$$R = A_{eff} \, \varepsilon \, \sigma \, [(t_{cl} + 273)^4 - (t_{mrt} + 273)^4] \qquad (kcal/hr) \qquad (18)$$

where A_{eff} = the effective radiation area of the clothed body (m²)

ε = the emittance of the outer surface of the clothed body

Table 2. *Data for Different Clothing Ensembles*

Clothing Ensemble	I_{cl} clo	f_{cl}
Nude....................................	0	1.0
Shorts..................................	0.1	1.0
Typical Tropical Clothing Ensemble:		
Shorts, open-neck shirt with short sleeves, light socks and sandals........................	0.3–0.4	1.05
Apollo Constant Wear Garment (astronauts):		
Light cotton undergarment with short sleeves and ankle length legs, cotton socks[1]..............	0.35	1.05
Light Summer Clothing:		
Long light-weight-trousers, open neck shirt with short sleeves...........................	0.5	1.1
Light Working Ensemble:		
Athletic shorts, woollen socks, cotton work shirt (open-neck), and work trousers, shirt tail out (208)	0.6	1.1
U.S. Army "Fatigues", Man's:		
Light-weight underwear, cotton shirt and trousers, cushion sole socks and combat boots[3].........	0.7	1.1
Combat Tropical Uniform:		
Same general components as U.S. Army fatigues but with shirt and trousers of cloth, wind resistant, poplin[3]................................	0.8	1.1
Typical Business Suit........................	1.0	1.15
Typical Business Suit + Cotton Coat...........	1.5	1.15
Light Outdoor Sportswear:		
Cotton shirt, trousers, T-shirt, shorts, socks, shoes and single ply poplin (cotton and dacron) jacket[2].	0.9	1.15
Heavy Traditional European Business Suit:		
Cotton underwear with long legs and sleeves, shirt, woollen socks, shoes, suit including trousers, jacket and vest (256)............................	1.5	1.15–1.2
U.S. Army Standard Cold-wet Uniform:		
Cotton-wool undershirt and drawers, wool and nylon flannel shirt, wind resistant, water repellent trousers and field coat, cloth mohair and wool coat liner and wool socks[3]	1.5–2.0	1.3–1.4
Heavy Wool Pile Ensemble:		
(Polar weather suit).......................	3–4	1.3–1.5

[1] James M. Waligora, Manned Spacecraft Center, Houston, personal communication.
[2] J. Jaax, Kansas State University, personal communication.
[3] J. R. Breckenridge, U.S. Army Research Institute, Natick, personal communication.

σ = the Stefan-Boltzmann constant: $4.96 \cdot 10^{-8}$ (kcal/m^2 hr$^\circ$K^4)

t_{mrt} = the mean radiant temperature ($^\circ$C). The mean radiant temperature, in relation to a given person placed at a given point with a given body position and a given clothing, is defined as that uniform temperature of a black enclosure which would result in the same heat loss by radiation from the person as the actual enclosure under study.

However, the geometry of radiant exchange between the body and the surroundings offers some difficulty because of the irregularity of body contours caused by appendages, protuberances and re-entrant angles. Since the human body is not everywhere convex there will be some interradiation between body parts and the area in formula (18) will therefore not be the actual surface area of the clothed body but a reduced area, called the effective radiation area,

$$A_{eff} = f_{eff} \, f_{cl} \, A_{Du} \qquad (m^2) \qquad\qquad (19)$$

where f_{eff} = the effective radiation area factor, i.e. the ratio of the effective radiation area of the clothed body to the surface area of the clothed body

f_{cl} = the ratio of the surface area of the clothed body to the surface area of the nude body

A_{Du} = DuBois area (the surface area of the nude body (m^2)).

The value of f_{eff} has been determined in the present study from comprehensive experiments described in chapter six. The effective radiation area factor was found to be 0.696 for sedentary body posture and 0.725 for standing posture, and these values seem to be independent of sex, weight, height, DuBois area or body build (see table 19 and figs. 36 and 37). Since the difference between the determined values for the two body postures is quite small, the mean value of $f_{eff} = 0.71$ will be used as a reasonable approximation for both postures in the expression for the radiant heat loss in the following.

The factor f_{cl} has been the subject of only a limited number of investigations. Nielsen and Pedersen (243) found a value for a heavy European business suit and Herrington (132) found a relationship between f_{cl} and clothing weight using a photographic silhouette method. In the present study f_{cl} was determined for a certain type of clothing (see chapter six). Table 2 includes a listing of estimated values of f_{cl} for different clothing ensembles, but more investigations in this area are needed.

Since the emittance for human skin is close to 1.0 (122, 220) and most types of clothing have emittances of about 0.95, a mean value of 0.97 is suggested for use. Emittance for skin and clothing is independent of the colour for low temperature radiation.

If the person is irradiated with short wave radiation (from, for instance, the sun or a high temperature radiant source), the total radiation heat transfer can still be calculated from eq. (18) using the strict definition for t_{mrt}. For calculation of t_{mrt} in this case, it is necessary to have information about the reflectance of the skin and the clothing, which for short wave radiation is highly dependent on the colour. Measurements of reflectances have been made by Hardy et al. (122, 125) and detailed studies concerning high temperature source radiation have been made by Gagge, Rapp, Hardy and Stolwijk (93, 94, 95, 98, 266).

Substituting for ε, σ and A_{eff} in eq. (18) gives

$$R = 3.4 \cdot 10^{-8} A_{Du} f_{cl} [(t_{cl} + 273)^4 - (t_{mrt} + 273)^4] \quad (kcal/hr) \quad (18a)$$

It might be noted that sometimes it can be advantageous to use the concept "effective radiant field" (ERF), recently introduced by Gagge et al. (98), to express the heat exchange by radiation. The effective radiant field is defined as the heat exchange by radiation (per unit body surface area) between the environment and a man-shaped object with a hypothetical black-body radiating surface temperature equal to the ambient air temperature. In other words, ERF expresses the radiant energy contribution (plus or minus) to the person, in addition to that case where the mean radiant temperature equals the air temperature. Application of this concept can in some cases simplify calculations. However, since the present calculations are performed on a digital computer, for strict accuracy eq. (18a) is used hereafter.

Heat Loss by Convection

The heat loss by convection from the outer surface of the clothed body can be expressed by the following equation:

$$C = A_{Du} f_{cl} h_c (t_{cl} - t_a) \quad (kcal/hr) \quad (20)$$

where h_c is the convective heat transfer coefficient ($kcal/m^2 \, hr\,°C$), the magnitude of h_c depending on the type of convection process. For low air velocities ("still air") the heat transfer takes place by free convection, so that h_c is a function of the temperature difference, $(t_{cl} - t_a)$.

For higher velocities forced convection exists and h_c then is a function of the velocity.

For the case of free convection, Nielsen and Pedersen (243) have made a comprehensive investigation using subjects and a manikin, both in seated and standing positions. The following formula for h_c, applicable both for standing and seated positions, was found to give excellent agreement between the subject and manikin tests:

$$h_c = 2.05 \, (t_{cl} - t_a)^{0.25} \qquad \text{(kcal/hr m}^2\,°\text{C)} \qquad (21)$$

The form of formula (21) is in agreement with the common formulae for free convection with laminar boundary layer (104):

$$\text{Nu} = \text{Const. (Gr Pr)}^{0.25} \qquad (22)$$

For the case of forced convection, Winslow, Gagge and Herrington (334) have investigated the convective heat transfer coefficient for subjects in a semi-reclining position with the velocity mainly downward. The following formula was found:

$$h_c = 10.4 \cdot \sqrt{v} \qquad \text{(kcal/hr m}^2\,°\text{C)} \qquad (23)$$

for $v < 2.6$ m/s
where v = the relative velocity (m/s).

Colin and Houdas (60) later found results for sedentary persons, wind direction head on, in reasonable agreement with eq. (23). The form of eq. (23) is also in agreement with common formulae for forced convection (104):

$$\text{Nu} = \text{Const. Re}^m \text{Pr}^n \qquad (24)$$

where m for the Re interval in question has values in the order of magnitude of 0.5 and Pr^n may be taken as $(0.71)^{0.33}$.

Although the velocity direction and the body position will have a certain influence on h_c, eq. (23) is assumed to give a reasonable approximation for seated or standing persons, when the air flow is across the body. For moving persons (for instance, walking) it must be noted that the velocity used in eq. (23) is the relative velocity, i.e., that velocity which, for a motionless person, will give the same convective heat transfer coefficient as for the person under study.

One must decide between forced and free convection controls for each particular case. Undoubtedly there will exist a transition zone between pure free convection and pure forced convection where both the temperature difference and the velocity influence the heat transfer process. Lacking transition formulae, it is proposed to use a common rule for the determination of convective heat transfer in the transition zone, namely, calculate h_c for both free and forced convection and use the larger value:

$$h_c = \begin{cases} 2.05(t_{cl} - t_a)^{0.25} \text{ for } 2.05(t_{cl} - t_a)^{0.25} > 10.4\sqrt{v} \\ 10.4\sqrt{v} \qquad \text{ for } 2.05(t_{cl} - t_a)^{0.25} < 10.4\sqrt{v} \end{cases} \tag{25}$$

The inequality condition, for most practical cases, will mean that the free convection formula should be used for $v < 0.10$ m/s and the forced convection formula for $v > 0.10$ m/s. This condition will suffice for approximate calculations but, since temperature difference is also involved, the inequalities in eq. (25) will be used in the subsequent calculations by digital computer.

The convective heat transfer formulae in eq. (25) are only applicable at normal barometric pressure at sea level. The effect of low and high air pressures, which can be of interest, e.g. in the mountains, aeroplanes, and in deep mines, will be discussed in chapter three.

Heat Balance Equation

Substituting all the heat loss terms derived above into the double heat balance eq. (5) and dividing by A_{Du} gives

$$\frac{M}{A_{Du}} (1 - \eta) - 0.35 [1.92t_s - 25.3 - p_a] - \frac{E_{sw}}{A_{Du}}$$

$$- 0.0023 \frac{M}{A_{Du}} (44 - p_a) - 0.0014 \frac{M}{A_{Du}} (34 - t_a) = \frac{t_s - t_{cl}}{0.18 I_{cl}} =$$

$$3.4 \cdot 10^{-8} f_{cl} [(t_{cl} + 273)^4 - (t_{mrt} + 273)^4] + f_{cl} h_c (t_{cl} - t_a) \tag{26}$$

CONDITIONS FOR THERMAL COMFORT

The first requirement for thermal comfort under steady state conditions, as exclusively considered below, is that the heat balance equation (26) be satisfied. This requirement is an expression for the purpose of man's thermoregulatory system: to maintain a reasonably constant internal body temperature. For a given activity level, skin temperature t_s and sweat secretion E_{sw} are seen to be the only physiological variables influencing the heat balance. For a given person with a given activity level, clothing and environment, a certain combination of t_s and E_{sw} will arise so that the heat balance equation is satisfied. Man's thermoregulatory system is quite effective and the heat balance can therefore be maintained within wide limits of the environmental variables, corresponding to wide limits of the physiological parameters (t_s, E_{sw}).

Satisfaction of the heat balance equation (26) is, however, far from being a sufficient condition for thermal comfort. Within the wide limits of the environmental variables for which a heat balance will be maintained, there is only a narrow interval which will create thermal comfort. Corresponding to this is a narrow interval of mean skin temperature t_s and sweat secretion E_{sw}.

In the following it is assumed that a condition for thermal comfort for a given person at a given activity level, is that his mean skin temperature t_s and his sweat secretion E_{sw} must have values inside narrow limits:

$$a < t_s < b \tag{27}$$

$$c < E_{sw} < d \tag{28}$$

The limiting values a, b, c and d are only applicable for an individual person at a particular activity level. The satisfaction of inequalities (27) and (28) is thus a condition for thermal comfort only for one individual person at a particular activity level (steady state).

Condition (27) agrees with several earlier investigations which have shown that the sensation of thermal comfort is related to the mean skin temperature t_s (Yaglou (348), Gagge et al. (90, 336), Hardy (124)). Chatonnet and Cabanac (54), Missenard (218) and Benzinger (26) state furthermore that some internal body temperature t_i, probably the hypothalamic temperature, influences the sensation of thermal comfort. A demand that t_i, at a given activity level, should lie within narrow limits is, however, in agreement with inequalities (27) and (28) since E_{sw} at a given activity level can be assumed to be a function of t_i and t_s.

The conditions given by eqs. (27) and (28) are claimed to be valid only for steady state conditions. For sudden, large changes of the environment special thermal sensation phenomena occur, as evidenced by Gagge, Stolwijk and Hardy (96). Thermal transients will be discussed in chapter three.

The inequalities (27) and (28) express that, for thermal comfort for a given person at a given activity level (steady state), his mean skin temperature and his sweat secretion must be within certain limits. The limiting values a, b, c and d can be expected to vary with the activity level and from person to person.

In an earlier study by Fanger (79) experimental values for mean skin temperature and sweat secretion were found for subjects at different activity levels, subjectively expressing thermal comfort. The subjects were American male and female college-age persons.

Fig. 1 shows the mean skin temperature as a function of the activity. Fig. 2 shows the evaporative heat loss as a function of the activity. From fig. 2 the sweat secretion was found by subtracting the diffusion and latent respiration heat losses. A regression analysis of the data gave, for persons in thermal comfort, the following functional dependency between skin temperature and activity level (internal heat production per unit surface area) and between sweat secretion and activity level:

$$\bar{t}_s = 35.7 - 0.032 \frac{H}{A_{Du}} \qquad (^\circ C) \qquad\qquad (29)$$

$$\bar{E}_{sw} = 0.42 A_{Du} \left(\frac{H}{A_{Du}} - 50 \right) \qquad (kcal/hr) \qquad (30)$$

It can be seen that for constant comfort, the mean skin temperature decreases with increasing activity (for $H/A_{Du} = 50$ kcal/hr m², $\bar{t}_s$ is 34°C, for $H/A_{Du} = 150$ kcal/hr m², $\bar{t}_s$ is 31°C). The sweat secretion at thermal comfort is zero for sedentary activity ($H/A_{Du} \sim 50$ kcal/hr m²). At higher activities moderate sweat secretions are necessary for thermal comfort (environments so cold that sweat secretion is completely suppressed would be felt much too cool for persons in activity).

It has often been claimed earlier that it was a condition for thermal comfort that the mean skin temperature was 33-34 °C, and that sweating did not occur. The present results show that this is approximately true only for sedentary persons. At higher activities the skin temperature necessary for comfort falls, and moderate sweating takes place.

For a given person in thermal comfort at a given activity level, only one value of t_s and of E_{sw} has been measured. These two measured values, however, give no indication of their exact locations within the subject's unknown comfort intervals a-b and b-c. However, for a large group of subjects in thermal comfort, and assuming that $\bar{t}_s$ and $\bar{E}_{sw}$ are normally distributed, it seems reasonable to take the mean of the measured mean skin temperatures $\bar{t}_s$ and the sweat secretions $\bar{E}_{sw}$ as an estimate of the mean of 0.5 (a + b) and 0.5 (c + d) for the actual activity level.

As the subjects concerned can be assumed to be representative of college-age persons, $\bar{t}_s$ and $\bar{E}_{sw}$ represent the values which, at the actual activity level, will fall inside the comfort limits (inequalities (27) and (28)) of the highest possible percentage of a large group of college-age persons.

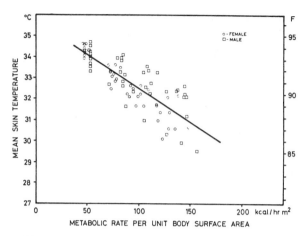

Fig. 1. Mean skin temperature as a function of the activity level for persons in thermal comfort. In order to maintain thermal comfort the ambient temperature was lower the higher the activity level.

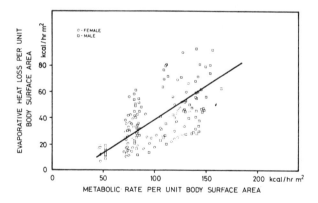

Fig. 2. Evaporative heat loss as a function of the activity level for persons in thermal comfort. In order to maintain comfort the ambient temperature was lower the higher the activity level. There are more points plotted than in fig. 1 since data by McNall et al. (206) are included in the analysis.

40

The expressions for $\bar{t}_s$ and $\bar{E}_{sw}$ given by eqs. (29) and (30) are therefore proposed as the second and third conditions for optimal thermal comfort.

A question could be raised as to whether the comfort values of skin temperature and sweat secretion at a given activity level will depend on how the clothing and the environmental variables are combined. However, in recent experiments at the Techn. Univ. of Denmark (Andersen and Olesen (7)), where a subject in 32 three-hour tests was exposed to different combinations of the variables (2 activities, 2 clo-values, 2 mean radiant temperatures, 2 velocities), it was found that in a state of thermal comfort no significant differences exist between the observed skin temperatures and sweat rates at a given activity, no matter whether the subject was exposed to a high t_{mrt} and a low t_a or vice versa, a velocity of 0.8 m/s or "still air", a clo-value of 0.6 or nude.

COMFORT EQUATION

Substituting the expressions for $\bar{t}_s$ and $\bar{E}_{sw}$ given by eqs. (29) and (30) in the double heat balance equation (26):

$$\frac{M}{A_{Du}}\left(1-\eta\right) - 0.35\left[43 - 0.061\,\frac{M}{A_{Du}}\left(1-\eta\right) - p_a\right] -$$

$$0.42\left[\frac{M}{A_{Du}}\left(1-\eta\right) - 50\right] - 0.0023\,\frac{M}{A_{Du}}\left(44 - p_a\right) -$$

$$0.0014\,\frac{M}{A_{Du}}\left(34 - t_a\right) = \frac{35.7 - 0.032\,\dfrac{M}{A_{Du}}\left(1-\eta\right) - t_{cl}}{0.18\,I_{cl}} = \tag{31}$$

$$3.4 \cdot 10^{-8}\,f_{cl}\left[(t_{cl} + 273)^4 - (t_{mrt} + 273)^4\right] + f_{cl}\,h_c\,(t_{cl} - t_a)$$

Solving the left part of the double equation (31) gives the following expression for t_{cl}:

$$t_{cl} = 35.7 - 0.032\,\frac{M}{A_{Du}}\left(1-\eta\right) - 0.18\,I_{cl}\left[\frac{M}{A_{Du}}\left(1-\eta\right) - \right.$$

$$0.35\left[43 - 0.061\cdot\frac{M}{A_{Du}}\left(1-\eta\right) - p_a\right] - 0.42\left[\frac{M}{A_{Du}}\left(1-\eta\right) - 50\right] -$$

$$\left. 0.0023\,\frac{M}{A_{Du}}\left(44 - p_a\right) - 0.0014\cdot\frac{M}{A_{Du}}\left(34 - t_a\right)\right] \qquad (°C) \tag{32}$$

Setting the left side of double equation (31) equal to the right side gives:

$$\frac{M}{A_{Du}}\left(1 - \eta\right) - 0.35 \left[43 - 0.061 \frac{M}{A_{Du}}\left(1 - \eta\right) - p_a\right] -$$

$$0.42 \left[\frac{M}{A_{Du}}\left(1 - \eta\right) - 50\right] - 0.0023 \frac{M}{A_{Du}}\left(44 - p_a\right) - \qquad (33)$$

$$0.0014 \frac{M}{A_{Du}}\left(34 - t_a\right) =$$

$$3.4 \cdot 10^{-8} f_{cl} \left[(t_{cl} + 273)^4 - (t_{mrt} + 273)^4\right] + f_{cl} h_c (t_{cl} - t_a)$$

Eq. (33) is the desired general comfort equation, in which t_{cl} is given by eq. (32) and h_c by eq. (25).

The comfort equation contains the following variables:

I_{cl}, f_{cl},	M/A_{Du}, η, v,	v, t_a, p_a, t_{mrt}
A function of the type of clothing	A function of the type of activity	Environmental variables

I_{cl} and f_{cl} are functions of the type of clothing (values for different clothing ensembles are shown in table 2). M/A_{Du}, η, and partially v, are functions of the type of activity (values for common daily activities are shown in table 1). t_a, p_a, t_{mrt} and partially v, are thermal environmental variables.

The comfort equation being obtained by inserting in the heat balance equation the comfort expressions found for skin temperature and sweat rate, satisfaction of the comfort equation therefore means at the same time satisfaction of the three basic comfort conditions. Satisfaction of the comfort equation is thus a necessary condition for optimal thermal comfort.

Using the comfort equation (33) it is possible, for any type of clothing (clo) and any type of activity (kcal/hr m²), to calculate all reasonable combinations of air temperature (°C), air humidity (mmHg), mean radiant temperature (°C), and relative velocity (m/s) which will create optimal thermal comfort for persons under steady state conditions.

The experimental work has covered activity levels only up to about 150 kcal/hr m². Furthermore, the comfort equation is based upon a series of assumptions and upon heat transfer equations which are applicable only within certain limits. It is therefore important to emphasize that the reliability of the comfort equation for extreme values of the variables is questionable without further experimental verification.

The comfort equation is based on experiments with American college-age persons exposed to a uniform environment under steady state conditions.

In the following chapter a discussion will be given based upon experiments carried out with the purpose of investigating the influence of national-geographic location and age on the application of the comfort equation. Furthermore, the influence on comfort of a number of special factors will be discussed. They concern the sex, body build, menstrual cycle, influence of ethnic differences, food, circadian rhythm, thermal transients, unilateral heating or cooling of the body (including asymmetric radiant fields, draught, and warm and cold floors), colour, crowding, and finally, the influence of air pressure. Fortunately, it appears that most of these factors have little or no effect upon the comfort conditions, and the comfort equation can therefore be used without modifications in the majority of cases in practice.

Comfort Diagrams

The comfort equation is quite complex, since the involved heat transfer processes are relatively complicated. Solution by hand would be laborious as multiple iteration is necessary. It has, therefore, been solved by digital computer, for all relevant combinations of the variables, and diagrams (figs. 3 to 11) for direct practical application have been prepared. Since the diagrams, and not the equation itself, should be used in practice, it was not neccessary – at the expense of accuracy – to simplify the comfort equation in order to make hand calculations easier.

The curves in figs. 3–11 represent comfort lines, i.e. lines through points (conditions) which satisfy the comfort equation and thus will provide optimal thermal comfort. In all the figures the mechanical efficiency η is set equal to zero, covering the great majority of practical applications.

Figs. 3 to 6 show combinations of activity level, clo-value, rel. velocity, humidity and ambient temperature, which will create optimal comfort, the mean radiant temperature being kept equal to air temperature. In the twelve diagrams, comfort lines (ambient temperature versus wet bulb temperature with relative velocity as parameter) have been plotted for four different clo-values, each at three different activity levels. These are particularly well suited to give a general view of the influence of the humidity.

It can be seen that the humidity influence for persons in thermal comfort is relatively moderate. A change from absolutely dry air (rh = 0%) to saturated air (rh = 100%) can be compensated for by a temperature decrease $\Delta t \sim 1.5 - 3\,°C$.

Since it is the vapour partial pressure and not the relative humidity which influences evaporation, a lower humidity effect might be expected when

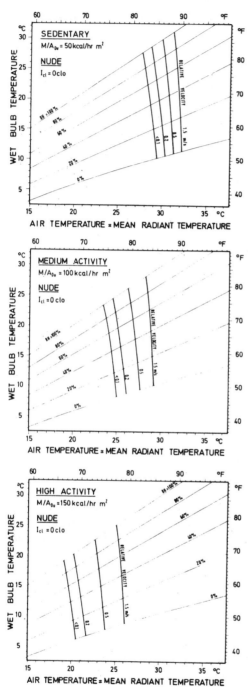

Fig. 3. Comfort lines (ambient temperature versus wet bulb temperature with relative air velocity as parameter) for *NUDE* persons ($I_{cl} = 0$ clo, $f_{cl} = 1.0$) at three different activity levels.

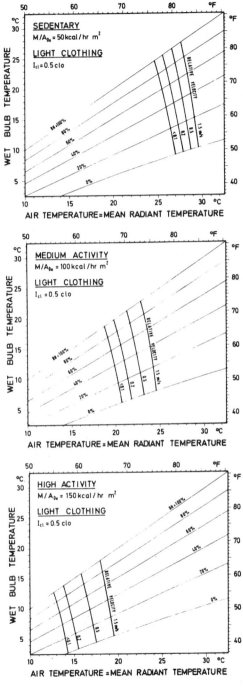

Fig. 4. Comfort lines (ambient temperature versus wet bulb temperature with relative air velocity as parameter) for persons with *LIGHT CLOTHING* (I_{cl} = 0.5 clo, f_{cl} = 1.1) at three different activity levels.

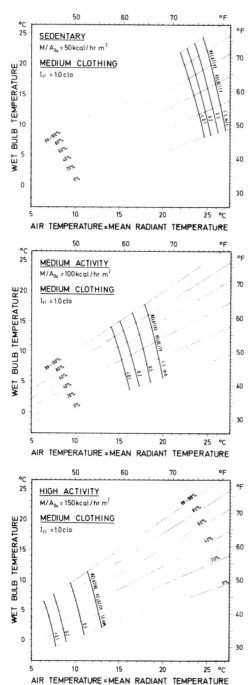

Fig. 5. Comfort lines (ambient temperature versus wet bulb temperature with relative air velocity as parameter) for persons with *MEDIUM CLOTHING* ($I_{cl} = 1.0$ clo, $f_{cl} = 1.15$) at three different activity levels.

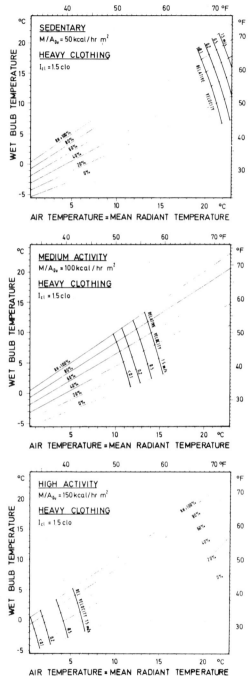

Fig. 6. Comfort lines (ambient temperature versus wet bulb temperature with relative air velocity as parameter) for persons with *HEAVY CLOTHING* (I_{cl} = 1.5 clo, f_{cl} = 1.2) at three different activity levels.

clo-value and/or activity level is high, since the comfort temperature then is low. As shown in the diagrams this is not, however, the case. The humidity effect is relatively independent of clo-value and activity level. The reason is that the lower vapour pressure at the lower temperatures is compensated for by the following: (a) for an increased clo-value by an increased change in ambient temperature necessary to create a given heat loss change, (b) for an increased activity level by an increased pulmonary ventilation.

The relatively small humidity effect applies only for persons in thermal comfort. At high ambient temperatures the degree of discomfort can be heavily influenced by the air humidity.

It should be noted that the comfort lines in figs. 3 to 6 are drawn for the entire humidity interval (rh = 0–100%). Although there is no reason, from a thermal comfort point of view, to avoid extreme humidity values, there can nevertheless be other, non-thermal, reasons for avoiding the extremes (dehydration of the mucous membranes, "wettedness" discomfort and damage to the structure and/or its contents).

It is important to emphasize that the moderate humidity effect is applicable only under steady state conditions. For short exposures the humidity effect can be greater due to absorption and desorption effects in the clothing and on the skin. Yaglou's effective temperature concept (343) was based on subjects exposed to different environments for a few minutes and a considerable humidity effect was therefore found. For long exposures Yaglou (348) found later a much smaller humidity effect which is in reasonable agreement with the present results. The moderate humidity effect is also in agreement with recent studies by Koch (163), Nevins (234) and McNall (206).

Fig. 7 shows also comfort lines (ambient temperature versus relative velocity with activity level as parameter) for four different clothings (clo-values). As in figs. 3 to 6, mean radiant temperature is equal to air temperature, but in this case the relative humidity is kept constant, at 50%. Fig. 7 is particularly well suited for evaluating the influence of relative velocity and activity level.

It will be seen from fig. 7 that the comfort lines have a vertical tangent for $v \sim 0$ m/s because free convection then controls the convective heat transfer process. Thus the necessary temperature for comfort is independent of the air velocity, when it is low. It will be seen that there is inflection for the comfort lines at 0.1 – 0.2 m/s, and that changes in velocity, especially in the interval 0.1–0.3 m/s, are important. An increase from 0.1 to 0.3 m/s must thus be compensated for by an increase in temperature of 1.5–3°C.

The considerable temperature changes necessary as compensation for changes in air velocity within the interval 0.1–0.3 m/s possibly give a partial

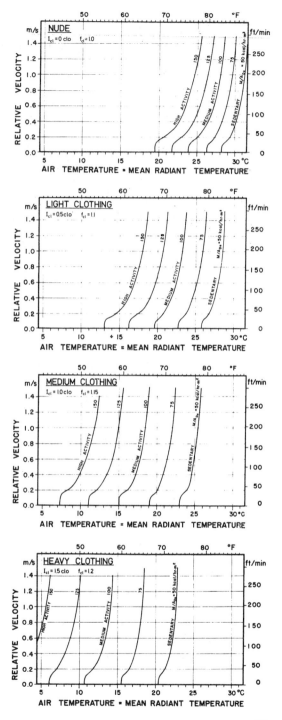

Fig. 7. Comfort lines (ambient temperature versus relative air velocity with activity level as parameter) at 4 different clo-values (rh = 50%).

explanation for the phenomenon of draught. One can compensate for an increase in the air velocity by increasing the temperature, but, since it is very difficult to create a uniform velocity field in a room, considerable differences in thermal sensation from point to point may easily arise. In order to obtain a uniform thermal climate in the occupied zone of a room, one normally attempts to keep the air velocities < 0.1 m/s where the heat transfer to the air is by free convection and therefore independent of the velocity.

By comparing the four diagrams in fig. 7 it can further be seen that the influence of clothing on the temperature necessary for comfort increases relatively sharply with increasing activity levels. An increase in clothing from 0 clo (nude) to 1.5 clo will thus decrease the necessary ambient temperature by 8°C for a sedentary person, but by 19°C for a person at high activity (150 kcal/hr m²). A sedentary person attired in polar clothing with a clo-value of 4, will prefer an ambient temperature as high as 8°C (v < 0.1 m/s). Even heavy polar clothing can therefore not substitute for the need of artificial heating of houses in winter.

Figs. 3 to 7 apply for mean radiant temperature equal to air temperature. However, it should be noted that in this case, table 13 in chapter four could also be used to determine the optimal temperature. The table is set up primarily for the practical assessment of a given room climate, but it can also be used for the determination of the optimal temperature, the "Predicted Mean Vote" (PMV) being set equal to zero.

Figs. 8 to 11 show comfort lines which should be used when the mean radiant temperature deviates from the air temperature. In these twelve diagrams, comfort lines (air temperature versus mean radiant temperature with relative velocity as parameter) have been plotted for four different clo-values, each at three different activity levels (rh = 50%). The comfort lines cross each other where the air temperature equals the mean temperature of the outer surface of the clothed body, since the convective heat transfer here will be zero, independent of the velocity. It is interesting to note that the tangent in the crossing point for v → 0 approaches a horizontal line since no convective (neither free nor forced) heat transfer takes place. For v → ∞ the comfort line approaches a vertical line through the crossing point. This is, however, of theoretical interest only since high velocities would, among other things, cause heat loss by intra-clothing ventilation.

To the left of the crossing point the temperature of the outer surface of the clothed body is higher than the air temperature and an increase in relative velocity will therefore necessitate an increase in air temperature (and/or mean radiant temperature) in order to maintain thermal comfort.

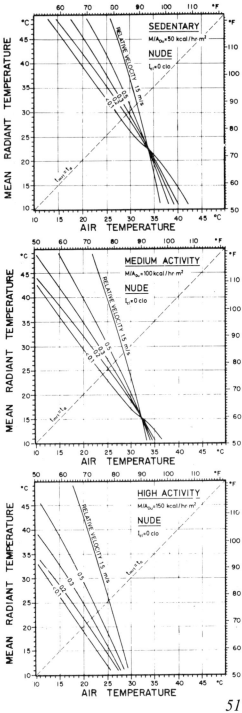

Fig. 8. Comfort lines (air temperature versus mean radiant temperature with relative air velocity as parameter) for *NUDE* persons ($I_{cl} = 0$ clo, $f_{cl} = 1.0$) at three different activity levels (rh = 50%).

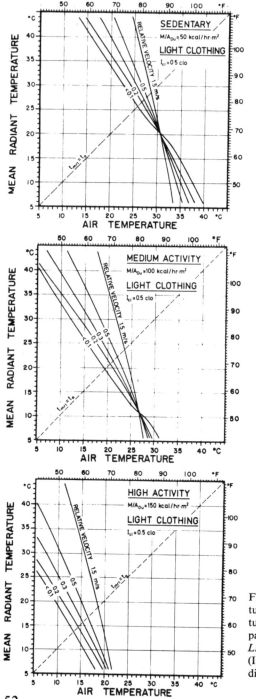

Fig. 9. Comfort lines (air temperature versus mean radiant temperature with relative air velocity as parameter) for persons with *LIGHT CLOTHING* (I_{cl} = 0.5 clo, f_{cl} = 1.1) at three different activity levels (rh = 50%).

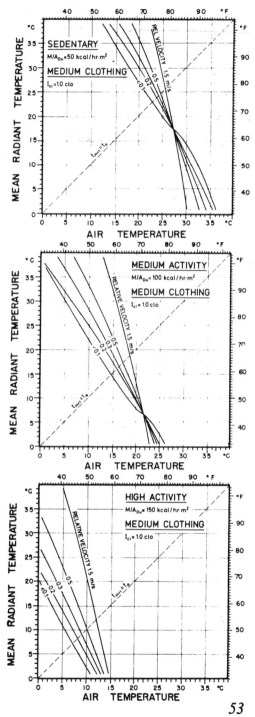

Fig. 10. Comfort lines (air temperature versus mean radiant temperature with relative air velocity as parameter) for persons with *MEDIUM CLOTHING* ($I_{cl} = 1.0$ clo, $f_{cl} = 1.15$) at three different activity levels (rh $= 50\%$).

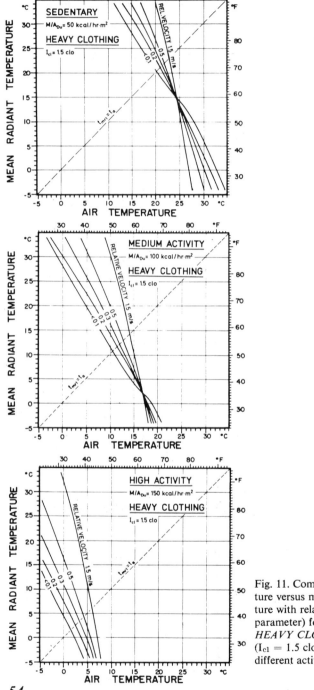

Fig. 11. Comfort lines (air temperature versus mean radiant temperature with relative air velocity as
parameter) for persons with
HEAVY CLOTHING
(I_{cl} = 1.5 clo, f_{cl} = 1.2) at three
different activity levels (rh = 50 %).

To the right of the crossing point the temperature of the outer surface of the clothed body is lower than the air temperature and an increase in relative velocity will necessitate a decrease in air temperature (and/or mean radiant temperature) since convective heat is transferred *to* the body in this case.

Practical Applications

In the following, a number of examples are given of the practical use of the comfort diagrams. In cases where it is obvious in advance that the mean radiant temperature can be considered equal to the air temperature, the diagrams in figs. 3 to 6 can be used. However, if the relative humidity deviates only moderately from 50%, it is easier to use fig. 7, which also gives greater accuracy of reading.

If the mean radiant temperature deviates from the air temperature, the diagrams in figs. 8 to 11 should be used, which strictly speaking are valid only for rh = 50%. For other humidities, eventual corrections can be made from fig. 13 given in the next section, but the influence of the humidity is fortunately moderate.

Example 1. At one end of an indoor swimming pool, rest places and a restaurant are provided. The comfort temperature for nude sedentary persons is to be determined, when v = 0.2 m/s, rh = 70%, and the mean radiant temperature is considered equal to the air temperature.

From the upper diagram in fig. 3, $t_a = t_{mrt} = 29.1\,°C$ is found.

Example 2. In a meeting room, sedentary persons in winter are considered to be clothed at 1.0 clo (normal business suit) while during the peak of the summer they are considered to be clothed at 0.6 clo (light summer trousers and light short-sleeved shirt and tie). With v < 0.1 m/s, rh = 40% in winter and rh = 70% in summer, it is desired to determine the optimal ambient temperatures (mean radiant temperature = air temperature) in both cases.

For winter conditions, $t_a = t_{mrt} = 23.3\,°C$ is found from the upper diagram in fig. 5; for summer conditions, $t_a = t_{mrt} = 24.9\,°C$ is found by interpolation between the upper diagrams in fig. 4 and fig. 5.

Example 3. It is desired to determine the optimal temperature in a "clean room" (laminar flow type), where the velocity in the whole of the occupied zone is 0.5 m/s and where persons are engaged in sedentary work (M/A_{Du} = 50 kcal/hr m^2), clothed in a special suit with I_{cl} = 0.75 clo, and with rh $=$ 50%. By interpolation between the two centre diagrams in fig. 7, $t_a = t_{mrt} = 0.5(24.5 + 27.5) = 26.0\,°C$ is found.

Example 4. The comfort temperature is to be determined for personnel in a shop, the activity corresponding to walking at 1.5 km/hr $(M/A_{Du} = 75$ kcal/hr m², rel. vel. v $= 1500/3600 = 0.4$ m/s) and $I_{cl} = 1.0$ clo, rh $=$ 50%.

From the third diagram in fig. 7, $t_a = t_{mrt} = 21.0\,°C$ is found.

Example 5. A special uniform is to be made for slaughterhouse workers who are employed in an environment of 8 °C. The necessary clo-value of the uniform must be determined, the activity level being set at 125 kcal/hr m², and the relative air velocity at 0.3 m/s.

From the last diagram in fig. 7 it can be seen that $I_{cl} = 1.5$ clo corresponds to the desired conditions.

Example 6. Under winter conditions, the mean radiant temperature in a long-distance bus is calculated to be 6 degrees lower than the air temperature. It is desired to determine the air temperature necessary for comfort, the passengers being presumed to be seated without overclothes $(I_{cl} = 1.0$ clo) and the velocity is 0.2 m/s (rh $= 50\%$).

From the upper diagram in fig. 10, $t_a = 26°C$ and $t_{mrt} = 20°C$ is found.

Example 7. A sidewalk restaurant is to be heated by high-intensity infra-red heaters, so that the restaurant can be used at air temperatures higher than 12°C, rh $= 50\%$. It is desired to calculate the mean radiant temperature necessary for comfort; the air velocity, by the use of suitable windbreaks, is controlled at 0.3 m/s, and the clothing of the guests is considered to be 1.5 clo (business suit + cotton coat).

By extrapolation of the upper diagram in fig. 11 it is found that the IR-heaters must create a mean radiant temperature of 40°C. For the calculation of IR-heaters, see chapter five.

Example 8. In a supersonic aircraft the outside surface reaches a temperature of 150°C. By suitable insulating and cooling arrangements, the mean radiant temperature in the passenger cabin is kept down to a level which is 10°C higher than the air temperature. It is desired to calculate the comfort air temperature for the sedentary passengers, the clo-value being 1.0 and the velocity 0.2 m/s.

56

From fig. 10, it will be found that the air temperature should be 20°C ($t_{mrt} = 30°C$).

Example 9. In a foundry, the mean radiant temperature in a workplace was measured at 50°C and the air temperature at 20°C (rh = 50%). The worker is lightly clad ($I_{cl} = 0.5$ clo) and has an activity level of 100 kcal/hr m². By erecting radiant shields, it is practically possible to bring the mean radiant temperature down to 35°C. Furthermore, it is suggested that an air jet be installed to increase the air velocity around the person. It is desired to determine the relative velocity necessary for comfort.

From the centre diagram in fig. 9, v = 1.5 m/s is found.

In several of the above-mentioned examples, the difference between the mean radiant temperature and the air temperature has been estimated. An accurate calculation of this difference can only be obtained by a detailed thermal analysis of the environment of the room in question. The theoretical basis for such an analysis, including the optimal comfort condition, is set forth in chapter seven.

A thermal analysis of a room gives a rational basis for the design of a given environmental system, but also the means for comparison among the various possible systems with the aim of optimization. Lee et al. (182, 183) have used the comfort equation as the basis for systems analysis and optimization of life support systems for confined spaces in aircraft and space vehicles.

Numerous other examples of the practical application of the comfort equation have been given by Moser (227), particularly for thermal environments in industry. Maes (201) used the basic experimental data in the comfort equation to write a computer program for calculating thermal comfort in passenger cabins in large aeroplanes.

The comfort equation could also be of importance in the design of room thermostats. The majority of existing room thermostats have a sensor which is sensitive to only one of the environmental variables, namely the air temperature. However, what is desired is not constant air temperature, but constant comfort. If the mean radiant temperature in a room is altered, e.g., due to changed outdoor conditions, or to crowding, or because lights are turned on, a different air temperature is required. The ideal would be a "comfortstat", integrating all the environmental variables in the same way the human body does. The comfort equation gives the mathematical basis for the construction of such a "comfortstat", which moreover could perhaps be constructed in such a way that one could set it at a given activity level and a given clo-value instead of at a given temperature. From a technical point of view, it is no doubt a complicated matter to construct a sensor arrangement which simulates the relationship between the variables given by the comfort equation. But a thermostat which was suitably sensitive to radiation would be an advance.

In connection with the design of life support systems and space suits for astronauts, the basic comfort conditions (eqs. (29) and (30)) for skin temperature and sweat secretion can be used, among other things as a basis for the automatic control system, so that it also provides thermal comfort. One possibility is to use thermal sensors on the skin, perhaps combined with an air humidity sensor, the set points being automatically adjusted so that the skin temperature and the sweat secretion become a function of the activity level, which, for example, could be sensed from the respiration rate or heart rate.

The comfort equation can also be of use in the design of special work suits (see ex. 5) and possibly also in connection with meteorological statistics and forecasts. Meteorologists normally give individual parameters independently of each other: air temperature, wind velocity, number of hours sunshine, etc. However, for outdoor work and from a recreational point of view, it is the combined effect of the variables which is of interest. For example, it can be of interest for different geographical locations to have statistical information as to how often the weather will be on the warm side of comfort, corresponding to different combinations of activity and clothing. The new thermal sensation index which is derived in chapter four, based on the comfort equation could be more suitable for a meteorological application, both for statistics and for weather forecasts.

RELATIVE INFLUENCE OF THE VARIABLES

A clear impression of the relative importance of each of the main variables in the comfort equation can be gained by partial differentiation of the equation, followed by the determination of the relevant differential coefficients in the comfort condition.

Thus, in fig. 12, $\delta t_a / \delta t_{mrt}$ is calculated and plotted by computer, as a function of the thermal resistance of the clothing with relative velocity as parameter, at three different activity levels. $\delta t_a / \delta t_{mrt}$ represents the change in air temperature necessary to maintain optimal comfort, when the mean radiant temperature is increased by 1°C. It should be emphasized that

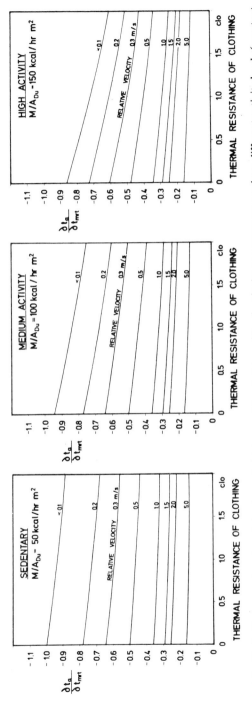

Fig. 12. $\delta t_a / \delta t_{mrt}$ as a function of the thermal resistance of the clothing with rel. velocity as parameter, at three different activity levels (constant vapour pressure). $\delta t_a / \delta t_{mrt}$ indicates the change in air temperature necessary to maintain optimal comfort when the mean radiant temperature is increased by 1°C

59

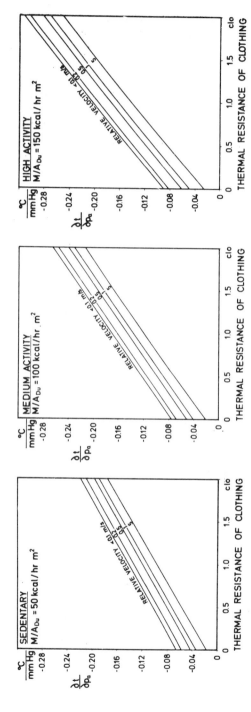

Fig. 13. $\delta t/\delta p_a$ as a function of the thermal resistance of the clothing with rel. velocity as parameter, at three different activity levels. $\delta t/\delta p_a$ indicates the change in ambient temperature (air temp. = mean rad. temp.) necessary to maintain optimal thermal comfort when the water vapour pressure is increased by 1 mm Hg.

60

$\delta t_a/\delta t_{mrt}$ is calculated in the comfort condition for $t_a = t_{mrt}$ and for a constant vapour pressure corresponding to rh = 50% in the comfort condition for each case.

$\delta t_a/\delta t_{mrt}$ is negative, as an increase in the mean radiant temperature must be compensated for by decreased air temperature. Moreover, the influence of mean radiant and air temperatures is nearly equal with light clothing and with still air, but $\delta t_a/\delta t_{mrt}$ falls with rising velocity due to the increased convective heat transfer coefficient. It will also be seen that $\delta t_a/\delta t_{mrt}$ falls slightly with increasing clo-value and also with increasing activity level, mainly because of the falling ambient temperature necessary for comfort with a consequently lower radiant heat transfer coefficient.

In fig. 13, $\delta t/\delta p_a$ is plotted in a similar manner, as a function of the thermal resistance of the clothing with relative velocity as parameter at three different activities. t means here the uniform value of air temperature and mean radiant temperature. $\delta t/\delta p_a$ therefore gives the change of air and mean radiant temperatures necessary to maintain optimal thermal comfort when the vapour pressure is increased by 1 mm Hg. $\delta t/\delta p_a$ is calculated in the comfort condition and for a vapour pressure corresponding to rh = 50%. It will be seen that $\delta t/\delta p_a$ is of moderate magnitude and that it is negative. Increased air humidity is compensated for by a lowering of the ambient temperature. In addition, $\delta t/\delta p_a$ will be seen to increase with increased clothing, because a rather large change in temperature is necessary to compensate for a given change in the evaporative heat loss when the clo-value is high.

In fig. 14, $\delta t/\delta v$ is shown as a function of the thermal resistance of the clothing with relative velocity as parameter. $\delta t/\delta v$ is calculated in the comfort condition for constant vapour pressure, corresponding to rh = 50%. $\delta t/\delta v$ indicates the change of air temperature and mean radiant temperature necessary to maintain optimal thermal comfort when the relative velocity is increased by 1 m/s. $\delta t/\delta v$ falls with rising velocity, i.e., a given change in the relative velocity has greatest influence when the velocity is moderate. However, $\delta t/\delta v$ is zero when the velocity is very small, as the convective heat transfer in this case occurs by free convection. The validity of the curve for v = 0.1 m/s is therefore subject to reservations, since the transition between free and forced convection often lies in this vicinity; in any case, this curve should only be used for positive values of δv.

Moreover, $\delta t/\delta v$ will be seen to be rather independent of the clothing but it rises with the activity level due to the fact that the temperature difference between outer body surface and the environment in the comfort condition is greater the higher the activity level.

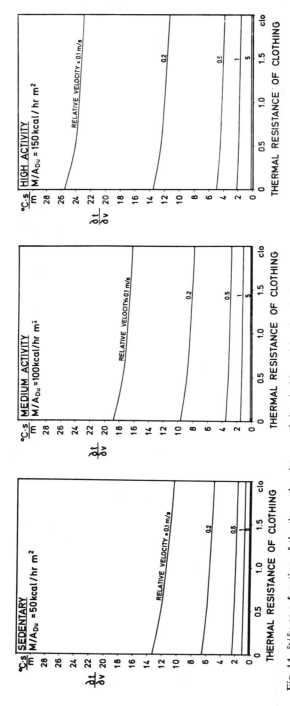

Fig. 14. $\delta t / \delta v$ as a function of the thermal resistance of the clothing with rel. velocity as parameter, at three different activity levels (*constant vapour pressure*). $\delta t / \delta v$ indicates the change in ambient temperature (air temp. = mean radiant temp.), necessary to maintain optimal thermal comfort when the velocity is increased by 1 m/s. The curve for v = 0.1 m/s is only applicable for positive values of δv.

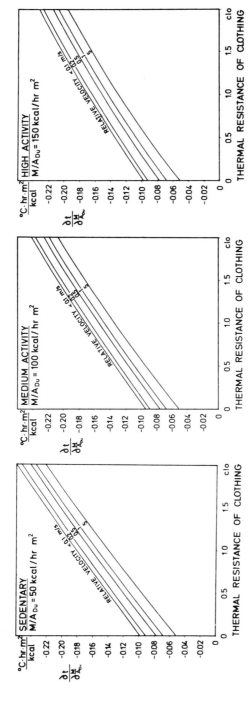

Fig. 15. $\delta t/\delta(M/A_{Du})$ as a function of the thermal resistance of the clothing with rel. velocity as parameter, at three different activity levels (constant vapour pressure). $\delta t/\delta(M/A_{Du})$ indicates the change in ambient temperature (air temp. = mean rad. temp.) necessary to maintain optimal thermal comfort when the metabolic rate is increased by 1 kcal/hr m².

The influence of the activity level will be seen from fig. 15, which shows $\delta t/\delta(M/A_{Du})$ as a function of the thermal resistance of the clothing with relative velocity as parameter. $\delta t/\delta(M/A_{Du})$ is calculated in the comfort condition for constant vapour pressure, corresponding to rh = 50%. $\delta t/\delta(M/A_{Du})$ indicates the equal change of air temperature and mean radiant temperature necessary to maintain thermal comfort when the metabolic rate is increased by 1 kcal/hr m². $\delta t/\delta(M/A_{Du})$ is negative, since an increase of the activity naturally necessitates a lower ambient temperature for comfort. $\delta t/\delta(M/A_{Du})$ is moderately dependent on the velocity (mostly with light clothing) whereas the activity level has very little influence. On the other hand, $\delta t/\delta(M/A_{Du})$ will be seen to rise sharply with increased clothing. An increase of the activity level of 5 kcal/hr m² thus necessitates, for nude persons, a lowering of the ambient temperature by approximately 0.5°C (v < 0.1 m/s) while a lowering of more than 1°C is necessary for a person clothed at 2 clo.

The relative influence of the clothing can be seen from fig. 16 which shows $\delta t/\delta I_{cl}$ as a function of I_{cl} with relative velocity as parameter. $\delta t/\delta I_{cl}$ is calculated in the comfort condition for constant vapour pressure, corresponding to rh = 50%. $\delta t/\delta I_{cl}$ indicates the equal change of air temperature and mean radiant temperature necessary to maintain thermal comfort when the clo-value is changed. $\delta t/\delta I_{cl}$ is negative, as an increase in the thermal resistance of the clothing necessitates a lower ambient temperature for comfort. In addition, $\delta t/\delta I_{cl}$ is seen to be practically independent of the clothing level and of the velocity. On the other hand, $\delta t/\delta I_{cl}$ rises moderately with increased activity level. An increase in the clothing of 0.1 clo thus necessitates, for sedentary activity, a decrease of 0.6°C, while a decrease of 1.5°C is necessary at high activity.

COMPARISON WITH EARLIER INVESTIGATIONS

As previously mentioned, many comfort studies involving large numbers of subjects have been undertaken over the years, both in the laboratory and in the field. But comparison with the comfort equation is only possible for a few of them. In most investigations one or more of the six main variables in the comfort equation have not been measured or reported. Information is often lacking concerning clo-value, activity level, mean radiant temperature or relative air velocity.

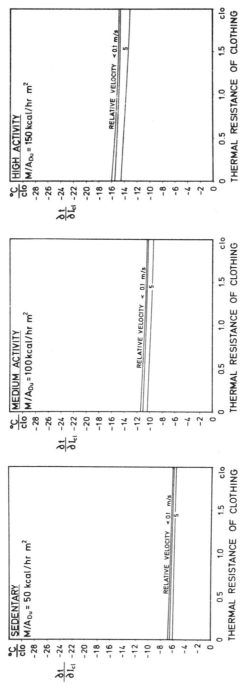

Fig. 16. $\delta t/\delta I_{cl}$ as a function of the thermal resistance of the clothing with rel. velocity as parameter, at three different activity levels (constant vapour pressure). $\delta t/\delta I_{cl}$ indicates the change in ambient temperature (air temperature = mean rad. temp.) necessary to maintain optimal thermal comfort when the clo-value is increased by 1 clo.

65

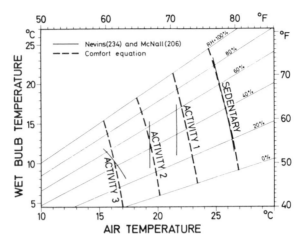

Fig. 17. Comparison between the comfort equation and the results of Nevins (234) and McNall (206). The curves are comfortlines corresponding to four different activities. The comfortlines of Nevins and McNall (solid lines) are determined by a purely statistical analysis of the thermal sensation votes of their subjects. The curves corresponding to the comfort equation (dashed lines) are calculated, the following values of the variables corresponding to the experimental conditions in Nevins' and McNall's experiments being inserted:

Sedentary: (720 subjects): $M/A_{Du} = 50$ kcal/m²hr; $v = 0.1$ m/s
Activity 1: (90 subjects): $M/A_{Du} = 80$ kcal/m²hr; $v = 0.2$ m/s
Activity 2: (150 subjects): $M/A_{Du} = 106$ kcal/m²hr; $v = 0.25$ m/s
Activity 3: (180 subjects): $M/A_{Du} = 135$ kcal/m²hr; $v = 0.32$ m/s

Subjects in standard clothing: 0.6 clo; mean radiant temperature equal to air temperature.

Comparison with experiments by Nevins et al. (234) and by McNall et al. (206) is possible, since large numbers of college-age persons have been used as subjects and since all the variables in the comfort equation have been well controlled during these experiments. The solid curves in fig. 17 are the comfort lines found by Nevins and McNall, while the dashed lines represent the solution using the comfort equation. It should be noted that fig. 17 is slightly different from the earlier published version (79) since the metabolic rates recently published by McNall (208) have been used.

For sedentary activity there is excellent agreement both for temperature level and temperature-humidity relationship (the lines ∽ identical). For the different activity levels good agreement was found for the temperature level (differences less than 1°C) but some differences appear in the temperature-humidity relationship. For activities 1 and 2, McNall et al. did not find humidity to be statistically significant. This might, however, have been due to the relatively narrow humidity range investigated (rh = 25–65%). In summary the agreement can be said to be reasonably good.

Recent studies of a similar purely empirical character, where the influence of the mean radiant temperature (205) and of the velocity (80) has been investigated, also show reasonable agreement with the comfort equation.

In all the above cases it must, however, be remembered that only "spot" comparisons are possible, since results of the "empirical" studies apply only at one constant value of each of four of the variables.

Chapter 3.

THE INFLUENCE OF CERTAIN
SPECIAL FACTORS ON THE
APPLICATION OF THE COMFORT
EQUATION

The comfort equation set up in the foregoing chapter is based on experiments performed during winter with American college-age subjects under exposures of three hours to uniform environments. In the present chapter, the general application of the comfort equation under other conditions will be discussed. The significance of a series of special factors which can conceivably influence the comfort condition is treated.

First, the influence of the national-geographic location will be discussed. It is often maintained that comfort conditions are different for different national-geographic locations, and it is thus a common belief that results from American comfort studies cannot, without modification, be applied in Europe. In order to study this problem, experiments have been undertaken involving 128 college-age Danish subjects who were exposed to the same thermal conditions and clothed in the same uniform as college-age subjects in a similar American study by Nevins et al. (234). These experiments are dealt with in the first section, which also includes a discussion of the application of the comfort equation for locations with extreme climates and at various times of the year.

Nearly all earlier comfort studies, including the experiments which form the basis for the comfort equation, have been performed with young subjects. In order to study the influence of age upon comfort conditions, experiments involving 128 elderly Danish subjects have been performed. These experiments, which are similar to those involving college-age subjects, are also dealt with in the first section which furthermore contains a discussion of the influence of the sex.

The experimental data also made possible a comparison between subjects of different body build and a study of the influence of the menstrual cycle on thermal comfort of the college-age female subjects. These factors, which sometimes are claimed to be of importance, are discussed in the following sections.

On the basis of a review of earlier studies and theoretical considerations a further discussion follows of the influence of various other factors which can possibly be of importance for the comfort conditions and thereby possibly modify the practical application of the comfort equation. This concerns the influence of ethnic differences, food, circadian rhythm, thermal transients, unilateral heating or cooling of the body (including asymmetric radiant fields, draught, and warm and cold floors), colour, crowding, and finally, the influence of air pressure.

NATIONAL-GEOGRAPHIC LOCATION, AGE AND SEX

The comfort equation is based on experiments with American college-age subjects. The question now is, to what extent the equation can be used for other national-geographic locations.

To investigate this problem, an experimental investigation was carried out involving 128 Danish college-age subjects. It was decided to perform the experiments under the same conditions as those employed by Nevins et al. (234), who used 720 untrained American college-age subjects clothed in a standard uniform (0.6 clo), at sedentary activity during three-hour laboratory tests.

Nevins' experimental data are especially appropriate as a basis for comparison, partly because all the environmental variables have been carefully controlled, and partly because the experiments included a large number of subjects who can be considered representative of the North American college-age population. In addition, Nevins' experimental results show extremely good agreement with the comfort equation (see fig. 17).

By far the greatest number of comfort studies to date have been carried out with young persons as subjects, and consequently the existing knowledge on the influence of age on the comfort conditions is slight. In order to investigate this aspect, an experimental investigation was carried out with 128 elderly persons (mean age: 68 years), who were exposed to exactly the same environmental conditions as the 128 students (mean age: 23 years). The large age difference (45 years) between the two groups was chosen primarily to investigate whether a significant age-conditioned difference exists at all.

As half of the subjects were females and half males, it was possible to study in addition, the influence of the sex on the comfort conditions.

Table 3. *Anthropometric Data for the Subjects*

Group	Sex	Number	Age	Height	Weight	DuBois Area	Ponderal Index
			years	cm	kg	m²	kg⁰·³³m⁻¹
College-age	Females	64	22.6 ± 2.0[1]	168.2 ± 5.4	57.1 ± 7.4	1.64 ± 0.12	2.25 ± 0.08
	Males	64	23.6 ± 2.3	179.6 ± 6.0	71.4 ± 8.1	1.90 ± 0.12	2.27 ± 0.08
	Females + Males	128	23.1 ± 2.2	173.9 ± 8.0	64.2 ± 10.5	1.77 ± 0.17	2.26 ± 0.08
Elderly	Females	64	66.5 ± 3.8	161.3 ± 5.4	63.9 ± 10.8	1.67 ± 0.14	2.44 ± 0.11
	Males	64	69.5 ± 5.1	171.4 ± 6.6	74.0 ± 11.9	1.85 ± 0.17	2.41 ± 0.11
	Females + Males	128	68.0 ± 4.7	166.4 ± 7.9	69.0 ± 12.4	1.77 ± 0.18	2.42 ± 0.11

[1] Standard deviation

Subjects

As subjects, 128 Danish college-age persons (64 males and 64 females) and 128 Danish elderly persons (64 males and 64 females) were used. The number of test persons was fixed on the basis of the statistical analysis of the American experimental data, in order to obtain a reasonable basis for comparison.

Only persons in general good health were allowed to participate. All subjects were volunteers, who were paid for participating in the experiments. The subjects were exposed to the thermal environment for three hours in groups of eight subjects.

Each subject participated in only one test, so as to preserve naïveté in the voting procedure. Different anthropometric data for the subjects are listed in table 3.

Clothing

All subjects were clothed in cotton twill shirts and trousers. The shirts were worn outside the trousers. Male subjects wore cotton undershorts,

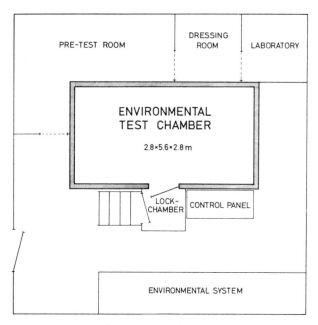

Fig. 18. Floor plan of the environmental facilities at the Techn. Univ. of Denmark.

but no undershirts or T-shirts. The women wore brassieres and pants. All subjects wore woollen sweat socks without shoes.

This clothing, which was procured from the U.S., is identical to the clothing used by Nevins et al. (234) for the American experiments at Kansas State University (KSU-standard-uniform). The clo-value of the uniform is 0.6 (208).

Experimental Facilities

The experimental programme was carried out in the new environmental chamber at the Technical University of Denmark, which was placed in operation in 1968 (a plan view of the chamber and adjoining facilities is shown in fig. 18). The chamber is 2.8 m wide by 5.6 m long with a ceiling height of 2.8 m. In the chamber all relevant combinations of air temperature, air humidity, mean radiant temperature and air velocity can be produced and accurately controlled.

By using a special arrangement, the mean radiant temperature can be controlled independent of the air temperature. Symmetric as well as asym-

71

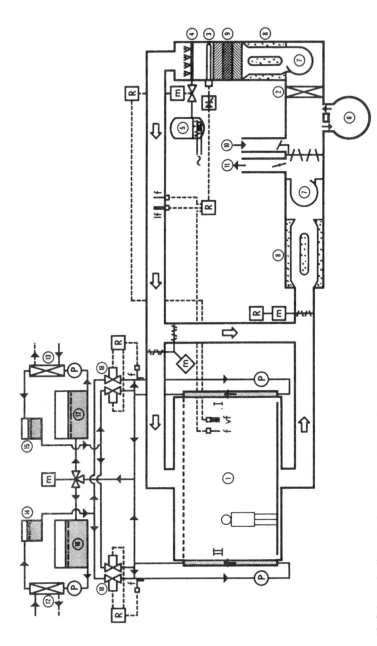

Fig. 19. Schematic diagram of environmental test chamber, air conditioning system and water system for end walls.
1: Chamber. 2: Air-cooling coil. 3: Air-heating coil. 4: Steam humidifier. 5: Steam generator. 6: Rotary dehumidification unit. 7: Fans. 8: Attenuators. 9: High-efficiency dust filters and activated charcoal filters. 10: Outdoor air intake. 11: Air discharge. 12: Heat exchanger (steam). 13: Heat exchanger (freon). 14: Heat accumulator. 15: Cold accumulator. 16: Heat receiver. 17: Cold receiver. 18: Solenoid valves, I and II: Water-cooled (-heated) end walls. R: Regulator. P: Pump. m: Motor. f: Temp. sensor. lf: Inlet duct temp. sensor. vf: Wet-bulb sensor.

metric radiation fields can be produced. All parameters are automatically recorded with a digital system. A schematic diagram of the environmental system is given in fig. 19.

In thermal comfort studies it is important that the assessment of the thermal environment is not disturbed by discomfort arising from other environmental variables; therefore, in the planning of the chamber, it was stressed that these variables should be kept at a suitable neutral level so that they would not give rise to discomfort.

The average illumination level, 0.8 m above floor level, is 150 lux. The sound level is 45 dB(A), and the sound pressure level is 63 dB (lin.). Dust concentration and odour level are kept suitably low by (a) the use of high-efficiency dust filters and activated charcoal filters, and (b) keeping the air change in the chamber at 40 hr^{-1}.

Outside the climate chamber the control panel, laboratory, dressing room and pre-test room are found, as shown in fig. 18.

Experimental Conditions

In the present experiments the condition in the chamber was held constant during each three-hour test period. The air temperature was maintained at four different levels: 21.1°C (70 F), 23.3°C (74 F), 25.6°C (78 F) and 27.8°C (82 F). The mean radiant temperature equalled the air temperature and the velocity was ∞ 0.1 m/s. Although the humidity dependency is well-established, two levels, rh = 30% and 70%, were used at each air temperature in order to obtain conditions analogous to those in Nevins' experiments and, to investigate different non-thermal effects of the humidity, not reported here.

Each of the eight test conditions were maintained during four experiments, namely for 8 college-age females, 8 college-age males, 8 elderly females, 8 elderly males. The three-hour test periods were conducted either in the afternoon (2–5 p.m.) or in the evening (7–10 p.m.) as in the experiments by Nevins et al. All 32 tests were conducted during the autumn 1968.

Experimental Procedure

The subjects reported for the tests at the time scheduled, having been asked to previously have a normal night's sleep, and a normal meal, the latter about an hour before arrival. After entering the pre-test room oral

73

temperatures were taken, no subject whose temperature was above 37.2°C being permitted to participate. It should be noted that even though 8 subjects actually participated in the test, an extra subject was scheduled in the event that one subject had an elevated temperature or failed to report for the test. The heights of the subjects were then measured, whereupon they donned the special clothing.

The subjects stayed in the pre-test room for thirty minutes and were here indoctrinated regarding the purpose of the study and the method of voting on the thermal sensation ballot. After entering the environmental test chamber the subjects were seated and asked to read, study or perform equally quiet activities. Quiet conversation was permitted but the subjects were not allowed to exchange views concerning the thermal environment. Smoking was allowed but the subjects were asked to keep it to a minimum.

After half an hour the subjects reported their thermal sensation by circling a number on a ballot with the following voting scale:

1. cold
2. cool
3. slightly cool
4. neutral
5. slightly warm
6. warm
7. hot

This psycho-physical voting scale is the one used in most of the ASHRAE comfort studies.

After this vote the ballots were collected and the votes were tallied: Half an hour later, the second vote was taken and recorded. This was repeated after each of the four subsequent half-hour periods or until six votes had been taken.

The subjects were weighed in a seated position, after the first vote and before the sixth vote on a precision balance in the chamber, in order to determine the evaporation loss. They were allowed to drink as much water as desired, with each subject's consumption being recorded, but no food was consumed.

After the sixth and final thermal sensation vote had been cast, a new type of ballot was distributed in order to obtain information about the subject's ability to connect comfort with the temperature scale. This ballot, which did not concern the main purpose of the experiment, included a rating scale, developed by Rohles (279), consisting of a vertical listing in random order of 24 temperatures ranging from 10°C to 33°C in one degree increments. Beside each temperature was a box in which the subject recorded his rating. The subjects were instructed to place a "C" beside the temperatures they considered to be comfortable, when seated and dressed as in the present experiment. If the temperature was considered cooler than comfortable they were asked to place a minus in the rating column and a plus if the temperature was considered warmer than comfortable. It should be noted that the questions were unrelated to the actual environmental conditions to which the subjects were exposed in the chamber.

Before leaving the chamber the subjects were furthermore asked to answer a questionnaire concerning meals, sleep, menstrual cycle etc., and were asked to vote on scales concerning several non-thermal factors, the results of which will be reported in a later study.

Results

Thermal Sensation Votes

In fig. 20, the mean value of all thermal sensation votes is given as a function of the time of the vote. It is seen that the mean vote is somewhat higher at the time of the first and the second votes, probably due to the subject's slightly higher activity before the test. To ensure steady-state conditions, it was decided to consider only the last three votes, i.e., the mean value of the last three votes was determined for each individual subject.

A regression analysis was then performed to determine the relationship between population mean vote and ambient temperature. As the influence of humidity has been well established, all experimental combinations of

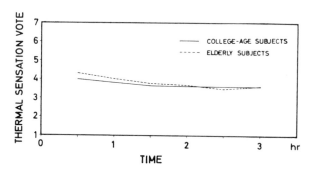

Fig. 20. Mean thermal sensation vote for Danish college-age and elderly subjects during the three-hour test period.

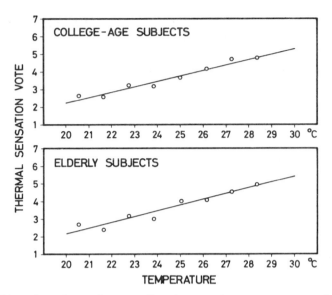

Fig. 21. Mean thermal sensation votes (last three votes) versus temperature for Danish college-age and elderly subjects. The curves are the regression lines.

ambient temperature and humidity were first converted to equivalent ambient temperatures at rh = 50%, using the humidity dependence given by the comfort equation.

In table 4 for the different groups of subjects, the calculated regression equations for the estimated mean thermal sensation vote are given as a function of ambient temperature. The regression lines and the corresponding points for college-age and elderly subjects are plotted in fig. 21.

Also in table 4, the corresponding equations for the American college-age subjects are given. The published regression analyses by Nevins et al. (234) were based on the subject's final vote only, but in order to obtain the best possible comparability with the present study, the raw data of Nevins were recalculated in the same way as the Danish data, utilizing the last three votes for each subject. It is these recalculated regression equations for the American subjects which are given in table 4, but it should be mentioned that there is very little difference compared with the original published equations (rh = 50%) by Nevins.

For each of the regression equations found, the temperature corresponding to a neutral mean vote is determined by inserting Y = 4. The results for the different groups are given in table 5, which also contains the neutral temperature predicted from the comfort equation.

Table 4. *Regression Equations*

Group	Number	Regression Equation[1]	Correlation Coefficient of Determination R	Estimated Residual Standard Deviation of Mean Votes $S_{Y|T}$
College-age Danish:				
Females + Males	128	$Y = -3.836 + 0.3048T$	0.716	0.768
Females	64	$Y = -5.963 + 0.3907T$	0.803	0.751
Males	64	$Y = -1.709 + 0.2190T$	0.615	0.731
Elderly Danish:				
Females + Males	128	$Y = -4.241 + 0.3206T$	0.667	0.925
Females	64	$Y = -6.090 + 0.4001T$	0.757	0.901
Males	64	$Y = -2.391 + 0.2412T$	0.569	0.906
College-age American:				
Females + Males	720	$Y = -4.625 + 0.3376T$	0.796	0.756
Females	360	$Y = -5.678 + 0.3735T$	0.834	0.727
Males	360	$Y = -3.574 + 0.3019T$	0.783	0.709

Y = Estimated Population Mean Vote.
T = Ambient Temperature (rh = 50%).

[1] The statistical analysis shows that the linear description of Y by T is not quite complete, and the model is therefore only an approximative description. By the comparison made in the following between the different groups, the magnitude of the test statistics will nevertheless serve as a good indicator for possible differences.

Table 5. *Neutral Temperatures for the Different Groups of Subjects* (°C)

Group	Females + Males	Females	Males
College-age Danish Subjects	25.71	25.50	26.07
Elderly Danish Subjects	25.71	25.22	26.50
College-age American Subjects	25.55	25.91	25.09
Comfort Equation	25.6		

Table 6. *Comparison Between Groups, Statistical Data*

Comparison between	Neutral Temp. °C	Diff. Between Neutral Temp. °C	Mean of Neutral Temp. T_m °C	Diff. Between Mean Votes at T_m ΔY	Estim. Variance of ΔY[1] $s^2_{\Delta Y}$	Degrees of Freedom for $s^2_{\Delta Y}$ df	T-value	Significance (5% level)
College-age Danish...........	25.71							
College-age American.........	25.55	0.16	25.63	−0.053	0.0061	840	−0.679	no
College-age Danish...........	25.71							
Elderly Danish...............	25.71	0.00	25.71	0.000	–	–	–	no
College-age Danish Females...	25.50							
College-age Danish Males.....	26.07	−0.57	25.78	0.173	0.0213	840	1.185	no
Elderly Danish Females.......	25.22							
Elderly Danish Males.........	26.50	−1.28	25.86	0.409	0.0552	124	1.740	no
College-age American Females..	25.91							
College-age American Males....	25.09	0.82	25.50	−0.278	0.0010	840	−8.968	yes

[1] The estimated variances of ΔY for all college-age groups are calculated on the basis of a common estimated residual variance $S^2{}_{Y}|_T = 0.520$ (df = 840), as a test of equality showed no significant difference in residual variances between Danes and Americans and between the sexes. For the elderly, the estimated residual variance is significantly higher and equal to $S^2{}_{Y}|_T = 0.817$ (df = 124), and this value has been used to calculate the estimated variance of ΔY for the elderly.

In table 6 the necessary statistical data are given for a comparison between the neutral temperatures found for Danish and American college-age subjects, Danish college-age and elderly subjects, and between the sexes within each group.

It is seen that there is no significant difference in preferred temperature between Danish and American college-age subjects, and no difference between Danish college-age and elderly subjects. A significant difference was found between American females and males, but not between the sexes of either the elderly or the college-age Danish group. Although the sex difference is not significant, it should be mentioned that the Danish males of both age-groups preferred a higher temperature than the females, while the opposite was the case for the Americans.

Evaporative Heat Losses

The measured evaporative heat losses are listed in table 7, the results for each of the groups being given for each of the two humidities, and further divided into the evaporative heat loss for subjects having a mean vote $Y \leq 4$ (neutral or colder than neutral) and subjects having a mean vote $Y > 4$ (warmer than neutral).

The division mentioned has been made as it can be expected that the evaporation for $Y \leq 4$ equals the perspiratio insensibilis (skin diffusion +

Table 7. *Evaporative Heat Losses*

Group	Sex	Evaporative Heat Loss (kcal/hr m²)			
		rh = 30%		rh = 70%	
		$Y \leq 4$	$Y > 4$	$Y \leq 4$	$Y > 4$
College-age	Females + Males...	14.1 ± 3.9[1]	19.3 ± 7.6	10.8 ± 2.9	15.2 ± 5.5
	Females..........	12.2 ± 3.1	14.8 ± 6.4	10.9 ± 2.7	14.6 ± 6.4
	Males............	16.0 ± 3.6	23.8 ± 6.1	10.8 ± 3.4	15.6 ± 5.0
Elderly	Females + Males...	11.1 ± 3.0	14.3 ± 5.3	8.9 ± 3.1	9.5 ± 4.2
	Females..........	10.3 ± 2.6	12.1 ± 4.2	7.9 ± 2.5	9.7 ± 3.6
	Males............	11.9 ± 3.3	16.8 ± 5.4	9.6 ± 3.3	9.0 ± 5.1

[1] Standard deviation.

respiratory evaporation), while for $Y > 4$ some sweating can be expected to occur. The evaporation for $Y \leq 4$ is, for the college-age subjects, found to be in reasonable agreement with the expression in the comfort equation for both humidity levels, due consideration being taken to the fact that subjects with a mean vote ≤ 4 can be expected to have a slightly lower skin temperature than the comfort value. It will be seen that the evaporation ($Y \leq 4$) for the elderly group is somewhat lower, and that the evaporation for females is slightly lower than that for males in both age-groups.

Comfort Estimates on the Temperature Scale

Each subject marked on the questionnaire a number of ambient temperatures which he judged would be felt as comfortable at the actual sedentary activity and in the actual standard clothing worn during the tests. For each subject the mean of the highest and lowest temperature estimated as comfortable was calculated. This value was taken to be the temperature which the person concerned would estimate as optimal for him under the given conditions. Moreover, the difference between the highest and lowest temperature was also calculated, this representing the range on the temperature scale within which the subject estimated that he would be comfortable. Mean values for the different groups are listed in table 8. As mentioned previously, this extra questionnaire bore no relation to the actual tests.

The estimated optimal temperatures are surprisingly similar for all groups, with no major differences either between the two age-groups or

Table 8. *Values on the Temperature Scale Estimated as Optimal by the Subjects*

Group	Sex	Estimated Optimal Temperature °C	Estimated Comfort Range °C
College-age	Females + Males.......	20.8 ± 2.0[1]	3.8 ± 1.7
	Females.............	20.6 ± 1.9	3.9 ± 1.8
	Males..............	20.9 ± 2.1	3.6 ± 1.7
Elderly	Females + Males.......	21.2 ± 1.8	3.0 ± 1.9
	Females.............	21.1 ± 1.7	2.8 ± 1.7
	Males..............	21.2 ± 1.8	3.4 ± 2.1

[1] Standard deviation.

between the sexes. For all groups, the temperature estimated by the subjects as optimal at the actual sedentary activity and in the actual clothing, is around 21°C, i.e., 4–5°C lower than the optimal temperature determined by analysis of their thermal sensation votes.

The results of this extra investigation show merely that the test persons apparently have little experience in relating comfort to the temperature scale. The subjects may have normally worn heavier clothing which may have biased their estimates. However, the result nevertheless shows that in practice, one should be cautious about relying on comfort temperatures estimated by subjects.

Discussion

National-geographic Location

The present experiments were designed to obtain the best possible comparison with the American study of Nevins (234). One might expect that the most reasonable method of checking the applicability of the comfort equation for other populations would be to duplicate the experiments on which the comfort equation is based. Experiments of this type are, however, more laborious and allow only one subject in the chamber at a time. Instead of performing such detailed experiments with relatively few subjects, it was decided to perform the present simpler experiments with many subjects. In this way comparison between different populations would be more credible since the samples cover a large number of subjects of each population.

The results (table 6) show surprising agreement between the temperatures desired for thermal neutrality for the two national-geographic groups. The Danish subjects preferred a slightly higher temperature than the Americans, but the difference is less than 0.2°C and is not statistically significant.

The experiments were performed for only one combination of clothing, activity and relative velocity, and for mean radiant temperature = air temperature. When agreement is found for this combination, however, there is little reason to believe that significant differences between the two groups should occur at other combinations of the variables.

Since the comfort equation agrees very well with the results of Nevins (see fig. 17), the results of this study suggest that the equation can readily be used for college-age persons in Denmark or, more generally, at national-geographic locations within the temperate climate zones. The actual differences in practice between preferred temperatures in the U.S. and in Europe which have been reported, especially in earlier field studies, probably reflect only differences in clothing habits and not adaptation arising from differences in outdoor climate, way of life, etc. as stated by several authors (345, 58, 22, 258, 259, 277, 180). The clo-value is, however, inserted as a variable in the comfort equation and values corresponding to the actual clothing habits at a given national-geographic location must therefore be considered for any practical application of the equation. It should be mentioned, however, that differences in clothing habits have been considerably reduced during the past few decades, with a strong trend in Europe away from the traditional heavy clothing toward lighter textiles such as those used generally in the U.S.

The present investigation does not indicate any difference in thermally neutral conditions within the temperate climate zone, but whether the comfort equation can also be applied at geographic locations outside that zone has yet to be determined, e.g., in the tropics, where people are more or less acclimatized to hot environments.

Acclimatization to heat is a well established phenomenon, which may be described as the series of physiological adjustments which occur when men who are accustomed to live in a cool climate are suddenly transferred to a hot climate. These adjustments ameliorate the physiological strain experienced on the initial exposure to heat. Just after the exposure to the hot climate the ability to perform muscular work will be impaired, an experience of lassitude and general high degree of subjective discomfort will often occur, and if the conditions are sufficiently severe, some acute heat disorder may take place. In the course of a period of one to two weeks (191) when under a training schedule of work, the ability to endure the environment will gradually improve, and the working capacity will increase. The acclimatization depends first and foremost on an increased ability for maximal sweating (186, 197, 73).

The question now is whether the acclimatization will influence the comfort conditions. Does the increased ability to endure and work in hot environments also mean that acclimatized persons will prefer a warmer environment for comfort? Or perhaps the well-known short-term acclimatization process mentioned above is without any great significance for the comfort conditions, while on the other hand, adaptation to heat over a long period could possibly be of significance.

As the present knowledge concerning these questions is inadequate, it is evident that more research is needed. The direct method of investigating the applicability of the comfort equation in the tropics would be to perform controlled laboratory experiments involving a suitable group of native subjects from a location having a hot climate throughout the whole year. Such a study has actually been initiated at the Technical University of Denmark, testing the subjects just after their arrival by plane from hot environments.

Some information regarding the applicability of the comfort equation in hot climates can already be gained by an analysis of different field studies which have been performed in the tropics (74, 75, 265, 12, 324, 325, 67, 222, 3, 339, 223, 161). In most of these investigations the values of several of the variables have not been measured or reported, but at least in some of the studies, sufficient information is given to enable a reasonable comparison with the comfort equation to be made.

This applies to a comfort study by Ellis (75) among 152 European and Asian residents in Singapore. An optimal temperature of 27°C was found at rh ∞ 80% and a mean relative velocity of 0.4 m/s for persons with typical tropical clothing, which can be estimated to have a clo-value equal to 0.4.[1] By insertion in the comfort equation an optimal temperature of 27.4°C is obtained, which is in reasonable agreement with the result of this field study. Ellis found no difference between the Europeans and the Asians. In another field study in Singapore, including only 14 subjects, Webb (325) found, under approximately the same conditions as Ellis, an optimal temperature of 28.5°C.

From a study in Port Harcourt, Nigeria, Ambler (3) found for sedentary European residents, an optimal temperature of 26°C at rh = 70%, v = 0.1 m/s, clothing: open necked shirts and shorts ∞ 0.4 clo. The comfort equation gives an optimal temperature of 26.0°C for these conditions. Rao (265) also reported 26°C as optimum for Indian subjects in Calcutta under similar conditions.

Crocott (114) refers to the practical experience of the Anglo-Iranian Oil Company, who have installed large air cooling and air-conditioning systems in their staff accommodation and offices in the Persian Gulf area, which in summertime is actually one of the hottest geographical locations in the world. Crocott recommends an indoor air temperature around 26°C at rh between 25 and 60%.

Recently Ballantyne et al. (12) have published a comfort study from Port Moresby, New Guinea, including 34 acclimatized Caucasian subjects. For tropically clothed persons, resting in still air, rh = 80%, Ballantyne found an optimal temperature of 25.8 °C, which is identical with the value calculated from the comfort equation. Similar data are given by Wyndham (339) from

---

[1] F. P. Ellis, Pierce Foundation Laboratory, Yale University, personal communication.

a comfort study at Weipa, Northern Australia, among 16 Caucasian residents.

The above-mentioned comparison between the comfort equation and results of field studies from different geographical locations in the tropics, shows surprisingly close agreement and indicates, therefore, that there is no significant difference in the thermally neutral conditions between temperate and tropical locations. Or, expressed rather more cautiously, if a difference does exist between the comfort conditions, then it is slight, and probably not of engineering significance.

Although acclimatized persons living in the tropics can better endure hot environments and have become used to accepting the discomfort due to heat, this seems to have only a slight influence, if any, on the thermal environment which they will actually prefer if given a choice. Therefore, the comfort equation can probably also be used in the tropics with reasonable accuracy. But because of the lighter clothing one must employ a lower clo-value in the equation.

If the above conclusions are true it does not seem probable either, that the comfort conditions are subject to any seasonal variation. This has been confirmed by a recent study in Kansas by McNall, Ryan and Jaax (207) who repeated during the summer, the winter experiments of Nevins et al. (234). The winter in Kansas was quite cool (mean temperature during the test period ∞ 0 °C). The summer was hot (mean of daily peaks in the four weeks prior to and during the test period: 36 °C). No significant difference in comfort conditions was found between the summer and the winter tests.

If one now considers the opposite extreme, namely exposure to cold over a long period, does man prefer lower temperatures for comfort? Unpublished results of comfort studies at the Technical University of Denmark involving subjects who had been working daily at a sedentary activity in refrigerated spaces in the meat packing industry at temperatures of 8–9 °C, indicate only minor differences in preferred temperatures relative to the calculated results from the comfort equation. In addition, Goromosov (110, 111) reports from a large-scale winter field study from 20 locations in the USSR that people in the northern parts of the country, where the outdoor temperature reaches −45 °C and lower, prefer *higher* indoor air temperatures than in the southern part. This is confirmed by another study from the northern USSR by Kandror (160). No information as to clothing is given, however, and the results are therefore difficult to interpret. The reason for this surprising observation could be that the mean radiant temperature in cold climates is lower due to the coupling of the surface temperatures of the enclosures with outside temperature.

84

The problem of extremely cold climates is perhaps mainly of academic interest, since people will normally endeavour to adjust their clothing for comfort when they are exposed to such environments. It is therefore presumably only in special cases that people really are exposed to cold stress over such a long period that it might be expected to cause a change in the comfort conditions, if indeed such a change can occur at all.

Conclusion. No significant difference in comfort conditions was observed between Danish and American college-age subjects and the comfort equation is therefore assumed to be applicable at national-geographic locations inside the temperate climate zones. Comparison between results from field studies in the tropics and the comfort equation suggests that the equation can also be used under these conditions. No seasonal variation in comfort conditions seems to exist.

Age

Comparison between elderly and college-age subjects also shows good agreement, the neutral temperatures for the two age-groups actually being found to be identical (table 6). Even though no systematic experiments with the purpose of investigating comfort conditions for the elderly have been performed previously, the hypothesis has often been suggested that elderly persons prefer warmer environments. In the ASHRAE Handbook of Fundamentals (5) it ,is thus stated that "all men and women over 40 years of age prefer a temperature for comfort 1.0 degree (F) effective temperature higher than that desired by persons below this age", but supportive evidence is not cited.

The reason that one expects an increased preferred temperature for the elderly is due to the fact that the basal metabolic rate decreases slightly with age. The difference in basal metabolic rate between subjects about 20 years old and those about 65 is approx. 4 kcal/m²hr (36, 83, 274). The same difference would be expected to occur for sedentary activity. However, the present results show that the insensible perspiration for the elderly is, on the other hand, lower than that for the college-age group (see table 7, $Y \leq 4$). The decrement found in the evaporative heat loss for the elderly is about the same as the decrement in metabolic rate. These offset each other in the heat balance, and offer a reasonable explanation as to why no difference in preferred temperature is found between the two age-groups. The reason for the decreased insensible perspiration for the elderly could be that a change in the vapour diffusion resistance of the skin occurs as a consequence of age.

A comfort study concerning the elderly was recently published by Rohles (279), who used a non-experimental method, sending questionnaires to a large number of elderly persons with a mean age of 75 years. As pointed out in the present study (table 8), this method may give rise to significant error, and the results must therefore be interpreted with caution. However, Rohles found no difference in preferred temperature between what the elderly reported as to their impressions of the temperature scale and the remainder of the population. On the other hand, Rudeiko (285), in a field study, found that 80–90 year old persons preferred slightly warmer environments than younger persons, but it is difficult to interpret the results since all of his variables were not reported.

Although no difference in preferred temperature has been found in the present study between elderly and college-age persons at the same activity, it might be remarked that behaviour, at least for very elderly persons, tends toward quiet activity. A person seated relaxed in an armchair all day will prefer a slightly warmer environment simply because of the low activity level. As the activity level is a variable in the comfort equation, this can naturally be taken into account in the design of environments for older people.

The present investigation comprised only adult persons. However, Partridge and MacLean (252) studied 7–14 year old Canadian children and found no difference between adults and children. Sevryukova (297) investigated comfort for preschool children, but the data are insufficient for comparison with adults. It is evident that more comprehensive studies are needed in order to give definite information on comfort conditions for children.

Conclusion: The present experiments show no difference in comfort conditions between elderly and college-age persons, and it seems reasonable, therefore, to assume that the comfort equation applies for adult persons. Further work is needed on children.

Sex

The present experiments showed for both age-groups that the males preferred a warmer environment than the females, but the difference is not statistically significant (5% level). Among the American subjects, however, the females preferred a slightly higher temperature than the males, and this difference was found to be statistically significant. Since no good reason has been found for believing that a possible sex-conditioned difference in preferred temperature should be dependent on the national-geographic location, it seems reasonable to consider all Danish and American subjects in common, and in this way it is found that the females prefer a temperature which is only 0.3 °C higher than that of the males, a difference which is too small to be of engineering significance.

In an earlier comfort study by McNall et al. (206) involving 420 subjects in standard clothing (0.6 clo) at three different activity levels, small differences were observed between the sexes, the males preferring a slightly warmer temperature at one activity level and a slightly cooler at another activity level than the females, while no difference was observed at a third activity level. In several field studies no difference in optimal temperature has been observed between the sexes (145, 310, 252, 8, 136, 75). In yet others, females have preferred slightly warmer environments than males (239, 286, 203, 33, 139). Yaglou and Messer (347) found from laboratory experiments in the late 1930's that comfort differences between the sexes which might be observed in practice are due to differences in clothing.

From a theoretical point of view it might be expected that females would prefer a slightly higher temperature since their metabolic rate per unit surface area under basal conditions as well as at sedentary activity (McNall et al. (208)) is a little lower than that for males. However, this seems to be counteracted by a slightly lower insensible perspiration for females as measured in the present experiments (table 7).

Although no significant difference in preferred temperature has been found between the sexes in the present experiments, females do seem to be more sensitive to a deviation from the optimum, i.e., assessing a given deviation as more uncomfortable than males would assess it. This difference, which appears from the regression equations (table 4), is found both for the two Danish age-groups as well as for the American college-age subjects.

Conclusion. The present experiments show no significant difference in comfort conditions between males and females, either among college-age persons or among elderly persons. If any difference does exist, it is small and of no engineering significance.

BODY BUILD

It is a rather wide-spread and popular opinion that obese persons prefer a cooler environment than persons of slighter build. Some information concerning this question can be obtained from the experimental data of the present comfort study, treated in the previous section, in that the 128 college-age subjects as well as the 128 elderly persons were divided into a "fat" group and a "thin" group and compared as to their thermal voting. The "fat" group comprises that half of the subjects having the highest values of the ponderal index, while the "thin" group comprises that half of the subjects having the lowest values of this index.

The ponderal index, defined as the third root of the weight divided by the height, is chosen here as an expression of the obesity of a given subject (42). As an expression of the fat content of the body, a suitably large number of measurements of the skin fold thickness on each subject would have been more satisfactory. Skin fold thicknesses were actually taken, but not extensively enough, and the ponderal index was thus chosen as a rough expression for obesity. For each group the neutral temperature was then determined on the basis of a regression analysis, the results being given in table 9.

It will be seen that there are very small differences in the neutral temperature between the groups. Among the college-age subjects, the fat group prefers a temperature approx. 0.2 °C lower than the thin group, while the reverse is the case for the elderly group, but none of the differences are statistically significant.

Even inspection of the votes of the most obese subjects (P. I.-values up to 0.284) and the thinnest subjects (P. I.-values down to 0.205) indicated no tendency towards an influence from the body build.

Wyon (340) came to the same conclusion in a recent field study among operating personnel, when he roughly assessed the build of each subject as being in one of five categories.

The present investigation comprises only sedentary subjects. It should be remembered, however, that the metabolic rate for a certain work involving body movements will tend to be higher for an obese person, and for this reason alone he may prefer a cooler environment during activity.

Conclusion. The present experiments indicate no significant influence of body build on the comfort conditions of sedentary subjects.

MENSTRUAL CYCLE

In the experiments described in the previous sections, the time of the test in relation to the menstrual cycle of each female college-age subject was

Table 9. *Comparison Between Neutral Temperatures for Thin and Obese Subjects*

Comparison Between	Ponderal Index	Neutral Temp.	Diff. Between Neutral Temp.	Mean of Neutral Temp. T_m	Diff. Between Mean Votes at T_m ΔY	Estim. Variance of ΔY $s^2_{\Delta Y}$	Degrees of Freedom for $s^2_{\Delta Y}$ df	T-value	Significance (5% level)
	kg$^{0.33}$/m	°C	°C	°C					
College-age Danish:									
Fattest Half...............	2.33	25.49	−0.26	25.62	0.080	0.0207	840	0.555	no
Thinnest Half.............	2.21	25.75							
Elderly Danish:									
Fattest Half...............	2.52	25.79	+0.17	25.71	−0.058	0.0320	124	0.324	no
Thinnest Half.............	2.23	25.63							

89

Table 10. *Comparison Between Neutral Temperatures for Groups of College-age Females in Different Periods of the Menstrual Cycle*

Comparison Between Groups	Number of Subjects	Neutral Temp. °C	Diff. Between Neutral Temp. °C	Mean of Neutral Temp. T_m °C	Diff. Between Mean Votes at T_m ΔY	Estim. Variance of ΔY $s^2_{\Delta Y}$	Degrees of Freedom for $s^2_{\Delta Y}$ df	T-value	Significance (5% level)
Menstrual or Premenstrual (D ≥ 26 or D ≤ 4)...............	22	25.38							
Remainder of Cycle (4 < D < 26)................	42	25.61	−0.23	25.49	+0.091	0.041	840	0.448	no
Preovulatory (10 ≤ D ≤ 17)...............	16	25.70							
Postovulatory (18 ≤ D ≤ 25)...............	18	25.15	+0.55	25.43	−0.218	0.083	840	−0.757	no

recorded and it was therefore possible to test whether any difference existed in preferred temperature between groups of subjects within different periods of the menstrual cycle.

It was found reasonable to first compare females who were either in the premenstrual or menstrual phase with females who were not in either of these phases of the menstrual cycle. The females were divided into two groups, one comprising subjects for whom $D \geq 26$ or $D \leq 4$, and the other comprising subjects for whom $4 < D < 26$, where D is the number of days after the beginning of the last menstruation. Regression analyses were made for the two groups and the neutral temperatures thus found are listed in table 10. No significant difference between these two groups was observed.

In addition, a comparison has been made between the following two groups of subjects: females in the preovulatory period $10 \leq D \leq 17$, and females in the postovulatory period $18 \leq D \leq 25$. Since the basal body temperature, according to Midgley and Jaffe (211), can be expected to be slightly higher in the second period than in the first, this fact could possibly have an influence on the comfort conditions. The neutral temperatures for these two groups are also listed in table 10. A difference of half a degree between the neutral temperatures was observed but this is not statistically significant (5% level).

The present experiments at least, do not indicate that the menstrual cycle has any practical influence on the comfort conditions. Possible minor fluctuations during the cycle must, however, be detected by a more refined experimental technique than the present one which was not primarily established to investigate this phenomenon. Determining neutral temperatures for individual subjects each day during a whole cycle, for example, would be preferable.

Conclusion. The present experiments indicate that the menstrual cycle has no practical influence on the comfort conditions. A more refined experimental technique is necessary in order to detect possible minor fluctuations during the cycle.

ETHNIC DIFFERENCES

Very little information exists on possible differences in comfort conditions between various ethnic groups. Some field studies have been carried out, but none have demonstrated any significant difference. This applies to a study by Ellis (75) among Asian and European residents in Singapore, a study by Angus (8) among students of many different races in London and a recently published investigation by Wyon et al. (340) in British operating rooms comprising subjects of different ethnic groups.

FOOD

The intake of food causes a certain increase in internal heat production. This would be expected to have an influence on thermal comfort. This increase, referred to as specific dynamic action of food (SDA), is highest for proteins, substantially lower for carbohydrates and smallest for fats. After most meals consisting of a mixed diet, the SDA amounts to an increase of 10%–15% (254) in relation to basal metabolic rate (equivalent to 3–5 kcal/m²hr) but can be somewhat higher if the meal is rich in protein. During exercise, SDA is low and normally negligible.

The SDA normally lasts a relatively long time (4–6 hours) after the intake of food, with a peak occurring 1–2 hours after the meal. With a normal daily food cycle consisting of three (or four) meals there are only 4–5 hours between the intake of food, so that SDA will take place practically the whole waking period each day and the mean value is already included in the internal heat production listed in table 1 for different activities. Some minor fluctuations will take place during the day of course. If a variation of ±2 kcal/m²hr is assumed, as well as low activity, low velocity and a clo-value around 0.5, calculations from the comfort equation indicate variations of ±0.3°C in optimal ambient temperature with the maximum occurring before the meal and minimum occurring 1–2 hours after the meal. After a heavy meal rich in protein, the influence could be greater, probably decreasing the optimal temperature up to 1°C for some hours.

The consumption of alcohol does not seem to change the internal heat production noticeably, either for small, just perceptible doses (11, 316) or by the intake of higher quantities of alcohol (103, 41, 317). If the popular notion that alcohol causes a certain sensation of warmth is true, it cannot therefore be due to a change in metabolic rate. It could be related to the skin vasodilatation, which is caused by the intake of alcohol (151). If any influence of alcohol on thermal sensation exists it would presumably tend to lower the optimal temperature, but no experimental evidence could be found.

At high doses of alcohol the resulting hypaesthesia will, of course, make the concept of thermal sensation and comfort meaningless.

CIRCADIAN RHYTHM

It is a well known phenomenon that the internal body temperature has a daily rhythm with a maximum occurring some time before the sleeping period and a minimum occurring some time before the person awakes. The amplitude of the oscillation is about 0.3–0.5°C. A rhythm in the comfort conditions is therefore feasible.

However, Nevins et al. (234) found no difference in optimal temperature between experiments performed in the afternoon and those performed in the evening, an observation which is confirmed in the present study. Nielsen (241) observed some changes during morning and afternoon experiments but no apparent differerence between the two periods of the day.

If any influence of circadian rhythm on comfort conditions exists it is probably so small as to be of no practical significance.

THERMAL TRANSIENTS

The comfort equation has been derived for steady state conditions, but this does not imply, however, that all variables need to be absolutely constant from one minute to the next. In practice, minor fluctuations in one or more of the variables will often occur, but as long as the mean value, taken over a suitable time interval, is reasonably constant, quasi-steady-state conditions exist, under which the comfort equation can also be employed.

For sudden large changes in one or more of the variables, the conditions are much more complicated since, among other things, the heat capacity of the body must also be considered. However, at present, only a few investigations have been made concerning comfort conditions under these circumstances, which are of practical importance especially in connection with short periods of occupancy in a room.

Recently important studies concerning thermal transients have been performed by Gagge, Stolwijk and Hardy (96, 101, 127, 306). In one type of experiment they exposed nude subjects alternately to cold and neutral and to hot and neutral environments. When proceeding from neutral to cold or warm environments, the changing thermal sensation was found to be correlated with the actual skin temperature and sweat rate in the same way as under steady state conditions. But when these transients were reversed, i.e. proceeding from a cold or hot to a neutral environment, they felt almost immediately comfortable, even though their skin temperature had not yet reached the steady state level considered comfortable. Gagge explains this by the rate of change of skin temperature which might cause a sensation that compensates for and predominates over the sensation of discomfort caused by the skin temperature itself. The thermal sensation "leads" the body temperature changes in this case and is thus "anticipatory". This hysteresis effect is an aid to man's reactions to fluctuating temperatures, since his thermal sensation changes more rapidly from discomfort to comfort than vice versa.

The sudden changes which occur when persons move from hot outdoor environments into an air-conditioned space (or vice versa) have sometimes been believed to cause an unhealthy "shock" effect. Studies by Keaton and others (108, 109, 135, 154, 156) have shown, however, that the necessary adjustments in the temperature regulatory mechanisms are prompt, unstressful and not unhealthy. Even ambulatory heart patients endure such changes with ease and the word "shock" to describe any part of these adjustments is, therefore, unwarranted.

With sudden changes in the humidity, special thermal phenomena occur due to absorption and desorption of water in the clothing and the skin. Textile fibres in equilibrium contain water in a quantity which is dependent on the relative humidity of the ambient air. If the air humidity is suddenly decreased, an evaporation of water will occur until the moisture content of the fibres corresponds to the new state of equilibrium. Evaporation requires heat and therefore, during this process, the environment will be perceived as cooler, when the humidity is suddenly decreased. Similarly, condensation will occur in the clothes with a consequent heat release when the humidity of the ambient air is increased suddenly.

This effect was already demonstrated in the 'twenties in Houghten and Yaglou's classic experiment which led to the setting up of the effective temperature (142, 342, 343). Subjects went back and forth between two chambers of different humidity, and the temperatures were changed until the persons found the rooms equally warm. A considerable humidity influence was found (as expressed in the effective temperature) which was thought to be of general validity. Twenty-five years later, however, Yaglou (348) realized that this significant moisture influence was probably caused by the transient character of the experiments.

The thermal effect of sudden changes in the humidity has later been examined by various textile research workers (52, 276, 62). It seems clear that the thermal effect is greatest immediately after the humidity change, after which it decreases relatively quickly. The effect seems to depend on the type of fibre; cotton, and especially wool, cause a greater thermal effect during humidity changes than synthetic fibres. However, this field has not been well examined as yet, and further research is obviously required.

In practice, the thermal effect of humidity changes causes the thermal discomfort to be diminished for persons who, in winter, are indoors for short periods with overclothes on. As the relative humidity in winter is high outdoors, the moisture content of the clothes will also be high, and the evaporation from the overclothes, on coming indoors, will therefore have an immediate cooling effect which delays the feeling of warm discomfort. Similarly, when the person exits, condensation will take place in the clothes, causing the outdoor environment to feel less cold at first. In rooms occupied by both lightly clad persons for long periods and heavily clad persons for short periods (shops, public offices, etc.), a low air humidity will be advantageous, as it decreases the thermal discomfort of the latter persons.

In the design of automatic control systems it is important to know which temperature fluctuations are acceptable from the point of view of comfort. This problem has recently been investigated by Sprague and McNall (302), who studied the influence on sedentary lightly clothed subjects of periodical fluctuations in air temperature, mean radiant temperature and all other variables being kept constant. They found that no serious occupancy complaints occur due to temperature fluctuations if

$$\Delta t^2 \,(\text{cph}) < 4.6 \qquad (°C^2/\text{hr})$$

where Δt is the peak to peak amplitude of the air temperature (°C) and cph is the cycling frequency (hr^{-1}). For example if $\Delta t = 1°C$, then cph < 4.6 cycles/hr would be an acceptable cycling rate. If cph $= 9.2$ cycles/hr, then $\Delta t < 0.7°C$ would be an acceptable peak to peak amplitude.

It is sometimes maintained that fluctuations in air temperature may actually be beneficial, since they should have a stimulating and invigorating effect on the organism, but this assertion is purely speculative and lacks documentation. It is certain, at least, that in rooms occupied by many persons there will, over a period, be a greater total number of dissatisfied when the temperature fluctuates beyond the limits stated above than when it is kept constant, as evidenced from the distribution of thermal sensation votes analysed in the next chapter.

UNILATERAL HEATING OR COOLING OF THE BODY

The satisfaction of the comfort equation is claimed to be a necessary condition for optimal thermal comfort. If a person is exposed to an asymmetric thermal flux it is not certain, however, that it is also a sufficient condition. Although a person may feel thermally neutral for the body in general, i.e., he would prefer neither a warmer nor a cooler environment, he might not be in thermal comfort if one part of the body is warm and another cold. To take an extreme case, a man who has one foot in ice-cold water and the other foot in hot water, can very well have a mean skin temperature and sweat secretion which, according to the comfort equation, condition thermal neutrality, but it is clear that because of the local effects he would be most uncomfortable! This extreme case shows that there must exist a limit for how asymmetric the heat loss from the body can be, without compromising thermal comfort. The question is, where this limit lies.

Discomfort due to unilateral heating or cooling of the body can be caused by an asymmetric radiant field, by air velocity (draught) or by warm or cold floors. In the following, each of these three cases will be discussed.

Asymmetric Radiant Fields

Several investigators have studied the influence on thermal comfort of asymmetric radiant fields, created for example by warm or cold panels in a wall or in the ceiling.

Bøje, Nielsen and Olesen (49) carried out a series of investigations with in all 32 sedentary subjects (14 elderly and 18 young men and women) who were exposed to unilateral radiant cooling from a vertical surface. It measured 1.2 × 1.4 m and was at a temperature of 10°C, placed 0.3 m to the left of the person (angle factor ∽ 0.20), while the temperature of the air and all other surfaces was regulated so that the persons in general were thermally neutral. Each person was exposed to this thermal environment for 6 hours daily for 15 days. The unilateral radiant cooling caused no discomfort, but a palpatoric examination showed, for a few of the subjects (in the course of the experimental period) a thickening of the cutaneous and subcutaneous tissues and an increased tension and soreness of the muscles on the side of the body exposed to the cold panel.

Gagge et al. (94, 95, 98) exposed four sedentary, nude subjects to radiation from two high-temperature radiant sources placed over the person. The air temperature was varied, and the person could adjust the radiant intensity himself until he felt that he was thermally neutral. Even in an air temperature as low as 10°C, the subjects had no difficulty in finding a suitable radiant intensity which created thermal comfort. A significant heat loss from the unirradiated parts of the body was compensated for by a heat gain on the irradiated parts, without causing any noticeable discomfort. The result of this investigation is in agreement with the everyday observation that nude persons sunbathing can be comfortable in an air temperature of 20°C, for example, (depending on the air velocity) even though the thermal influence on the body is obviously very heterogeneous.

On the other hand, Chrenko (57) maintains, on the basis of short-exposure experiments, that a heat radiation from above which causes an increase of more than 2°C in the mean radiant temperature (in relation to the head), may result in an unpleasant radiation influence on the upper parts of the body, especially the head. Later on, Kollmar (166, 167, 168) used this limit as grounds for a mathematical deduction of limit curves for the highest permissible ceiling temperatures, depending on the angle factor of the ceiling. It is probable, however, that some of the symptoms which Chrenko found in a number of his subjects can be a consequence of general warm discomfort and not just of the asymmetric radiant field, as in the experiments no compensation was made for the added radiation (e.g., by decreasing the air temperature). If Chrenko's criterion was valid in general, all exposure to solar radiation would be uncomfortable, as this unilateral radiation involves a mean radiant temperature which can be about 30–40°C higher than the air temperature. This is much more than his recommended upper limit of 2°C, which seems to be on the conservative side.

Wenzel and Müller (328), in experiments of a similar nature, have exposed standing subjects to radiation from a 5.6 × 5.9 m ceiling (height = 3.8 m), the exposure time in most of the experiments being 5–10 min. Some discomfort was observed for ceiling temperatures higher than 37°C, but no influence on local skin temperature was observed, in contradiction to Ronge and Löfstedt (281) who found a significant influence of a cold ceiling on shoulder temperature.

Experiments of an extreme nature have been carried out by Hall and Klemm (120). Their objective was to study the physiological response to disparate thermal environments as a result of re-entry and extravehicular aspects of aerospace flights. Six lightly-clad subjects (0.3 clo) were placed lying on a net in a narrow test chamber arranged in such a way that the part of the body facing upwards was exposed to a radiant temperature of 82–93°C, and that underneath was exposed to one of −7°C, while the air temperature was 21–24°C. Even when exposed to such extreme skew influences, it was possible to bring the subjects into a state where they reported overall thermal comfort, despite the existence of an anterior-posterior skin temperature difference of around 9°C.

The most comprehensive experiments so far concerning the effect of asymmetric radiation in practical environments have recently been performed at Kansas State University. Schlegel and McNall (292) exposed 90 sedentary subjects clothed in standard uniforms (0.6 clo) to an asymmetric radiant field. One side wall in a test chamber (angle factor between subject and wall = 0.2) was kept in one series of experiments 7°C lower, and in another series 7°C higher, than the balance of the chamber surface temperatures. In comparison with similar experiments in uniform radiant fields, no discomfort as a result of the asymmetry was found.

In continuation of these experiments, McNall and Biddison (209) exposed 234 subjects to more extreme asymmetries. Subjects were exposed to a ceiling (angle factor = 0.15) with a temperature which in one series of experiments was 30°C higher and in another series 15°C lower than the balance of the chamber surface temperatures. In a third series of experiments, subjects were exposed to a wall (angle factor = 0.20) 11°C lower than ambient. In all these three cases no discomfort due to the asymmetry was found, the subjects reacting in the same way as in uniform surroundings with the same mean radiant temperature. Discomfort due to asymmetry was observed only in a test where the wall was 30°C warmer than ambient temperature.

In the above, various unilateral external influences due to asymmetric radiant fields have been mentioned. It must be remembered, however, that even for a nude man in a completely uniform thermal field where the air velocity is zero, the heat flux density is by no means uniform over the whole body surface. There will be considerable differences because (a) even in a state of comfort, the skin temperature is not absolutely uniform, (b) the convective heat transfer coefficient is not equal over the whole of the body surface, partly due to the differences in characteristic dimension (compare trunk and little finger), and (c) the heat loss to the surroundings by radiation is less for some skin areas because of radiant interchange with other parts of the body (e.g., between the legs).

If one now considers a clothed man, e.g., clad in a normal business suit, this attire will further cause significant variations in the heat flux between the unclothed and clothed parts of the body and between skin areas where the clothing has a different thermal resistance. If, moreover, the subject is lying down, e.g. on a well-upholstered divan, the heat flux from the posterior part of the body will be almost zero, an extreme case of asymmetric heat flux.

From these examples it can be seen that clothing, etc., increases the non-uniformity of the heat loss from a person. Nevertheless, it is well known from practice that thermal comfort can easily be created in such cases –

despite the significant non-uniformity caused by the clothing which is often greater than most asymmetries originating from the surroundings. On the basis of the foregoing considerations and the previous experiments referred to above, it seems reasonable to assume that the comfort equation can be used even in relatively skew thermal fields. At present, however, it is difficult to give reliable quantitative limits as to the magnitude of thermal asymmetry under which thermal comfort is impossible.

Even though thermal effects which are quite non-uniform do not prevent the creation of thermal comfort, this does not necessarily mean that these effects cannot give rise to unfavourable effects on the state of health of a person over prolonged exposures. This point needs further research.

Draught

Draught is often defined as an unwanted local convective cooling of a person. It is noted that also radiant cooling is sometimes included in the definition of draught. Only convective draught will be discussed here, but many of the considerations regarding unilateral radiant cooling which are set forth in the previous section, are also valid when speaking of convective cooling.

Experiments at the Techn. University of Denmark (7) and at Kansas State University (80) have shown that at least with normal clothing, it is not difficult to create thermal comfort for a single person exposed to a relatively high velocity, e.g. about 1 m/s, unilaterally exposed to the entire body, if only the ambient temperature is regulated according to the comfort equation. These observations are also in agreement with experiments carried out by Houghten (146) and Norbäck (247), the results of which are expressed in formulae and diagrams by Rydberg (287, 288, 289) and Olingsberg (250). The non-uniformity in the heat loss from the different parts of the body due to exposure to a high velocity from a given direction seems, therefore, at least for normal clothing, to be of only minor importance as long as the subject is in general, thermally neutral. This is also in agreement with the fact that people can feel thermally comfortable outdoors although air velocities here are often much higher than indoors. The very fact that a walking subject can be comfortable, although the movement in itself creates relative velocities of 1–2 m/s, points to the same conclusion.

Complaints about draughts can nevertheless be a serious practical problem. This is presumably a consequence of two factors. Firstly, optimal comfort for a group of persons does not mean that all are comfortable. In a large group there will always be some who feel cool and some who feel warm and this will be discussed in detail in the next chapter. Those who generally feel cool will, according to Cabanac (50), be much more sensitive to a local cold stimulus. If this stimulus is caused by the air velocity, the person will be liable to complain of draught. Secondly, there can often be significant differences in air velocity within the occupied zone. Even though, for example, all velocities lie in the interval 0–0.3 m/s, this will bring about quite significant differences in the thermal effect on subjects at different locations (see fig. 14). As will be seen in the following chapter, the percentage of subjects who feel cold (or warm) discomfort will increase, the larger the variations found from point to point in a room. Therefore, the fraction of persons likely to feel discomfort because of draught will be increased. To obtain as uniform conditions as possible in the occupied zone, one normally designs, in practice, for velocities so small that the heat loss from the human body occurs by free convection where the heat transfer coefficient is independent of the velocity.

The sensation of draught seems, at least to some extent, to be a function of the general thermal state of the body. If a person feels warm he is likely to assess a local convective cooling as pleasant while the same stimulus might be felt unpleasant, i.e. as a draught, if he generally feels cool (50). It is possible that also the velocity fluctuations are of importance for the sensation of draught.

It must be said that up to the present, problems in connection with draught have been insufficiently examined and further research is, therefore, urgently needed.

Cold and Warm Floors

Because of the direct conduction contact between feet and floor, unpleasant local cooling or heating of the feet can occur if the floor is too hot or too cold. In the design of heated or cooled floors and in the choice of insulating and floor materials, it is essential to be aware of the limits for permissible floor temperatures.

It is important to point out that complaints of cold feet need not necessarily have anything to do with the floor temperature. If a person generally feels cool, he will often notice it most perceptively in the feet, as the skin temperature there, because of the vasoconstriction, is normally lowest (123, 241). And a person with cold feet will often be likely to think that the floor is cold, although the cold feet may actually be only a symptom of general cold discomfort. Likewise, uncomfortably warm feet can be due merely to general warm discomfort.

Although the foot temperature, as demonstrated by Nielsen (242), mainly is a function of the thermal state of the whole body, the temperature of the floor will nevertheless have a certain influence with a consequent possibility for local discomfort, even though the person generally feels thermally neutral. The limits for permissible temperatures depend on whether or not the persons wear shoes, and these two cases will therefore be treated separately.

With Footwear

Local discomfort must obviously be connected with the heat loss from the feet, which depends on the footwear (especially the sole) and on the floor temperature. On the other hand, studies of Muncey (228, 229), Munro and Chrenko (230), Billington (29, 30) and Frank (84, 85), indicate that the flooring material has no influence on foot discomfort. The old superstition that concrete floors feel cold does not apply for persons with footwear.

The upper and lower limits for permissible floor temperatures depend on the kind of footwear, so that both limits must be higher the lighter the footwear. For a person wearing heavy winter boots, the upper and lower limits could be $+ 10\,°C$ and $- 10\,°C$ respectively, so that in normal indoor environments his feet would be too warm. The example shows that specifications regarding footwear are necessary in order to give reasonable limits for the floor temperature.

Comprehensive American experiments involving in all 61 subjects in light shoes, have recently been carried out by Nevins et al. (232, 233, 303), who found that floor surface temperatures as high as 29 °C did not cause serious discomfort for sedentary and walking subjects during 3-hour exposures. For shorter exposures (1 hr) Nevins (231) found a limit as high as 35 °C for seated persons. Standing persons will require lower limits due to the constant contact with the floor (30). Earlier European studies (56, 51, 217) indicate somewhat lower maximum temperatures, probably because of heavier footwear.

Cold floors were also investigated by Nevins (235) who, for 48 subjects with light shoes, found results which indicate a lower comfort limit for floor temperatures of approx. 17–18 °C.

In all the above-mentioned experiments, both for warm and for cold floors, some of the observed foot-discomfort votes might just be a symptom of general bodily discomfort. If only subjects in general bodily neutrality were observed, the range of permissible floor temperatures would probably become wider.

Bare Feet

In rooms where people go barefooted (bathrooms, bedrooms) it is not only the floor temperature but also the flooring material which is of importance for foot comfort. Immediately after the foot touches the floor, the sole takes on the contact temperature which is a function of the floor temperature and the contact coefficient b of the surface material of the floor defined by

$$b = \sqrt{k \rho c} \qquad\qquad (34)$$

where k = conductivity
       ρ = density
       c = specific heat

A concrete floor has a much higher contact coefficient than a wooden floor and therefore will feel colder because the contact temperature is lower.

That the purely physical calculation of the contact temperature gives reasonable results has been confirmed experimentally by Schüle (294) and Billington (29, 30), but large-scale investigations with subjects are lacking in order to fix the upper and lower comfort limits for the contact temperatures.

In the absence of experimental evidence, one can make a rough calculation of comfort intervals for various flooring materials by setting the initial foot

Table 11. *Temperature Limits for Different Flooring Materials, Bare Feet*

Flooring Material (without surface finishing)	Contact Coefficient	Comfort Range of Floor Temperature	Pain Limits	
			lower	upper
	kcal/m² hr$^{0.5}$ °C	°C	°C	°C
Steel.....................	180	29–32	14	45
Concrete..................	25	27–34	4	54
Linoleum, rubber..........	9	24–35	−12	67
Oak wood................	7	22–35	−20	74
Pine wood...............	4	17–39	−53	84
Cork....................	2	5–42	−140	150

temperature at 32 °C and the upper and lower comfort limits at 33 °C and 29 °C respectively, the contact coefficient for the skin being assumed to be approximately 16 kcal/m² hr$^{0.5}$ °C (294).

The results are given in table 11, which also gives limits for floor temperatures which will actually give rise to a pain sensation, as the pain limits for the skin are set at 15 and 45 °C. It must be emphasized, however, that the table should be used with caution, as in the absence of experimental evidence, it is calculated on the basis of estimated skin temperatures.

Moreover, the calculation can be assumed to be valid when a person with bare feet remains only a short time on the floor in question. This, however, is normally the case of greatest practical interest.

COLOUR

It seems to be a commonly accepted idea that colour in a room influences the feeling of warmth. For instance an individual is presumed to feel warmer in an environment finished in a colour scheme in which red predominates, as compared with one in which blue is the prevailing colour.

Green and blue are considered to be "cool" colours, whereas red and orange are considered "warm" (2). When coloured lights are used to illuminate stage scenes, the "cool" hues give the audience the impression of a low temperature on stage, while the illusion of heat is produced by "warm" lighting (282).

The question is whether a person's thermal sensation really can be biased by the colour of his surroundings. The problem is of considerable interest as an affirmative answer could undoubtedly lead to interesting energy-saving consequences: e.g., by "colour conditioning", more or less substituting for air conditioning.

The first experimental study with bearing on this question was conducted by Morgensen and English (224), who asked subjects to judge the temperature of heating coils wrapped in paper of different colours. Subjects apparently judged the green ones as hottest.

Houghten et al. (149) studied the problem in an environmental chamber where subjects successively were exposed to red, white and blue environments. Houghten found no influence of colour, either on physiological measurements or on thermal sensation votes.

The most comprehensive study concerning the influence of colour upon thermal sensation was conducted by Berry (27) who exposed each of 25 subjects to 5 colours: blue, green, white, yellow and amber. In each test the ambient temperature was slowly increased and the subject was told to indicate by a switch when he was beginning to feel uncomfortably warm. As the subjects were led to believe that the tests concerned the effects of coloured illumination upon imagined driving performance, it was possible to conduct the experiments so that they were unaware of the experimenter's interest in their judgement of comfort. The results showed no change in the upper limit of comfort as a function of the colour.

The results of the above-mentioned investigations are in agreement with the fact that the colour of the surrounding surfaces has no influence on man's heat loss, with the exception of those special cases where the wave-length of special high-intensity radiant sources can possibly influence the mean radiant temperature.

As colour has no thermal influence on man, any influence on the thermal sensation must therefore be of a psychological nature. None of the investigations carried out up till now, however, indicate that such an influence exists.

CROWDING

It is sometimes maintained that crowding will influence the conditions for thermal comfort, i.e., that persons would prefer a lower temperature in a room packed with many persons than in the same room occupied only by a few.

Rohles et al. (278) studied the effect of subject crowding by exposing groups of 8, 18 and 32 test persons to the same thermal environments in a test chamber measuring $3.6 \times 7.3 \times 2.4$ m³ equivalent to respectively 3.3, 1.5 and 0.8 m² floor area per subject and 8.0, 3.5 and 2.0 m³ room volume per subject. The results showed no influence of crowding on the physiological responses of the subjects. The experiments were performed under warm conditions, where the effect of reciprocal radiant exchange between the subjects had negligible influence. However, in cooler environments this effect would tend to increase the mean radiant temperature slightly and therefore decrease the optimal air temperature in crowded rooms. Yaglou and Drinker (345) found that this increment of the mean radiant temperature is the only effect from crowding.

If, however, the crowding is so extreme that the boundary layers of the subjects begin to interact upon each other (e.g. in trains and buses at peak hours), the convective heat transfer will also be impaired, necessitating a lower air temperature for comfort.

An example of extreme crowding is the classical case in the Black Hole of Calcutta (14), where 146 British prisoners in 1773 were locked up in a 23 m² room, only 23 being alive after one night. But this has certainly nothing to do with thermal comfort and therefore falls outside the frame of the present study. It has been established beyond doubt, however, that these deaths were caused by heat stress and not suffocation.

Apart from the increment in mean radiant temperature, there is little reason to believe that crowding will normally influence the comfort conditions. But crowding will of course, have a dominating influence on the sizing of the environmental equipment which is to provide thermal comfort in the actual room, due to the added heat sources of the occupants.

AIR PRESSURE

The comfort equation is derived for an air pressure equivalent to normal sea level pressure (= 760 mm Hg). The question now is to what extent a deviation from the normal air pressure will influence the preferred thermal environment. Daily meteorological pressure fluctuations represent only a small percentage of the total air pressure and have therefore no noticeable thermal effect. But for a number of practical applications there can occur significant deviations from the atmospheric pressure at sea level. This mainly concerns high mountainous elevations and aeroplanes (space craft) where the pressure is lower than normal. Deep mines, pressurized chambers for medical care (hyperbaric), and ocean floor sea-laboratories, where the pressure can be considerably higher than the normal atmospheric pressure at sea level, are also becoming more important.

The air pressure influences some of the terms in the heat balance for the human body and can therefore also be expected to have a certain significance for the preferred thermal environment.

Considering the various heat losses from the body, the radiation is practically independent of the air pressure. The same applies to conduction through the clothing, as the thermal conductivity of the air is not dependent on the pressure.

The convective heat loss will, however, be changed. Of those properties of air which are significant for convective heat transfer, the absolute viscosity, the thermal conductivity, the specific heat, and the coefficient of expansion are all independent of the air pressure, while the density is proportional to the pressure. By inserting the properties in eqs. (22) and (24), it follows from this that the convective heat transfer coefficient for both free and forced convection is proportional to the square root of the pressure. The convective heat loss will thus be less at low pressure, e.g. in high mountains.

This is counteracted, however, by an increased evaporative heat loss. Increases occur partly in the vapour diffusion through the skin which is inversely dependent on air pressure (119), and partly in the latent inspiration heat loss because the lung ventilation, expressed as volume flow, increases (depending on the activity level) when the air pressure falls (351). Since the quantitative influence of air pressure on evaporative heat loss is not completely known at the present time, it is therefore difficult to give reliable corrections to the comfort equation. For low pressures, slightly increased optimal temperatures may be expected, as the increment in evaporative heat loss more than compensates for the decrement in convective heat loss. For those pressures which are many times higher than normal pressure, an increased optimal temperature may also be expected.

For the relatively moderate deviations from the normal pressure, which are of predominant importance in practice ($\pm 30\%$, equivalent to ± 3000 m in height), it seems clear, however, that only small corrections are necessary. The comfort equation can therefore be applied without modifications as a reasonable approximation in these cases. At low air pressures a greater humidity dependency can be expected.

For extreme high and low pressures which naturally occur only under exceptional conditions, the existing knowledge concerning, among other things, vapour diffusion through the skin, is insufficient to enable the setting up of reliable corrections.

Chapter 4.
PRACTICAL ASSESSMENT OF THERMAL ENVIRONMENTS

In the foregoing chapters the conditions for optimal thermal comfort have been discussed. In the design and operation of environmental systems, it is these conditions which are of primary interest when optimal thermal comfort is desired.

But in practice how should one evaluate an existing room climate, and how should one rate the quality of a given thermal environment? It is possible to measure the environmental variables at a suitable number of points in the occupied zone in a given space, but how should these measurements be interpreted? How can one quantify the deviation from the comfort condition, and how great a non-uniformity can one tolerate within the occupied zone? In short, how can one, on the basis of measurements taken in practice, determine whether a given indoor climate is satisfactory or not. A method of determining this is, of course, of the greatest importance in order to obtain any meaningful result from practical measurements, and it is a necessary prerequisite for the establishment of reasonable standards which can be guaranteed in the field. However, up till now, no suitable method has been available.

In the present chapter a new and rational method will be set up for the evaluation, in practice, of a given thermal environment. First, starting from the comfort equation, a new thermal sensation index will be derived, which makes it possible to predict the mean thermal sensation vote on a standard scale for a large group of persons for any given combination of the four thermal environmental variables, the activity level and the clo-value of clothing worn by the occupants.

The mathematical expression derived for the calculation of the "Predicted Mean Vote" (PMV) is rather complicated; tables and diagrams have therefore been prepared which simplify the determination of PMV. On the basis of an analysis of data from experiments involving nearly one thousand three hundred subjects, another factor is then introduced in the following section, namely "Predicted Percentage of Dissatisfied" (PPD), i.e., that percentage of a large group of persons who can be expected to feel definitely uncomfortable in a given environment. As it is precisely the decidedly dissatisfied who in fact will be inclined to complain about the thermal environment, PPD would seem to be a meaningful factor in rating the quality of a given indoor climate. The Predicted Percentage of Dissatisfied can be determined after PMV has been found for a series of different locations in the occupied zone in the actual room.

The more non-uniform a thermal field in a room, the greater the number of dissatisfied persons to be expected. On the basis of measurements taken in the field, one can calculate the "Lowest Possible Percentage of Dissatisfied" (LPPD) which it is possible to obtain in the actual room by altering the temperature level. The magnitude of LPPD is an expression for the non-uniformity of the thermal environment and is therefore suitable for characterizing the heating or air-conditioning system in the actual space under consideration.

The method makes possible a prediction of how many dissatisfied persons can be expected for the conditions under which the measurements are taken, as well as an estimation of how low it is possible to bring the percentage of dissatisfied in the given space, with its actual heating or air-conditioning system.

After going through the practical procedure for the use of the new method for evaluating thermal environments, the present chapter gives, finally, a short summary of suitable methods for measuring the four environmental variables in practice.

EARLIER THERMAL INDICES

Over the years a large number of thermal indices have been set up, with various objectives, which in different ways should enable an estimation to be made of the thermal environment or of the thermal state of man. But only a few of them refer at all to man's thermal sensation.

One group of indices had the specific objective of making possible an evaluation of extreme heat stress. This concerns the P4SR-index (Mc Ardle et al. (202, 200, 299)), the Heat Stress Index (Belding and Hatch (23, 24)), the Oxford Index (Lind et al. (190, 186)), the Index of Physiological Effect (Robinson et al. (275)), the Thermal Acceptance Ratio (Ionides et al. (157, 262)), the Relative Strain Index (Lee and Henschel (184, 152, 71)), Yaglou and Minard's WBGT-index (349), Givoni's Index of Thermal Stress (105,

106), the Nomogrammes of Vogt and Metz (323) and Lustinec's Predictive System (195, 196).

These indices are set up as a basis for the assessment of physiological severity in hot environments, so that, among other things, safety limits and tolerance time can be set for workers in mines and hot industries. They are, however, unsuitable for the assessment of ordinary non-extreme environments.

Another group comprises indices where it has been attempted, within certain limits, to combine the effect on man of two or more of the surrounding variables to a single variable. This concerns the Effective Temperature, developed by Yaglou and associates (142, 144, 342, 343, 344, 346, 348), the Belgian Effective Temperature (Bidlot and Ledent (28)), the Operative Temperature (Gagge et al. (88, 91)), the Resulting Temperature (Nielsen and Pedersen (243, 244), Missenard (219)), the Equivalent Temperature (Dufton and Bedford (69, 21)), the Equivalent Warmth (Bedford (21)), the Wind Chill Index (Siple and Passel (157, 262)).

Belonging to the same group is also a large number of instruments which have been developed over the years for the purpose of integrating the effect of two or more of the environmental variables into one value: The Homöotherm (Frankenhaüser (87)), the Katathermometer (137, 138, 16, 70, 38, 293, 291, 296), the Frigorimeter (Dorno (66), Thilenius (311), Schüle (296), Frank (86)), the Coolometer (Weeks (327)), the Eupatheostat and Eupatheoscope (Dufton (68, 69)), the Thermointegrator (Winslow et al. (331, 332, 333)), the Frigorigraph (Pfleiderer and Büttner (260)), the Trifrigorigraph (Pfleiderer (261)), Globethermometers of different types (320, 321, 131, 17, 216, 177, 178, 45), the Directional Thermometer (Bisgaard (31, 32)), the Klimasonde (Riedel (273)), different thermal manikins (Pedersen (256), Newling (238) and Tredre (312), Korsgaard and Lund Madsen (175)), and the R-meter (Gagge (99)).

In order to evaluate the ability of a given climate to create satisfactory conditions for the subjects, it is necessary to have an index which predicts the thermal sensation of the subjects, but only few such indices exist.

In the 'thirties, Bedford (21) set up an index on the basis of a comprehensive field study among female British industrial workers. This index, which is found from a correlation analysis, gives the observed mean vote as a function of the four environmental variables. Neither activity level nor clothing are included in the index, and it is therefore obvious that it is valid only for the non-specified clothing and activity under which the measurements have been taken in the actual field study. The same applies for an index set up by van Zuilen (350, 37) in the 'forties. Both Bedford's and van Zuilen's indices give, at small velocities, optimal ambient temperatures as low as 16–17 °C.

Likewise, Webb (324) has set up an Equatorial Comfort Index based on a field study in Singapore involving 20 persons, but this index does not give the activity level or the clo-value as variables either, and is thus also of limited applicability under other conditions.

Recently theoretical approaches have been made by Nishi et al. (245, 153) and Lustinec (194, 196), who express the influence of clothing and environmental variables by a hypothetical skin temperature necessary to keep heat balance for the human body.

None of the existing indices seem to be generally applicable for a detailed assessment of thermal environments in practice.

PREDICTED MEAN VOTE

The satisfaction of the comfort equation is a condition for optimal thermal comfort. However, the equation only gives information as to how the variables should be combined in order to create optimal thermal comfort, and it is thus not directly suitable for ascertaining the thermal sensation of persons in an arbitrary climate where the variables cannot be expected to satisfy the equation. With the comfort equation as a starting point, an index will be derived in the present section which makes possible a prediction of the thermal sensation for any given combination of activity level, clo-value, and the four thermal environmental parameters.

As a measure for the thermal sensation the commonly used seven point psycho-physical ASHRAE scale will be used:

$$
\begin{aligned}
-\ 3 & \quad \text{cold} \\
-\ 2 & \quad \text{cool} \\
-\ 1 & \quad \text{slightly cool} \\
0 & \quad \text{neutral} \\
+\ 1 & \quad \text{slightly warm} \\
+\ 2 & \quad \text{warm} \\
+\ 3 & \quad \text{hot}
\end{aligned}
$$

the numerical values in the scale being here diminished, however, by four so that the scale ranges from − 3 to + 3 instead of from 1 to 7. A scale is thus obtained which is easier to remember, as it is symmetrical around the zero point, so that a positive value corresponds to the warm side and a negative value to the cold side of neutral.

A connection must now be found between the thermal sensation expressed on the above-mentioned scale and the thermal variables. When the comfort equation is satisfied one will expect, for a large group of persons, a mean vote equal to zero (neutral). How then can a physical expression having relation to the thermal sensation, be established for deviations from the comfort equation?

It is well known that the human body is capable of maintaining heat balance within wide limits of the environmental variables, by the use of its effector mechanisms: vasodilatation and vasoconstriction, sweat secretion and shivering. But within these wide limits there is only a small interval which is regarded as comfortable. It is therefore reasonable to assume that the degree of discomfort is greater, the more the load on the effector mechanisms deviates from the comfort condition. Therefore, in the following, we will assume that the thermal sensation at a given activity level is a function of the thermal load L of the body, defined as the difference between the internal heat production and the heat loss to the actual environment for a man hypothetically kept at the comfort values of the mean skin temperature and the sweat secretion at the actual activity level.

According to this definition, the thermal load (per unit body surface area) can be expressed mathematically as follows, using the expressions for heat loss set up in the derivation of the comfort equation, and the experimentally determined comfort values for skin temperature and sweat secretion:

$$
L = \frac{M}{A_{Du}} \left(1 - \eta\right) - 0.35 \left[43 - 0.061 \frac{M}{A_{Du}} \left(1 - \eta\right) - p_a\right] -
$$
$$
0.42 \left[\frac{M}{A_{Du}} \left(1 - \eta\right) - 50\right] - 0.0023 \frac{M}{A_{Du}} \left(44 - p_a\right) -
$$
$$
0.0014 \frac{M}{A_{Du}} \left(34 - t_a\right) - \tag{35}
$$
$$
3.4 \cdot 10^{-8} f_{cl} \left[(t_{cl} + 273)^4 - (t_{mrt} + 273)^4\right] -
$$
$$
f_{cl} h_c (t_{cl} - t_a) \qquad (kcal/m^2 \, hr)
$$

where t_{cl} is found iteratively from the equation

$$
t_{cl} = 35.7 - 0.032 \frac{M}{A_{Du}} \left(1 - \eta\right) - \tag{36}
$$
$$
0.18 I_{cl} \left[3.4 \cdot 10^{-8} f_{cl} \left[\left(t_{cl} + 273\right)^4 - \left(t_{mrt} + 273\right)^4\right] +
$$
$$
f_{cl} h_c \left(t_{cl} - t_a\right)\right] \qquad (°C)
$$

and h_c is determined by eq. (25).

In the comfort condition the thermal load will be equal to zero. In other environments the body's effector mechanisms will change the mean skin temperature and the sweat secretion in order to maintain the heat balance of the body. The thermal load is therefore an expression for the physiological strain upon the effector mechanisms of the body, and it seems reasonable to assume that the thermal sensation at a given activity level is related to this strain. This relationship can be expressed mathematically as follows:

$$Y = f\left(L, \frac{H}{A_{Du}}\right) \tag{37}$$

where the thermal sensation is expressed by the mean vote Y on the scale mentioned earlier. The proviso is here made that the functional connection between the thermal sensation (the mean vote Y) and the thermal load L might vary with the internal heat production H/A_{Du}.

It is clear that equation (37) can only be quantified on the basis of experiments where the subjects cast thermal sensation votes, and where the clothing, activity and all the surrounding variables have been carefully controlled so that the thermal load can be calculated. In order to obtain a reasonable statistical basis for the quantification of equation (37), it is further necessary that a large number of subjects have participated in the experiments. Fortunately, results are available from experiments which satisfy the above-mentioned demands and which therefore can be used to determine the functional dependence in equation (37).

For sedentary persons, the experimental data of Nevins et al. (234) can be used, and this can be pooled with the data from the analogous experiments in the present study (see chapter 3). For higher activity levels the experimental results of McNall et al. (206) can be used. These three investigations have covered in all 1396 subjects clothed in the KSU-standard uniform (0.6 clo) and exposed for three hours to constant environments, where all the variables have been well controlled.

For the four activity levels investigated, connections between mean vote Y, and ambient temperature t (air temperature = mean radiant temperature) were found as shown in table 12. By inserting the experimentally determined values of the different variables in eq. (35) it is possible, for each of the four activity levels, to determine a connection between t and L and thus, by an insertion in the equations in table 12, also a connection between Y and L. After this, $\delta Y/\delta L$ can be determined graphically for Y = 0, since it is especially the relationship around the neutral point which is of interest. Moreover, the gradient of the curves is very slight, so that the error in the approximation made is negligible.

Table 12. *Connection between Mean Vote and Ambient Temperature at Four Activity Levels*

Activity Level	M/A_{Du}	I_{cl}	v	Mean Vote Y at rh = 50%
	kcal/hr m²	clo	m/s	
Sedentary........	50	0.6	0.1	$Y = -8.471 + 0.331t$
Low.............	80	0.6	0.2	$Y = -3.643 + 0.175t$
Medium.........	106	0.6	0.25	$Y = -3.356 + 0.174t$
High............	135	0.6	0.32	$Y = -4.158 + 0.265t$

In fig. 22, the values of $\delta Y/\delta L$ found are plotted with the four activity levels. It can be seen that $\delta Y/\delta L$ is considerably higher for sedentary activity than it is for the other activities. In perusing the plotted points one could believe at first that $\delta Y/\delta L$ had a minimum value. This, however, is not likely. It seems more probable that $\delta Y/\delta L$ decreases monotonously with the activity and therefore an exponential curve has been drawn which gives an acceptable approximation to the points. The curve is drawn through the point, equivalent to $M/A_{Du} = 50$ kcal/m²hr, as this is based on a much larger number of subjects than the other points. The equation for the curve is

$$\frac{\delta Y}{\delta L} = 0.352\, e^{-0.042\, (M/A_{Du})} + 0.032 \qquad (\text{m}^2\text{hr/kcal}) \qquad (38)$$

By integration we then arrive at

$$Y = (0.352\, e^{-0.042\, (M/A_{Du})} + 0.032)\, L \qquad (39)$$

since $Y = 0$ for $L = 0$.

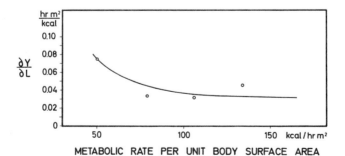

Fig. 22. $\delta Y/\delta L$ as a function of the metabolic rate.

113

The expression for Y given by eq. (39) will, in the following, be referred to as the "Predicted Mean Vote" (PMV). By inserting in eq. (39) the expression for L found by eq. (35), the following formula for PMV is obtained:

$$PMV = \left(0.352\, e^{-0.042\,(M/A_{Du})} + 0.032\right)\left[\frac{M}{A_{Du}}\left(1 - \eta\right) - \right.$$

$$0.35\left[43 - 0.061\frac{M}{A_{Du}}\left(1 - \eta\right) - p_a\right] -$$

$$0.42\left[\frac{M}{A_{Du}}\left(1 - \eta\right) - 50\right] - \tag{40}$$

$$0.0023\frac{M}{A_{Du}}\left(44 - p_a\right) - 0.0014\frac{M}{A_{Du}}\left(34 - t_a\right) -$$

$$\left. 3.4\cdot 10^{-8}\, f_{cl}\,[(t_{cl} + 273)^4 - (t_{mrt} + 273)^4] - f_{cl}\, h_c(t_{cl} - t_a)\right]$$

where t_{cl} is determined by the equation

$$t_{cl} = 35.7 - 0.032\frac{M}{A_{Du}}\left(1 - \eta\right) -$$

$$0.18\, I_{cl}\left[3.4\cdot 10^{-8}\, f_{cl}\left[\left(t_{cl} + 273\right)^4 - \left(t_{mrt} + 273\right)^4\right] + \right.$$

$$\left. f_{cl}\, h_c\left(t_{cl} - t_a\right)\right] \qquad (^\circ C) \tag{41}$$

and h_c by

$$h_c = \begin{cases} 2.05\,(t_{cl} - t_a)^{0.25} & \text{for } 2.05\,(t_{cl} - t_a)^{0.25} > 10.4\,\sqrt{v} \\[2mm] 10.4\,\sqrt{v} & \text{for } 2.05\,(t_{cl} - t_a)^{0.25} < 10.4\,\sqrt{v} \end{cases} \tag{25}$$

Equation (40) establishes the thermal sensation index desired, which gives the Predicted Mean Vote (PMV) for a large group of persons as a function of activity (kcal/hrm²), clothing (clo), air temperature (°C), mean radiant temperature (°C), relative air velocity (m/s) and air humidity (mmHg).

As with the comfort equation, the mathematical expression for PMV is rather complicated and therefore hardly suitable for calculations by hand. For use in practice the predicted mean vote has been determined on a digital computer and set up in table 13 for about 3500 combinations of the variables.

The table covers 8 different activity levels, 7 clo-values, 9 relative air velocities and 8 ambient temperatures (air temperature = mean radiant temperature). At the higher activity levels the lowest velocities are unreal-

Table 13. *Predicted Mean Vote*

Activity Level 50 kcal/m²hr

Clothing	Ambient Temp.	Relative Velocity (m/s)								
clo	°C	<0.10	0.10	0.15	0.20	0.30	0.40	0.50	1.00	1.50
0	26.	−1.62	−1.62	−1.96	−2.34					
	27.	−1.00	−1.00	−1.36	−1.69					
	28.	−0.39	−0.42	−0.76	−1.05					
	29.	0.21	0.13	−0.15	−0.39					
	30.	0.80	0.68	0.45	0.26					
	31.	1.39	1.25	1.08	0.94					
	32.	1.96	1.83	1.71	1 61					
	33.	2.50	2.41	2.34	2.29					
0.25	24.	−1.52	−1.52	−1.80	−2.06	−2.47				
	25.	−1.05	−1.05	−1.33	−1.57	−1.94	−2.24	−2.48		
	26.	−0.58	−0.61	−0.87	−1.08	−1.41	−1.67	−1.89	−2.66	
	27.	−0.12	−0.17	−0.40	−0.58	−0.87	−1.10	−1.29	−1.97	−2.41
	28.	0.34	0.27	0.07	−0.09	−0.34	−0.53	−0.70	−1.28	−1.66
	29.	0.80	0.71	0.54	0.41	0.20	0.04	−0.10	−0.58	−0.90
	30.	1.25	1.15	1.02	0.91	0.74	0.61	0.50	0.11	−0.14
	31.	1.71	1.61	1.51	1.43	1.30	1.20	1.12	0.83	0.63
0.50	23.	−1.10	−1.10	−1.33	−1.51	−1.78	−1.99	−2.16		
	24.	−0.72	−0.74	−0.95	−1.11	−1.36	−1.55	−1.70	−2.22	
	25.	−0.34	−0.38	−0.56	−0.71	−0.94	−1.11	−1.25	−1.71	−1.99
	26.	0.04	−0.01	−0.18	−0.31	−0.51	−0.66	−0.79	−1.19	−1.44
	27.	0.42	0.35	0.20	0.09	−0.08	−0.22	−0.33	−0.68	−0.90
	28.	0.80	0.72	0.59	0.49	0.34	0.23	0.14	−0.17	−0.36
	29.	1.17	1.08	0.98	0.90	0.77	0.68	0.60	0.34	0.19
	30.	1.54	1.45	1.37	1.30	1.20	1.13	1.06	0.86	0.73
0.75	21.	−1.11	−1.11	−1.30	−1.44	−1.66	−1.82	−1.95	−2.36	−2.60
	22.	−0.79	−0.81	−0.98	−1.11	−1.31	−1.46	−1.58	−1.95	−2.17
	23.	−0.47	−0.50	−0.66	−0.78	−0.96	−1.09	−1.20	−1.55	−1.75
	24.	−0.15	−0.19	−0.33	−0.44	−0.61	−0.73	−0.83	−1.14	−1.33
	25.	0.17	0.12	−0.01	−0.11	−0.26	−0.37	−0.46	−0.74	−0.90
	26.	0.49	0.43	0.31	0.23	0.09	0.00	−0.08	−0.33	−0.48
	27.	0.81	0.74	0.64	0.56	0.45	0.36	0.29	0.08	−0.05
	28.	1.12	1.05	0.96	0.90	0.80	0.73	0.67	0.48	0.37
1.00	20.	−0.85	−0.87	−1.02	−1.13	−1.29	−1.41	−1.51	−1.81	−1.98
	21.	−0.57	−0.60	−0.74	−0.84	−0.99	−1.11	−1.19	−1.47	−1.63
	22.	−0.30	−0.33	−0.46	−0.55	−0.69	−0.80	−0.88	−1.13	−1.28
	23.	−0.02	−0.07	−0.18	−0.27	−0.39	−0.49	−0.56	−0.79	−0.93
	24.	0.26	0.20	0.10	0.02	−0.09	−0.18	−0.25	−0.46	−0.58
	25.	0.53	0.48	0.38	0.31	0.21	0.13	0.07	−0.12	−0.23
	26.	0.81	0.75	0.66	0.60	0.51	0.44	0.39	0.22	0.13
	27.	1.08	1.02	0.95	0.89	0.81	0.75	0.71	0.56	0.48
1.25	16.	−1.37	−1.37	−1.51	−1.62	−1.78	−1.89	−1.98	−2.26	−2.41
	18.	−0.89	−0.91	−1.04	−1.14	−1.28	−1.38	−1.46	−1.70	−1.84
	20.	−0.42	−0.46	−0.57	−0.65	−0.77	−0.86	−0.93	−1.14	−1.26
	22.	0.07	0.02	−0.07	−0.14	−0.25	−0.32	−0.38	−0.56	−0.66
	24.	0.56	0.50	0.43	0.37	0.28	0.22	0.17	0.02	−0.06
	26.	1.04	0.99	0.93	0.88	0.81	0.76	0.72	0.61	0.54
	28.	1.53	1.48	1.43	1.40	1.34	1.31	1.28	1.19	1.14
	30.	2.01	1.97	1.93	1.91	1.88	1.85	1.83	1.77	1.74
1.50	14.	−1.36	−1.36	−1.49	−1.58	−1.72	−1.82	−1.89	−2.12	−2.25
	16.	−0.94	−0.95	−1.07	−1.15	−1.27	−1.36	−1.43	−1.63	−1.75
	18.	−0.52	−0.54	−0.64	−0.72	−0.82	−0.90	−0.96	−1.14	−1.24
	20.	−0.09	−0.13	−0.22	−0.28	−0.37	−0.44	−0.49	−0.65	−0.74
	22.	0.35	0.30	0.23	0.18	0.10	0.04	0.00	−0.14	−0.21
	24.	0.79	0.74	0.68	0.63	0.57	0.52	0.49	0.37	0.31
	26.	1.23	1.18	1.13	1.09	1.04	1.01	0.98	0.89	0.84
	28.	1.67	1.62	1.58	1.56	1.52	1.49	1.47	1.40	1.37

Table 13. *Predicted Mean Vote* (continued)

Activity Level 60 kcal/m²hr

Clothing clo	Ambient Temp. °C	Relative Velocity (m/s) <0.10	0.10	0.15	0.20	0.30	0.40	0.50	1.00	1.50
0	25.	−1.33	−1.33	−1.59	−1.92					
	26.	−0.83	−0.83	−1.11	−1.40					
	27.	−0.33	−0.33	−0.63	−0.88					
	28.	0.15	0.12	−0.14	−0.36					
	29.	0.63	0.56	0.35	0.17					
	30.	1.10	1.01	0.84	0.69					
	31.	1.57	1.47	1.34	1.24					
	32.	2.03	1.93	1.85	1.78					
0.25	23.	−1.18	−1.18	−1.39	−1.61	−1.97	−2.25			
	24.	−0.79	−0.79	−1.02	−1.22	−1.54	−1.80	−2.01		
	25.	−0.42	−0.42	−0.64	−0.83	−1.11	−1.34	−1.54	−2.21	
	26.	−0.04	−0.07	−0.27	−0.43	−0.68	−0.89	−1.06	−1.65	−2.04
	27.	0.33	0.29	0.11	−0.03	−0.25	−0.43	−0.58	−1.09	−1.43
	28.	0.71	0.64	0.49	0.37	0.18	0.03	−0.10	−0.54	−0.82
	29.	1.07	0.99	0.87	0.77	0.61	0.49	0.39	0.02	−0.22
	30.	1.43	1.35	1.25	1.17	1.05	0.95	0.87	0.58	0.39
0.50	18.	−2.01	−2.01	−2.17	−2.38	−2.70				
	20.	−1.41	−1.41	−1.58	−1.76	−2.04	−2.25	−2.42		
	22.	−0.79	−0.79	−0.97	−1.13	−1.36	−1.54	−1.69	−2.17	−2.46
	24.	−0.17	−0.20	−0.36	−0.48	−0.68	−0.83	−0.95	−1.35	−1.59
	26.	0.44	0.39	0.26	0.16	0.01	−0.11	−0.21	−0.52	−0.71
	28.	1.05	0.98	0.88	0.81	0.70	0.61	0.54	0.31	0.16
	30.	1.64	1.57	1.51	1.46	1.39	1.33	1.29	1.14	1.04
	32.	2.25	2.20	2.17	2.15	2.11	2.09	2.07	1.99	1.95
0.75	16.	−1.77	−1.77	−1.91	−2.07	−2.31	−2.49			
	18.	−1.27	−1.27	−1.42	−1.56	−1.77	−1.93	−2.05	−2.45	
	20.	−0.77	−0.77	−0.92	−1.04	−1.23	−1.36	−1.47	−1.82	−2.02
	22.	−0.25	−0.27	−0.40	−0.51	−0.66	−0.78	−0.87	−1.17	−1.34
	24.	0.27	0.23	0.12	0.03	−0.10	−0.19	−0.27	−0.51	−0.65
	26.	0.78	0.73	0.64	0.57	0.47	0.40	0.34	0.14	0.03
	28.	1.29	1.23	1.17	1.12	1.04	0.99	0.94	0.80	0.72
	30.	1.80	1.74	1.70	1.67	1.62	1.58	1.55	1.46	1.41
1.00	16.	−1.18	−1.18	−1.31	−1.43	−1.59	−1.72	−1.82	−2.12	−2.29
	18.	−0.75	−0.75	−0.88	−0.98	−1.13	−1.24	−1.33	−1.59	−1.75
	20.	−0.32	−0.33	−0.45	−0.54	−0.67	−0.76	−0.83	−1.07	−1.20
	22.	0.13	0.10	0.00	−0.07	−0.18	−0.26	−0.32	−0.52	−0.64
	24.	0.58	0.54	0.46	0.40	0.31	0.24	0.19	0.02	−0.07
	26.	1.03	0.98	0.91	0.86	0.79	0.74	0.70	0.57	0.50
	28.	1.47	1.42	1.37	1.34	1.28	1.24	1.21	1.12	1.06
	30.	1.91	1.86	1.83	1.81	1.78	1.75	1.73	1.67	1.63
1.25	14.	−1.12	−1.12	−1.24	−1.34	−1.48	−1.58	−1.66	−1.90	−2.04
	16.	−0.74	−0.75	−0.86	−0.95	−1.07	−1.16	−1.23	−1.45	−1.57
	18.	−0.36	−0.38	−0.48	−0.55	−0.66	−0.74	−0.81	−1.00	−1.11
	20.	0.02	−0.01	−0.10	−0.16	−0.26	−0.33	−0.38	−0.55	−0.64
	22.	0.42	0.38	0.31	0.25	0.17	0.11	0.07	−0.08	−0.16
	24.	0.81	0.77	0.71	0.66	0.60	0.55	0.51	0.39	0.33
	26.	1.21	1.16	1.11	1.08	1.03	0.99	0.96	0.87	0.82
	28.	1.60	1.56	1.52	1.50	1.46	1.43	1.41	1.34	1.30
1.50	12.	−1.09	−1.09	−1.19	−1.27	−1.39	−1.48	−1.55	−1.75	−1.86
	14.	−0.75	−0.75	−0.85	−0.93	−1.03	−1.11	−1.17	−1.35	−1.45
	16.	−0.41	−0.42	−0.51	−0.58	−0.67	−0.74	−0.79	−0.96	−1.05
	18.	−0.06	−0.09	−0.17	−0.22	−0.31	−0.37	−0.42	−0.56	−0.64
	20.	0.28	0.25	0.18	0.13	0.05	0.00	−0.04	−0.16	−0.23
	22.	0.63	0.60	0.54	0.50	0.44	0.39	0.36	0.25	0.19
	24.	0.99	0.95	0.91	0.87	0.82	0.78	0.76	0.67	0.62
	26.	1.35	1.31	1.27	1.24	1.20	1.18	1.15	1.08	1.05

116

Table 13. *Predicted Mean Vote* (continued)

Activity Level 70 kcal/m²hr

Clothing clo	Ambient Temp. °C	Relative Velocity (m/s)								
		<0.10	0.10	0.15	0.20	0.30	0.40	0.50	1.00	1.50
0	24.	−1.14	−1.14	−1.35	−1.65					
	25.	−0.72	−0.72	−0.95	−1.21					
	26.	−0.30	−0.30	−0.54	−0.78					
	27.	0.11	0.11	−0.14	−0.34					
	28.	0.52	0.48	0.27	0.10					
	29.	0.92	0.85	0.69	0.54					
	30.	1.31	1.23	1.10	0.99					
	31.	1.71	1.62	1.52	1.45					
0.25	22.	−0.95	−0.95	−1.12	−1.33	−1.64	−1.90	−2.11		
	23.	−0.63	−0.63	−0.81	−0.99	−1.28	−1.51	−1.71	−2.38	
	24.	−0.31	−0.31	−0.50	−0.66	−0.92	−1.13	−1.31	−1.91	−2.31
	25.	0.01	0.00	−0.18	−0.33	−0.56	−0.75	−0.90	−1.45	−1.80
	26.	0.33	0.30	0.14	0.01	−0.20	−0.36	−0.50	−0.98	−1.29
	27.	0.64	0.59	0.45	0.34	0.16	0.02	−0.10	−0.51	−0.78
	28.	0.95	0.89	0.77	0.68	0.53	0.41	0.31	−0.04	−0.27
	29.	1.26	1.19	1.09	1.02	0.89	0.80	0.72	0.43	0.24
0.50	18.	−1.36	−1.36	−1.49	−1.66	−1.93	−2.12	−2.29		
	20.	−0.85	−0.85	−1.00	−1.14	−1.37	−1.54	−1.68	−2.15	−2.43
	22.	−0.33	−0.33	−0.48	−0.61	−0.80	−0.95	−1.06	−1.46	−1.70
	24.	0.19	0.17	0.04	−0.07	−0.22	−0.34	−0.44	−0.76	−0.96
	26.	0.71	0.66	0.56	0.48	0.35	0.26	0.18	−0.07	−0.23
	28.	1.22	1.16	1.09	1.03	0.94	0.87	0.81	0.63	0.51
	30.	1.72	1.66	1.62	1.58	1.52	1.48	1.44	1.33	1.25
	32.	2.23	2.19	2.17	2.16	2.13	2.11	2.10	2.05	2.02
0.75	16.	−1.17	−1.17	−1.29	−1.42	−1.62	−1.77	−1.88	−2.26	−2.48
	18.	−0.75	−0.75	−0.87	−0.99	−1.16	−1.29	−1.39	−1.72	−1.92
	20.	−0.33	−0.33	−0.45	−0.55	−0.70	−0.82	−0.91	−1.19	−1.36
	22.	0.11	0.09	−0.02	−0.10	−0.23	−0.32	−0.40	−0.64	−0.78
	24.	0.55	0.51	0.42	0.35	0.25	0.17	0.11	−0.09	−0.20
	26.	0.98	0.94	0.87	0.81	0.73	0.67	0.62	0.47	0.37
	28.	1.41	1.36	1.31	1.27	1.21	1.17	1.13	1.02	0.95
	30.	1.84	1.79	1.76	1.73	1.70	1.67	1.65	1.58	1.53
1.00	14.	−1.05	−1.05	−1.16	−1.26	−1.42	−1.53	−1.62	−1.91	−2.07
	16.	−0.69	−0.69	−0.80	−0.89	−1.03	−1.13	−1.21	−1.46	−1.61
	18.	−0.32	−0.32	−0.43	−0.52	−0.64	−0.73	−0.80	−1.02	−1.15
	20.	0.04	0.03	−0.07	−0.14	−0.25	−0.32	−0.38	−0.58	−0.69
	22.	0.42	0.39	0.31	0.25	0.16	0.10	0.05	−0.12	−0.21
	24.	0.80	0.76	0.70	0.65	0.57	0.52	0.48	0.35	0.27
	26.	1.18	1.13	1.08	1.04	0.99	0.95	0.91	0.81	0.75
	28.	1.55	1.51	1.47	1.44	1.40	1.37	1.35	1.27	1.23
1.25	12.	−0.97	−0.97	−1.06	−1.15	−1.28	−1.37	−1.45	−1.67	−1.80
	14.	−0.65	−0.65	−0.75	−0.82	−0.94	−1.02	−1.09	−1.29	−1.40
	16.	−0.33	−0.33	−0.43	−0.50	−0.60	−0.67	−0.73	−0.91	−1.01
	18.	−0.01	−0.02	−0.10	−0.17	−0.26	−0.32	−0.37	−0.53	−0.62
	20.	0.32	0.29	0.22	0.17	0.09	0.03	−0.01	−0.15	−0.22
	22.	0.65	0.62	0.56	0.52	0.45	0.40	0.36	0.25	0.18
	24.	0.99	0.95	0.90	0.87	0.81	0.77	0.74	0.65	0.59
	26.	1.32	1.28	1.25	1.22	1.18	1.14	1.12	1.05	1.00
1.50	10.	−0.91	−0.91	−1.00	−1.08	−1.18	−1.26	−1.32	−1.51	−1.61
	12.	−0.63	−0.63	−0.71	−0.78	−0.88	−0.95	−1.01	−1.17	−1.27
	14.	−0.34	−0.34	−0.43	−0.49	−0.58	−0.64	−0.69	−0.84	−0.92
	16.	−0.05	−0.06	−0.14	−0.19	−0.27	−0.33	−0.37	−0.50	−0.58
	18.	0.24	0.22	0.15	0.11	0.04	−0.01	−0.05	−0.17	−0.23
	20.	0.53	0.50	0.45	0.40	0.34	0.30	0.27	0.17	0.11
	22.	0.83	0.80	0.75	0.72	0.67	0.63	0.60	0.52	0.47
	24.	1.13	1.10	1.06	1.03	0.99	0.96	0.94	0.87	0.83

Table 13. *Predicted Mean Vote* (continued)

Activity Level 80 kcal/m²hr

Clothing clo	Ambient Temp. °C	<0.10	0.10	0.15	0.20	0.30	0.40	0.50	1.00	1.50
0	23.	−1.12	−1.12	−1.29	−1.57					
	24.	−0.74	−0.74	−0.93	−1.18					
	25.	−0.36	−0.36	−0.57	−0.79					
	26.	0.01	0.01	−0.20	−0.40					
	27.	0.38	0.37	0.17	0.00					
	28.	0.75	0.70	0.53	0.39					
	29.	1.11	1.04	0.90	0.79					
	30.	1.46	1.38	1.27	1.19					
0.25	16.	−2.29	−2.29	−2.36	−2.62					
	18.	−1.72	−1.72	−1.83	−2.06	−2.42				
	20.	−1.15	−1.15	−1.29	−1.49	−1.80	−2.05	−2.26		
	22.	−0.58	−0.58	−0.73	−0.90	−1.17	−1.38	−1.55	−2.17	−2.58
	24.	−0.01	−0.01	−0.17	−0.31	−0.53	−0.70	−0.84	−1.35	−1.68
	26.	0.56	0.53	0.39	0.29	0.12	−0.02	−0.13	−0.52	−0.78
	28.	1.12	1.06	0.96	0.89	0.77	0.67	0.59	0.31	0.12
	30.	1.66	1.60	1.54	1.49	1.42	1.36	1.31	1.14	1.02
0.50	14.	−1.85	−1.85	−1.94	−2.12	−2.40				
	16.	−1.40	−1.40	−1.50	−1.67	−1.92	−2.11	−2.26		
	18.	−0.95	−0.95	−1.07	−1.21	−1.43	−1.59	−1.73	−2.18	−2.46
	20.	−0.49	−0.49	−0.62	−0.75	−0.94	−1.08	−1.20	−1.59	−1.82
	22.	−0.03	−0.03	−0.16	−0.27	−0.43	−0.55	−0.65	−0.98	−1.18
	24.	0.43	0.41	0.30	0.21	0.08	−0.02	−0.10	−0.37	−0.53
	26.	0.89	0.85	0.76	0.70	0.60	0.52	0.46	0.25	0.12
	28.	1.34	1.29	1.23	1.18	1.11	1.06	1.01	0.86	0.77
0.75	14.	−1.16	−1.16	−1.26	−1.38	−1.57	−1.71	−1.82	−2.17	−2.38
	16.	−0.79	−0.79	−0.89	−1.00	−1.17	−1.29	−1.39	−1.70	−1.88
	18.	−0.41	−0.41	−0.52	−0.62	−0.76	−0.87	−0.96	−1.23	−1.39
	20.	−0.04	−0.04	−0.15	−0.23	−0.36	−0.45	−0.52	−0.76	−0.90
	22.	0.35	0.33	0.24	0.17	0.07	−0.01	−0.07	−0.27	−0.39
	24.	0.74	0.71	0.63	0.58	0.49	0.43	0.38	0.21	0.12
	26.	1.12	1.08	1.03	0.98	0.92	0.87	0.83	0.70	0.62
	28.	1.51	1.46	1.42	1.39	1.34	1.31	1.28	1.19	1.14
1.00	12.	−1.01	−1.01	−1.10	−1.19	−1.34	−1.45	−1.53	−1.79	−1.94
	14.	−0.68	−0.68	−0.78	−0.87	−1.00	−1.09	−1.17	−1.40	−1.54
	16.	−0.36	−0.36	−0.46	−0.53	−0.65	−0.74	−0.80	−1.01	−1.13
	18.	−0.04	−0.04	−0.13	−0.20	−0.30	−0.38	−0.44	−0.62	−0.73
	20.	0.28	0.27	0.19	0.13	0.04	−0.02	−0.07	−0.23	−0.32
	22.	0.62	0.59	0.53	0.48	0.41	0.35	0.31	0.17	0.10
	24.	0.96	0.92	0.87	0.83	0.77	0.73	0.69	0.58	0.52
	26.	1.29	1.25	1.21	1.18	1.14	1.10	1.07	0.99	0.94
1.25	10.	−0.90	−0.90	−0.98	−1.06	−1.18	−1.27	−1.33	−1.54	−1.66
	12.	−0.62	−0.62	−0.70	−0.77	−0.88	−0.96	−1.02	−1.21	−1.31
	14.	−0.33	−0.33	−0.42	−0.48	−0.58	−0.65	−0.70	−0.87	−0.97
	16.	−0.05	−0.05	−0.13	−0.19	−0.28	−0.34	−0.39	−0.54	−0.62
	18.	0.24	0.22	0.15	0.10	0.03	−0.03	−0.07	−0.20	−0.28
	20.	0.52	0.50	0.44	0.40	0.33	0.29	0.25	0.14	0.07
	22.	0.82	0.79	0.74	0.71	0.65	0.61	0.58	0.49	0.43
	24.	1.12	1.09	1.05	1.02	0.97	0.94	0.92	0.84	0.79
1.50	8.	−0.82	−0.82	−0.89	−0.96	−1.06	−1.13	−1.19	−1.36	−1.45
	10.	−0.57	−0.57	−0.65	−0.71	−0.80	−0.86	−0.92	−1.07	−1.16
	12.	−0.32	−0.32	−0.39	−0.45	−0.53	−0.59	−0.64	−0.78	−0.85
	14.	−0.06	−0.07	−0.14	−0.19	−0.26	−0.31	−0.36	−0.48	−0.55
	16.	0.19	0.18	0.12	0.07	0.01	−0.04	−0.07	−0.19	−0.25
	18.	0.45	0.43	0.38	0.34	0.28	0.24	0.21	0.11	0.05
	20.	0.71	0.68	0.64	0.60	0.55	0.52	0.49	0.41	0.36
	22.	0.97	0.95	0.91	0.88	0.84	0.81	0.79	0.72	0.68

Table 13. *Predicted Mean Vote* (continued)

Activity Level 90 kcal/m²hr

Clothing clo	Ambient Temp. °C	Relative Velocity (m/s)								
		<0.10	0.10	0.15	0.20	0.30	0.40	0.50	1.00	1.50
0	22.	−1.05	−1.05	−1.19	−1.46					
	23.	−0.70	−0.70	−0.86	−1.11					
	24.	−0.36	−0.36	−0.53	−0.75					
	25.	−0.01	−0.01	−0.20	−0.40					
	26.	0.32	0.32	0.13	−0.04					
	27.	0.66	0.63	0.46	0.32					
	28.	0.99	0.94	0.80	0.68					
	29.	1.31	1.25	1.13	1.04					
0.25	16.	−1.79	−1.79	−1.86	−2.09	−2.46				
	18.	−1.28	−1.28	−1.38	−1.58	−1.90	−2.16	−2.37		
	20.	−0.76	−0.76	−0.89	−1.06	−1.34	−1.56	−1.75	−2.39	−2.82
	22.	−0.24	−0.24	−0.38	−0.53	−0.76	−0.95	−1.10	−1.65	−2.01
	24.	0.28	0.28	0.13	0.01	−0.18	−0.33	−0.46	−0.90	−1.19
	26.	0.79	0.76	0.64	0.55	0.40	0.29	0.19	−0.15	−0.38
	28.	1.29	1.24	1.16	1.10	0.99	0.91	0.84	0.60	0.44
	30.	1.79	1.73	1.68	1.65	1.59	1.54	1.50	1.36	1.27
0.50	14.	−1.42	−1.42	−1.50	−1.66	−1.91	−2.10	−2.25		
	16.	−1.01	−1.01	−1.10	−1.25	−1.47	−1.64	−1.77	−2.23	−2.51
	18.	−0.59	−0.59	−0.70	−0.83	−1.02	−1.17	−1.29	−1.69	−1.94
	20.	−0.18	−0.18	−0.30	−0.41	−0.58	−0.71	−0.81	−1.15	−1.36
	22.	0.24	0.23	0.12	0.02	−0.12	−0.22	−0.31	−0.60	−0.78
	24.	0.66	0.63	0.54	0.46	0.35	0.26	0.19	−0.04	−0.19
	26.	1.07	1.03	0.96	0.90	0.82	0.75	0.69	0.51	0.40
	28.	1.48	1.44	1.39	1.35	1.29	1.24	1.20	1.07	1.00
0.75	12.	−1.15	−1.15	−1.23	−1.35	−1.53	−1.67	−1.78	−2.13	−2.33
	14.	−0.81	−0.81	−0.89	−1.00	−1.17	−1.29	−1.39	−1.70	−1.89
	16.	−0.46	−0.46	−0.56	−0.66	−0.80	−0.91	−1.00	−1.28	−1.44
	18.	−0.12	−0.12	−0.22	−0.31	−0.43	−0.53	−0.61	−0.85	−0.99
	20.	0.22	0.21	0.12	0.04	−0.07	−0.15	−0.21	−0.42	−0.55
	22.	0.57	0.55	0.47	0.41	0.32	0.25	0.20	0.02	−0.09
	24.	0.92	0.89	0.83	0.78	0.71	0.65	0.60	0.46	0.38
	26.	1.28	1.24	1.19	i.15	1.09	1.05	1.02	0.91	0.84
1.00	10.	−0.97	−0.97	−1.04	−1.14	−1.28	−1.39	−1.47	−1.73	−1.88
	12.	−0.68	−0.68	−0.76	−0.84	−0.97	−1.07	−1.14	−1.38	−1.51
	14.	−0.38	−0.38	−0.46	−0.54	−0.66	−0.74	−0.81	−1.02	−1.14
	16.	−0.09	−0.09	−0.17	−0.24	−0.35	−0.42	−0.48	−0.67	−0.78
	18.	0.21	0.20	0.12	0.06	−0.03	−0.10	−0.15	−0.31	−0.41
	20.	0.50	0.48	0.42	0.36	0.29	0.23	0.18	0.04	−0.04
	22.	0.81	0.78	0.73	0.68	0.62	0.57	0.53	0.41	0.35
	24.	1.11	1.08	1.04	1.00	0.95	0.91	0.88	0.78	0.73
1.25	8.	−0.84	−0.84	−0.91	−0.99	−1.10	−1.19	−1.25	−1.46	−1.57
	10.	−0.59	−0.59	−0.66	−0.73	−0.84	−0.91	−0.97	−1.16	−1.26
	12.	−0.33	−0.33	−0.40	−0.47	−0.56	−0.63	−0.69	−0.86	−0.95
	14.	−0.07	−0.07	−0.14	−0.20	−0.29	−0.35	−0.40	−0.55	−0.63
	16.	0.19	0.18	0.12	0.06	−0.01	−0.07	−0.11	−0.24	−0.32
	18.	0.45	0.44	0.38	0.33	0.26	0.22	0.18	0.06	0.00
	20.	0.71	0.69	0.64	0.60	0.54	0.50	0.47	0.37	0.31
	22.	0.98	0.96	0.91	0.88	0.83	0.80	0.77	0.69	0.64
1.50	−2.	−1.63	−1.63	−1.68	−1.77	−1.90	−2.00	−2.07	−2.29	−2.41
	2.	−1.19	−1.19	−1.25	−1.33	−1.44	−1.52	−1.58	−1.78	−1.88
	6.	−0.74	−0.74	−0.80	−0.87	−0.97	−1.04	−1.09	−1.26	−1.35
	10.	−0.29	−0.29	−0.36	−0.42	−0.50	−0.56	−0.60	−0.74	−0.82
	14.	0.17	0.17	0.11	0.06	−0.01	−0.05	−0.09	−0.20	−0.26
	18.	0.64	0.62	0.57	0.54	0.49	0.45	0.42	0.34	0.29
	22.	1.12	1.09	1.06	1.03	1.00	0.97	0.95	0.89	0.85
	26.	1.61	1.58	1.56	1.55	1.52	1.51	1.50	1.46	1.44

Table 13. *Predicted Mean Vote* (continued)

Activity Level 100 kcal/m²hr

Clothing	Ambient Temp.	Relative Velocity (m/s)								
clo	°C	<0.10	0.10	0.15	0.20	0.30	0.40	0.50	1.00	1.50
0	18.		−2.00	−2.02	−2.35					
	20.		−1.35	−1.43	−1.72					
	22.		−0.69	−0.82	−1.06					
	24.		−0.04	−0.21	−0.41					
	26.		0.59	0.41	0.26					
	28.		1.16	1.03	0.93					
	30.		1.73	1.66	1.60					
	32.		2.33	2.32	2.31					
0.25	16.		−1.41	−1.48	−1.69	−2.02	−2.29	−2.51		
	18.		−0.93	−1.03	−1.21	−1.50	−1.74	−1.93	−2.61	
	20.		−0.45	−0.57	−0.73	−0.98	−1.18	−1.35	−1.93	−2.32
	22.		0.04	−0.09	−0.23	−0.44	−0.61	−0.75	−1.24	−1.56
	24.		0.52	0.38	0.28	0.10	−0.03	−0.14	−0.54	−0.80
	26.		0.97	0.86	0.78	0.65	0.55	0.46	0.16	−0.04
	28.		1.42	1.35	1.29	1.20	1.13	1.07	0.86	0.72
	30.		1.88	1.84	1.81	1.76	1.72	1.68	1.57	1.49
0.50	14.		−1.08	−1.16	−1.31	−1.53	−1.71	−1.85	−2.32	
	16.		−0.69	−0.79	−0.92	−1.12	−1.27	−1.40	−1.82	−2.07
	18.		−0.31	−0.41	−0.53	−0.70	−0.84	−0.95	−1.31	−1.54
	20.		0.07	−0.04	−0.14	−0.29	−0.40	−0.50	−0.81	−1.00
	22.		0.46	0.35	0.27	0.15	0.05	−0.03	−0.29	−0.45
	24.		0.83	0.75	0.68	0.58	0.50	0.44	0.23	0.10
	26.		1.21	1.15	1.10	1.02	0.96	0.91	0.75	0.65
	28.		1.59	1.55	1.51	1.46	1.42	1.38	1.27	1.21
0.75	10.		−1.16	−1.23	−1.35	−1.54	−1.67	−1.78	−2.14	−2.34
	12.		−0.84	−0.92	−1.03	−1.20	−1.32	−1.42	−1.74	−1.93
	14.		−0.52	−0.60	−0.70	−0.85	−0.97	−1.06	−1.34	−1.51
	16.		−0.20	−0.29	−0.38	−0.51	−0.61	−0.69	−0.95	−1.10
	18.		0.12	0.03	−0.05	−0.17	−0.26	−0.32	−0.55	−0.68
	20.		0.43	0.34	0.28	0.18	0.10	0.04	−0.15	−0.26
	22.		0.75	0.68	0.62	0.54	0.48	0.43	0.27	0.17
	24.		1.07	1.01	0.97	0.90	0.85	0.81	0.68	0.61
1.00	8.		−0.95	−1.02	−1.11	−1.26	−1.36	−1.45	−1.71	−1.86
	10.		−0.68	−0.75	−0.84	−0.97	−1.07	−1.15	−1.38	−1.52
	12.		−0.41	−0.48	−0.56	−0.68	−0.77	−0.84	−1.05	−1.18
	14.		−0.13	−0.21	−0.28	−0.39	−0.47	−0.53	−0.72	−0.83
	16.		0.14	0.06	0.00	−0.10	−0.16	−0.22	−0.39	−0.49
	18.		0.41	0.34	0.28	0.20	0.14	0.09	−0.06	−0.14
	20.		0.68	0.61	0.57	0.50	0.44	0.40	0.28	0.20
	22.		0.96	0.91	0.87	0.81	0.76	0.73	0.62	0.56
1.25	−2.		−1.74	−1.77	−1.88	−2.04	−2.15	−2.24	−2.51	−2.66
	2.		−1.27	−1.32	−1.42	−1.55	−1.65	−1.73	−1.97	−2.10
	6.		−0.80	−0.86	−0.94	−1.06	−1.14	−1.21	−1.41	−1.53
	10.		−0.33	−0.40	−0.47	−0.56	−0.64	−0.69	−0.86	−0.96
	14.		0.15	0.08	0.03	−0.05	−0.11	−0.15	−0.29	−0.37
	18.		0.63	0.57	0.53	0.47	0.42	0.39	0.28	0.22
	22.		1.11	1.08	1.05	1.00	0.97	0.95	0.87	0.83
	26.		1.62	1.60	1.58	1.55	1.53	1.52	1.47	1.45
1.50	−4.		−1.52	−1.56	−1.65	−1.78	−1.87	−1.95	−2.16	−2.28
	0.		−1.11	−1.16	−1.24	−1.35	−1.44	−1.50	−1.69	−1.79
	4.		−0.69	−0.75	−0.82	−0.92	−0.99	−1.04	−1.20	−1.29
	8.		−0.27	−0.33	−0.39	−0.47	−0.53	−0.58	−0.72	−0.79
	12.		0.15	0.09	0.05	−0.02	−0.07	−0.11	−0.22	−0.29
	16.		0.58	0.53	0.49	0.44	0.40	0.37	0.28	0.23
	20.		1.01	0.97	0.94	0.91	0.88	0.85	0.79	0.75
	24.		1.47	1.44	1.43	1.40	1.38	1.36	1.32	1.29

Table 13. *Predicted Mean Vote* (continued)

Activity Level 120 kcal/m²hr

Clothing clo	Ambient Temp. °C	Relative Velocity (m/s)								
		<0.10	0.10	0.15	0.20	0.30	0.40	0.50	1.00	1.50
0	16.			−1.88	−2.22					
	18.			−1.34	−1.63					
	20.			−0.79	−1.05					
	22.			−0.23	−0.44					
	24.			0.34	0.17					
	26.			0.91	0.78					
	28.			1.49	1.40					
	30.			2.07	2.03					
0.25	14.			−1.31	−1.52	−1.85	−2.12	−2.34		
	16.			−0.89	−1.08	−1.37	−1.61	−1.81	−2.49	
	18.			−0.47	−0.63	−0.89	−1.10	−1.27	−1.87	−2.26
	20.			−0.05	−0.19	−0.41	−0.58	−0.73	−1.24	−1.58
	22.			0.39	0.28	0.09	−0.05	−0.17	−0.60	−0.88
	24.			0.84	0.74	0.60	0.48	0.39	0.05	−0.17
	26.			1.28	1.22	1.11	1.02	0.95	0.70	0.53
	28.			1.73	1.69	1.62	1.56	1.51	1.35	1.24
0.50	12.			−0.97	−1.11	−1.34	−1.51	−1.65	−2.12	−2.40
	14.			−0.62	−0.76	−0.96	−1.11	−1.24	−1.65	−1.91
	16.			−0.28	−0.40	−0.58	−0.71	−0.82	−1.19	−1.42
	18.			0.07	−0.03	−0.19	−0.31	−0.41	−0.73	−0.92
	20.			0.42	0.33	0.20	0.10	0.01	−0.26	−0.43
	22.			0.78	0.71	0.60	0.52	0.45	0.22	0.08
	24.			1.15	1.09	1.00	0.94	0.88	0.70	0.59
	26.			1.52	1.47	1.41	1.36	1.32	1.19	1.11
0.75	10.			−0.71	−0.82	−0.99	−1.11	−1.21	−1.53	−1.71
	12.			−0.42	−0.52	−0.67	−0.79	−0.88	−1.16	−1.33
	14.			−0.13	−0.22	−0.36	−0.46	−0.54	−0.79	−0.94
	16.			0.16	0.08	−0.04	−0.13	−0.20	−0.42	−0.56
	18.			0.45	0.38	0.28	0.20	0.14	−0.05	−0.17
	20.			0.75	0.69	0.60	0.54	0.49	0.32	0.22
	22.			1.06	1.01	0.94	0.88	0.84	0.70	0.62
	24.			1.37	1.33	1.27	1.23	1.20	1.09	1.02
1.00	6.			−0.78	−0.87	−1.01	−1.12	−1.20	−1.45	−1.60
	8.			−0.54	−0.62	−0.75	−0.85	−0.92	−1.15	−1.29
	10.			−0.29	−0.37	−0.49	−0.57	−0.64	−0.86	−0.98
	12.			−0.04	−0.11	−0.22	−0.29	−0.36	−0.55	−0.66
	14.			0.21	0.15	0.06	−0.01	−0.07	−0.24	−0.34
	16.			0.47	0.41	0.33	0.27	0.22	0.07	−0.02
	18.			0.73	0.68	0.60	0.55	0.51	0.38	0.30
	20.			0.98	0.94	0.88	0.84	0.80	0.69	0.62
1.25	−4.			−1.46	−1.56	−1.72	−1.83	−1.91	−2.17	−2.32
	0.			−1.05	−1.14	−1.27	−1.37	−1.44	−1.67	−1.80
	4.			−0.62	−0.70	−0.81	−0.90	−0.96	−1.16	−1.27
	8.			−0.19	−0.26	−0.35	−0.42	−0.48	−0.64	−0.74
	12.			0.25	0.20	0.12	0.06	0.02	−0.12	−0.20
	16.			0.70	0.66	0.60	0.55	0.52	0.41	0.35
	20.			1.16	1.13	1.08	1.05	1.02	0.94	0.90
	24.			1.65	1.63	1.60	1.57	1.56	1.51	1.48
1.50	−8.			−1.44	−1.53	−1.67	−1.76	−1.83	−2.05	−2.17
	−4.			−1.07	−1.15	−1.27	−1.35	−1.42	−1.61	−1.72
	0.			−0.70	−0.77	−0.87	−0.94	−1.00	−1.17	−1.27
	4.			−0.31	−0.37	−0.46	−0.53	−0.57	−0.72	−0.80
	8.			0.07	0.02	−0.05	−0.10	−0.14	−0.27	−0.34
	12.			0.47	0.43	0.37	0.33	0.29	0.19	0.14
	16.			0.88	0.85	0.80	0.77	0.74	0.66	0.62
	20.			1.29	1.27	1.24	1.21	1.19	1.13	1.10

Table 13. *Predicted Mean Vote* (continued)

Activity Level 150 kcal/m²hr

Clothing	Ambient Temp.	Relative Velocity (m/s)								
clo	°C	<0.10	0.10	0.15	0.20	0.30	0.40	0.50	1.00	1.50
0	14.				−1.92	−2.49				
	16.				−1.36	−1.87				
	18.				−0.80	−1.24				
	20.				−0.24	−0.61				
	22.				0.34	0.04				
	24.				0.93	0.70				
	26.				1.52	1.36				
	28.				2.12	2.02				
0.25	12.				−1.19	−1.53	−1.80	−2.02		
	14.				−0.77	−1.07	−1.31	−1.51	−2.21	
	16.				−0.35	−0.61	−0.82	−1.00	−1.61	−2.02
	18.				0.08	−0.15	−0.33	−0.48	−1.01	−1.36
	20.				0.51	0.32	0.17	0.04	−0.41	−0.71
	22.				0.96	0.80	0.68	0.57	0.21	−0.03
	24.				1.41	1.29	1.19	1.11	0.83	0.64
	26.				1.87	1.78	1.71	1.65	1.45	1.32
0.50	10.				−0.78	−1.00	−1.18	−1.32	−1.79	−2.07
	12.				−0.43	−0.64	−0.79	−0.92	−1.34	−1.60
	14.				−0.09	−0.27	−0.41	−0.52	−0.90	−1.13
	16.				0.26	0.10	−0.02	−0.12	−0.45	−0.65
	18.				0.61	0.47	0.37	0.28	0.00	−0.18
	20.				0.96	0.85	0.76	0.68	0.45	0.30
	22.				1.33	1.24	1.16	1.10	0.91	0.79
	24.				1.70	1.63	1.57	1.53	1.38	1.28
0.75	6				−0.75	−0.93	−1.07	−1.18	−1.52	−1.72
	8.				−0.47	−0.64	−0.76	−0.86	−1.18	−1.36
	10				−0.19	−0.34	−0.45	−0.54	−0.83	−1.00
	12.				0.10	−0.03	−0.14	−0.22	−0.48	−0.63
	14.				0.39	0.27	0.18	0.11	−0.12	−0.26
	16.				0.69	0.58	0.50	0.44	0.24	0.12
	18.				0.98	0.89	0.82	0.77	0.59	0.49
	20.				1.28	1.20	1.14	1.10	0.95	0.87
1.00	−6.				−1.68	−1.88	−2.03	−2.14	−2.50	−2.70
	−2.				−1.22	−1.39	−1.52	−1.62	−1.94	−2.12
	2.				−0.74	−0.90	−1.01	−1.10	−1.37	−1.53
	6.				−0.26	−0.39	−0.49	−0.56	−0.80	−0.93
	10.				0.22	0.12	0.04	−0.02	−0.22	−0.33
	14.				0.73	0.64	0.58	0.53	0.38	0.29
	18.				1.24	1.18	1.13	1.09	0.97	0.91
	22.				1.77	1.73	1.69	1.67	1.59	1.54
1.25	−8.				−1.36	−1.52	−1.64	−1.73	−2.00	−2.15
	−4				−0.95	−1.10	−1.20	−1.28	−1.52	−1.65
	0.				−0.54	−0.66	−0.75	−0.82	−1.03	−1.15
	4.				−0.12	−0.22	−0.30	−0.36	−0.54	−0.64
	8.				0.31	0.22	0.16	0.11	−0.04	−0.13
	12.				0.75	0.68	0.63	0.59	0.47	0.40
	16.				1.20	1.15	1.11	1.08	0.98	0.93
	20.				1.66	1.62	1.59	1.57	1.50	1.46
1.50	−10.				−1.13	−1.26	−1.35	−1.42	−1.64	−1.76
	−6.				−0.76	−0.87	−0.96	−1.02	−1.21	−1.32
	−2.				−0.39	−0.49	−0.56	−0.62	−0.79	−0.88
	2.				−0.01	−0.10	−0.16	−0.21	−0.36	−0.44
	6.				0.38	0.30	0.25	0.21	0.08	0.01
	10.				0.76	0.70	0.66	0.62	0.52	0.46
	14.				1.17	1.12	1.09	1.06	0.98	0.93
	18.				1.58	1.54	1.52	1.50	1.44	1.40

istically small (due to unavoidable body movements) and have therefore been omitted from the table. The PMV index can be expected to be less accurate at the combination: low clo-value (nude) and high velocity, since the actual skin temperature is quite close to the air temperature in this case. These combinations have therefore also been omitted from table 13.

The ambient temperatures given in the table have been chosen so that the predicted mean votes fall nearly symmetrically around zero. The table has been calculated for a relative humidity of 50%, but as mentioned before, humidity has only a moderate influence on the thermal sensation near the comfort conditions. If the actual rh deviates greatly from 50%, a correction to the table is given in fig. 25, which will be discussed later.

The table is set up for the mean radiant temperature equal to the air temperature. If the mean radiant temperature deviates from the air temperature, this correction is given in fig. 24 which will also be discussed later.

The evaluation process, in practice, for a given room climate is as follows. The activity level and clo-value are first estimated (see tables 1 and 2) with due consideration to the intended use of the room. The environmental variables are then measured, i.e., air temperature, mean radiant temperature, air velocity and humidity, at a suitable number of points in the occupied zone. The water vapour pressure will normally be the same over the whole room, and a single measurement of the humidity is thus sufficient. Methods for the measurement of the individual variables will be treated in a later section of this chapter.

Using table 13, the predicted mean vote at each measuring point in the occupied zone can then be determined. One might further sketch in iso-PMV-curves, i.e., curves through those points having the same predicted mean vote, in order to gain a general idea of how the condition deviates from the optimal in the different areas of the occupied zone. The "Predicted Percentage of Dissatisfied" can then be calculated; this will be dealt with in detail in the following section.

Prior to this, however, the relative influence of some of the individual variables on the predicted mean vote will be considered. This influence is determined by differentiation of equation (40) with regard to the individual variables. The partial differential coefficient is determined for PMV $= 0$, i.e., in the neutrality point, as it is the influence near this point which is of greatest interest. The differential coefficients have been plotted by computer in the diagrams shown in figs. 23 to 25.

Fig. 23 shows the influence of the ambient temperature t on the predicted mean vote. $\delta(\text{PMV})/\delta t$ is plotted at three different activity levels as a function of the clo-value with the velocity as parameter. $\delta(\text{PMV})/\delta t$ gives the change

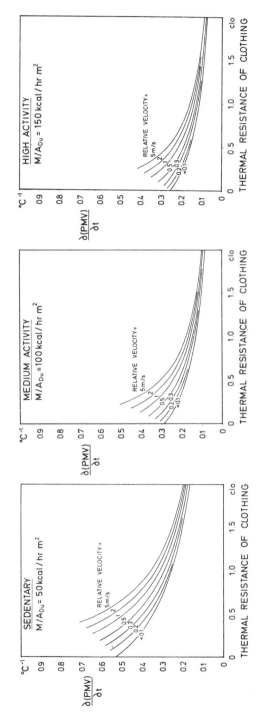

Fig. 23. $\delta(PMV)/\delta t$ as a function of the thermal resistance of the clothing with rel. velocity as parameter, at three different activity levels. $\delta(PMV)/\delta t$ is determined for PMV = 0 and indicates the increment of predicted mean vote, when air temperature (= mean radiant temperature) is increased by 1°C. (Constant vapour pressure.)

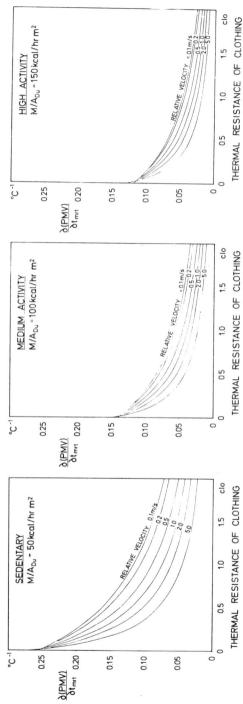

Fig. 24. $\delta(PMV)/\delta t_{mrt}$ as a function of the thermal resistance of the clothing with rel. velocity as parameter, at three different activity levels. $\delta(PMV)/\delta t_{mrt}$ is determined for PMV = 0 and indicates the increment of predicted mean vote, when mean radiant temperature is increased by 1°C. (Constant vapour pressure.)

125

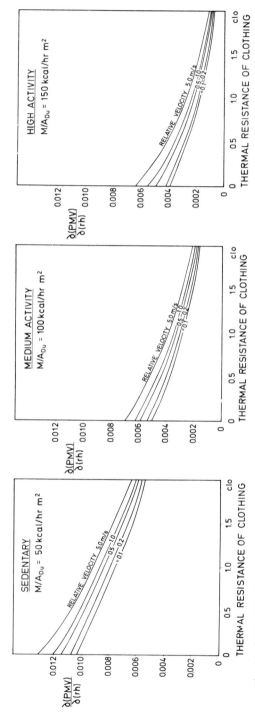

Fig. 25. $\delta(\text{PMV})/\delta(\text{rh})$ as a function of the thermal resistance of the clothing with rel. velocity as parameter, at three different activity levels. $\delta(\text{PMV})/\delta(\text{rh})$ is determined for PMV $= 0$, rh $= 50\%$ and indicates the increment of predicted mean vote, when the relative humidity is increased by 1%.

in the predicted mean vote when the ambient temperature is increased by 1°C, all the other variables being kept constant. It will be seen that a given temperature change has a greater effect the smaller the amount of clothing worn, the higher the velocity and the lower the activity level. By temperature change is meant here an equal alteration of air and mean radiant temperature.

Fig. 24 shows analogously the influence of the mean radiant temperature alone. $\delta(PMV)/\delta t_{mrt}$ is less, the higher the relative velocity, the clo-value, and the activity level. Fig. 24 should be used in practice for correcting the PMV value determined from table 13 if the mean radiant temperature deviates from the air temperature. If, for example, the air temperature is measured at 23.5°C and the air velocity at 0.10 m/s, for sedentary activity and 1 clo, a predicted mean vote equal to 0.06 will be obtained from table 13. If, however, the mean radiant temperature is measured at 2.6°C higher than the air temperature, then PMV $= 0.06 + 2.6 \cdot 0.12 = 0.37$, $\delta(PMV)/\delta t_{mrt}$ ($=$ the change of PMV through a change of t_{mrt} of 1°C) being determined from fig. 24 as 0.12.

The influence of the humidity can be seen from fig. 25, which for three different activity levels shows $\delta(PMV)/\delta(rh)$ as a function of the clo-value with the relative velocity as parameter. $\delta(PMV)/\delta(rh)$ gives the change in PMV when the relative humidity increases by 1%. The influence of a given change in the relative humidity will be seen to be less, the lower the velocity, the higher the clo-value, and the higher the activity level, but otherwise, as anticipated, the influence of the humidity is small. Fig. 25 can be used for correcting the PMV value determined from table 13 which is tabulated for rh $= 50\%$, but the corrections are, as mentioned earlier, only necessary for large deviations. If, for example, rh is measured at 30%, from fig. 25 one obtains for sedentary persons, $I_{cl} = 0.5$ clo, v $= 0.2$ m/s, a value of $\delta(PMV)/\delta(rh)$ equal to 0.0095; the correction to the PMV value found from the table will therefore be $(30–50) 0.0095 = -0.19$. The correction is negative, as 30% humidity will be felt to be slightly cooler than 50%.

It must be remembered that the thermal sensation index is derived on the basis of experimental conditions which have differed only moderately from thermal neutrality (slight discomfort), and it is therefore also in this interval that the greatest accuracy can be expected from the index. For PMV-values smaller than -2 and greater than $+2$, the index should definitely be used with care. Especially in the hot end of the scale, significant errors can occur due to problems with the evaporation of secreted sweat.

Moreover, the discussion in chapter three concerning the influence of certain special factors (national-geographic location, age, sex, etc.) on the comfort conditions and the precautions which are taken here, also apply in general for the thermal sensation index.

PREDICTED PERCENTAGE OF DISSATISFIED

The thermal sensation index derived in the previous section gives the predicted mean vote of a large group of persons exposed to a given combination of the variables. The mean vote is indeed an expression for the general degree of discomfort for the group as a whole, but it is nevertheless difficult to interpret what the magnitude of PMV determined in a practical case can imply. What does it mean, for example, when the predicted mean vote is found to be −0.30, i.e., a value between neutral and slightly cool? Is this acceptable? If one imagined that all persons were identical, corresponding to an "average person", the answer would be Yes, and it could then be expected that all would be comfortable enough not to complain.

However, as is well known, people are not alike. There will naturally be a certain variance in the thermal sensations of a group of persons exposed to the same environment. The persons of particular interest will be those who are decidedly uncomfortable, since it is obviously these dissatisfied persons who in practice will be inclined to complain about the environment.

Instead of just giving the predicted mean vote as an expression for the thermal environment, it seems, therefore, to be more meaningful to state what percent of persons can be expected to be decidedly dissatisfied, since this can readily be interpreted by both the engineer and the layman. The percentage of dissatisfied is simply an expression for the number of "potential complainers".

A relationship between the percentage of dissatisfied and the mean vote can be found from an analysis of the voting from the present Danish experiments (see chapter three) and the analogous American experiments of Nevins et al. (234) and Rohles (280).

The analysis comprises in all 1296 subjects from these three studies. In the experiments each subject was clothed in a standard uniform (0.6 clo) and exposed for three hours to a given ambient temperature. The subjects were seated and voted every half hour on their thermal sensation. Details of the experimental procedure are described in chapter three.

The mean of the last three votes for each subject was calculated and reckoned to the nearest vote (integer). The distribution of these mean votes at each ambient temperature in the interval from 66 F (18.9°C) to 90 F (32.2°C) are listed in table 14.

Table 14. *Distribution of Thermal Sensation Votes (%)*

Amb. Temperature		Number of Subjects	Votes							Dissatisfied		
F	°C		-3	-2	-1	0	+1	+2	+3	Cold (-3) and (-2)	Warm (+2) and (+3)	Total (-3), (-2), and (+2), (+3)
66	18.9	80	42.4	36.3	16.2	3.8	1.3	–	–	78.7	–	78.7
68	20.0	80	28.8	48.7	15.0	7.5	–	–	–	77.5	–	77.5
70	21.1	144	12.5	30.5	45.2	10.4	1.4	–	–	43.0	–	43.0
72	22.2	80	8.8	33.7	31.2	26.3	–	–	–	42.5	–	42.5
74	23.3	144	5.6	11.1	47.2	33.3	2.1	0.7	–	16.7	0.7	17.4
76	24.4	80	–	3.8	22.5	62.5	11.2	–	–	3.8	–	3.8
78	25.6	144	0.7	2.1	18.1	57.5	18.8	2.8	–	2.8	2.8	5.6
80	26.7	80	–	–	3.8	57.5	31.2	5.0	2.5	–	7.5	7.5
82	27.8	144	–	–	4.2	38.8	41.0	14.6	1.4	–	16.0	16.0
84	28.9	80	–	–	–	17.5	41.3	30.0	11.2	–	41.2	41.2
86	30.0	80	–	–	–	25.0	45.0	26.3	3.7	–	30.0	30.0
88	31.1	80	–	–	–	8.8	38.7	36.3	16.2	–	52.5	52.5
90	32.2	80	–	–	–	5.0	16.3	50.0	28.7	–	78.7	78.7

The dissatisfied are defined here as those who vote −2 (cool) or −3 (cold), +2 (warm) or +3 (hot). One could perhaps object that those voting −1 or +1 were not included also, but as evidenced by Gagge et al. (96), real discomfort is first expressed by those voting higher than +2 or lower than −2. It has therefore been decided here to describe as dissatisfied, only those persons who feel decided discomfort according to the above definition. However, the following relative considerations would not be vitally affected if perhaps a slightly different definition had been chosen.

The percentages of warm and cold dissatisfied, listed in table 14, were then the object of a probit analysis (82), applied earlier in comfort studies by Chrenko (58) and Wyon (340). In fig. 26 the probits of the proportions "cold dissatisfied" and "warm dissatisfied" are plotted against ambient temperature. This transformation gives a straight line relationship.

The lines cross each other at 25.6°C, equal to the optimal temperature given by the comfort equation and also equal to the preferred temperature determined from the same data but in another way in chapter three (table 5). Smoothed estimates of the proportions of cold and warm dissatisfied were then obtained from these lines and they were added in one curve shown in fig. 27. This curve illustrates in a semi-logarithmic plot the total percentage of dissatisfied as a function of the predicted mean vote. The transformation of the abscissa from ambient temperature to PMV could easily be done since all variables were well controlled and measured during the experiments.

In the following, the "Predicted Percentage of Dissatisfied" (PPD) shown by the curve in fig. 27 will be used as the basis for an evaluation of thermal environments. It will be seen that the curve is symmetric and it has a minimum of 5% dissatisfied for a mean vote equal to zero. This point corresponds to the optimal comfort condition mentioned many times previously, and established by the comfort equation. It is this optimum condition which should be sought, and thermal environments should be judged according to the extent to which the actual PPD exceeds the minimum value of 5%.

As will be seen from fig. 27, PPD increases the more the mean vote deviates from zero, and the curve does not have a crisp at PMV = 0, but is rounded considerably. However, already with a mean vote of ± 0.35, there will be half as many more dissatisfied than at the minimum point. After this, PPD increases quite rapidly, and for PMV = ± 0.5 it is twice as great, and for PMV = ± 1 it is over five times as great as the minimum value of 5%.

As fig. 27 shows, it is impossible to satisfy all persons in a large group sharing a collective climate. Even with a perfect environmental system, which creates absolutely uniform conditions in the occupied zone, one

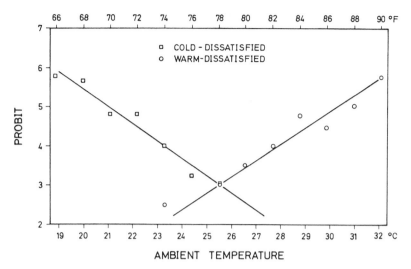

Fig. 26. Proportion of individuals thermally dissatisfied at various ambient temperatures. Left line shows the probit of the percentage "cold dissatisfied". Right line shows the probit of the percentage "warm dissatisfied".

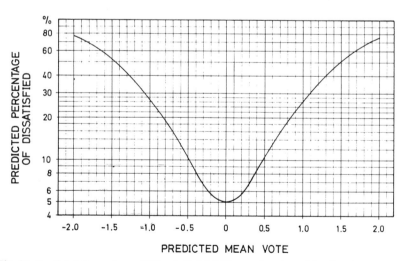

Fig. 27. Predicted Percentage of Dissatisfied (PPD) as a function of Predicted Mean Vote (PMV).

Table 15. *Distribution Between Cold- and Warm-Dissatisfied*

PMV	Predicted Percentage of Dissatisfied		
	Cold	Warm	Total
− 2.0	76.4	–	76.4
− 1.5	52.0	–	52.0
− 1.0	26.8	–	26.8
− 0.9	22.5	–	22.5
− 0.8	18.7	0.1	18.8
− 0.7	15.3	0.2	15.5
− 0.6	12.4	0.3	12.7
− 0.5	9.9	0.4	10.3
− 0.4	7.7	0.6	8.3
− 0.3	6.0	0.9	6.9
− 0.2	4.5	1.3	5.8
− 0.1	3.4	1.8	5.2
0	2.5	2.5	5.0
+ 0.1	1.8	3.4	5.2
+ 0.2	1.3	4.5	5.8
+ 0.3	0.9	5.9	6.8
+ 0.4	0.6	7.7	8.3
+ 0.5	0.4	9.8	10.2
+ 0.6	0.3	12.2	12.5
+ 0.7	0.2	15.2	15.4
+ 0.8	0.1	18.5	18.6
+ 0.9	–	22.2	22.2
+ 1.0	–	26.4	26.4
+ 1.5	–	51.4	51.4
+ 2.0	–	75.7	75.7

cannot attain a PPD value lower than 5% for similarly clothed people in the same activity.

This point is often overlooked in practice where any complaints, however few, are often taken as an indication that the system is defective or a least badly operated. It is thus rather common for operating personnel to change the temperature level simply because of complaints from individual persons in a large group. These particular persons will perhaps then be satisfied, but on the other hand, others will become dissatisfied. Even a larger number than before may complain, if an optimal condition existed previously. Complaints cannot be avoided, but they should be kept to a minimum, corresponding to the curve in fig. 27.

It has previously been rather usual to speak of more or less randomly defined comfort zones corresponding to wide temperature intervals. In practice, these comfort zones were often employed so that as long as the condition of the room lay within the wide interval concerned, it was considered as satisfactory. For an individual person, there is an interval within which he will feel comfortable. For a large group of persons, however, as shown in fig. 27, there will only be one point which will be optimal for the group. Certain practical limits for permissible deviations must of course be allowed, e.g., that the number of dissatisfied must not be more than half as large again as the minimum value, i.e., PPD = 7.5%; the predicted mean vote must lie between -0.35 and $+0.35$ in this case. In project planning, such a limit can naturally be linked with a design meteorological condition so that it would be required that the capacity of the environmental system be sufficient to keep PPD under the stated limit, at the design weather conditions.

Besides considering the total percent of decidedly dissatisfied, it may be of interest to know how many are uncomfortable because of heat, and how many are uncomfortable because of cold. The distribution is given in table 15. It can be seen from this that in the optimal condition, there are just as many cold as warm dissatisfied, while the distribution becomes more and more skew the more the mean vote deviates from zero. For PMV $> +1$ or < -1, one can expect that the dissatisfied will make up a homogenous group who either feel uncomfortably warm or uncomfortably cold. While at the optimal condition there is thus a balance between the two groups of dissatisfied, a deviation from the zero point will not only mean a greater percentage of dissatisfied, but also a skew composition of the dissatisfied, which must be expected to result in a massive demand for a unilateral change.

THERMAL NON-UNIFORMITY OF ROOMS

In the previous section, the relation between predicted mean vote and percentage of dissatisfied has been discussed, presupposing that all persons are exposed to exactly the same thermal conditions.

If the thermal field in a room is uniform, the predicted mean vote will of course be the same over the whole occupied zone, and by adjusting the temperature level, one can obtain a mean vote of zero, corresponding to the minimum percentage of dissatisfied of 5%.

If, on the other hand, there are thermal differences from point to point in the occupied zone, one can still, by changing the temperature level, achieve an average of zero for the PMV values for all points in the occupied zone, but the predicted percentage of dissatisfied will now be higher than the minimum value.

133

If, in practice, one measures the thermal variables at a number of points suitably distributed within the occupied zone, one can determine from table 13 the predicted mean vote, and from fig. 27 the corresponding value of the PPD for each measuring point. PPD for the room (the entire occupied zone) can then be determined as the average of the PPD values for all measuring points, and the difference between this percentage and 5% is then a "figure of merit" for the quality of the actual measured thermal environment.

Part of this difference could be due to the temperature level, and a part could be due to the thermal non-uniformity of the room. By changing the temperature level, the minimum value of PPD for the room can be determined. This value is the "Lowest Possible Percentage of Dissatisfied" (LPPD) in the actual room. The difference between LPPD and the 5% dissatisfied which it is possible to obtain in a thermally uniform environment is a figure of merit for the non-uniformity of the room and thus characterizes the heating or air-conditioning system in the actual room.

In determining the LPPD, the temperature level is altered. It should be noted that for moderate alterations this will have only a negligible effect on the velocity field and on the temperature differences in the space, and therefore on the thermal non-uniformity of the room.

In practice the operating personnel should maintain a suitable temperature level in the space (if the capacity of the system makes this possible), while it is the task of the engineer who designs the heating and air conditioning to propose a system which will give as uniform thermal conditions as possible in the occupied zone, i.e., so that the LPPD value comes as close as possible to the ideal minimum value of 5%.

Only large groups of persons have been referred to in the foregoing. However, the same method can well be used to characterize rooms intended to be occupied by only a few persons. In these rooms also the greatest possible uniformity will be demanded so that one can occupy, and be comfortable in, the entire occupied zone, and LPPD is an applicable expression for the non-uniformity in this case as well.

With larger air-conditioning projects it is rather usual, as a part of the design, to perform model experiments, where at least air velocities and temperatures are measured at a large number of points in the occupied zone. Also in this case the calculation of LPPD is a suitable means by which to evaluate the measured results, which otherwise can be very difficult to interpret.

The question now is where should the upper limit be set for permissible values of LPPD ? As with most quality demands, this limit must be established by using professional judgement. It is suggested here that in rooms intended for long-term occupancy, this limit be set at 6% under normal working conditions, i.e. the non-uniformity in the room is permitted to increase the number of dissatisfied by only one-fifth. This demand may seem severe, but it should be noted that the non-uniformity will cause a much greater increase of PPD if the temperature level is not optimum, due to the steep slope of the curve in fig. 27.

If outer walls exist in a room, the magnitude of LPPD is not only a function of the environmental system, but also of the outdoor climate, since this influences the thermal field in the room. The meteorological data should therefore be noted, when determining the LPPD in practice. Furthermore, the quality demand for an environmental system as regards thermal uniformity in a room must be set in relation to normal outdoor conditions. For example, the following demand can be set for a heating system: at an outdoor mean 24–hour temperature of between 0 and 5°C, LPPD for the actual room must not exceed 6%. And for an air-conditioning system, for example: at an outdoor mean 24-hour temperature between 15 and 20°C and with a clear sky, LPPD must not exceed 6%. These demands for the thermal uniformity of a room are of course in addition to the demands for PPD under design conditions, as mentioned in the previous section.

It should be emphasized that the non-uniformity expressed by LPPD refers to the thermal variations from place to place in the occupied zone and not to the directional variations in heat loss from the human body. Unilateral heating or cooling of the body must be evaluated separately. However, as noted in chapter three, quite significant asymmetries in the heat loss from the human body seem to be acceptable without discomfort.

PRACTICAL PROCEDURE

On the basis of the new method of rating the quality of thermal environments described above, the following procedure is now suggested for use in the evaluation of indoor climates in practice.

1. A suitable number of measuring points should be chosen, equally distributed over the occupied zone in the particular space. If the space is intended for sedentary persons, the measurements should be taken 0.6 m above floor level, for standing persons 1.0 m above floor level. With more detailed investigations, measurements can be taken at each place for three heights: 0.2, 0.6 and 1.0 m above floor level for sedentary

135

persons, and 0.3, 1.0 and 1.7 m above floor level in rooms intended for standing persons.

2. The air temperature, the mean radiant temperature and the air velocity should be measured at each of the measuring points. The water vapour pressure is normally the same over the whole room, and it is therefore sufficient to measure the humidity at one point. Various methods of measuring the environmental variables are mentioned in the last section of this chapter. The measurements at the different points should preferably take place within a relatively short time period, so that possible changes in the temperature level have no effect. Corrections can be made, however, for time fluctuations in the temperature level, by registering the air temperature at one point on a recorder and then correcting all the measured points accordingly (assuming equal fluctuations in the entire occupied zone).

3. The activity level and clo-value should be established from tables 1 and 2, with due consideration to the intended use of the room. At high activity levels where the body movements increase the relative air velocity, all the velocities measured should be supplemented by this value.

4. On the basis of the values measured, the predicted mean vote for each measuring point is then determined from table 13. If the mean radiant temperature deviates from the air temperature, the value in the table is corrected by using fig. 24. If the air humidity deviates to any great extent from 50%, the value in the table can be corrected by using fig. 25. If, for each location, measurements are taken at three heights, the mean is determined from the PMV values at each height. This mean value is suggested as representative of the location in question.

5. For each location the PPD value is now determined from fig. 27 or table 15, and the mean for the whole space is calculated. The predicted percentage of dissatisfied in the space is the suggested "figure of merit" for the quality of the thermal environment at the time of measuring.

6. The predicted mean vote for the whole occupied zone is calculated as the average of the mean votes found for each location. If this average is higher (lower) than zero, it means that the temperature level should be lowered (raised), and the magnitude of the change can be determined from table 13 or fig. 23.

7. The mean vote for the whole occupied zone found from 6. above is subtracted from the mean votes determined at each location, and the corresponding PPD values are found from fig. 27. The mean value of the new PPD values found gives the lowest possible percentage of dissatisfied (LPPD) in the actual room, and the difference between LPPD and 5%

136

is the suggested "figure of merit" for the thermal non-uniformity of the room.

8. If LPPD is too high, the reasons therefor must be examined in more detail in order to discover possibilities for design improvements. In this connection, it can be helpful to draw iso-PMV-curves, i.e., curves through points having the same PMV value. The curves are drawn on the basis of the PMV values at the measuring points, determined from 4. above. By examining the iso-PMV-curves, a general view of the problems is obtained, making it easier to suggest where something is wrong and where design changes are desirable.

Example 10. In a lecture hall of the size shown in fig. 28, it is desired to assess the room climate. In the occupied zone an imaginary square grid is constructed and measurements are taken of the air temperature, air velocity and mean radiant temperature in the centre of each square. In this example 30 measuring points in all (0.6 m above floor level) have been chosen. The values found from the measurements are listed in table 16 (hypothetical figures). For one location in the room the water vapour pressure is measured at 10 mm Hg. Since this corresponds to an rh close to 50%, it is not necessary to correct for the humidity in determining the PMV. The activity is sedentary ($M/A_{Du} = 50$ kcal/hr m^2), and the clo-value is estimated at 1.0.

From table 13 a PMV value corresponding to the air temperature and velocity measured (PMV$_{air}$) is now determined for each measuring point, and a correction Δ(PMV) is then made as the mean radiant temperature deviates from the air temperature. The correction is found by first determining δ(PMV)/δt_{mrt} from fig. 24 and then multiplying by $\Delta t = t_{mrt} - t_a$. PMV is then determined as the sum of PMV$_{air}$ and Δ(PMV), and for each point the corresponding PPD value is found.

The mean value is then determined for all points of PMV ($= -0.42$) and of PPD ($= 11.3\%$). Thus, between twice and two-and-a-half times as many decidedly dissatisfied can be expected than under optimal conditions.

By increasing the PMV value at each point by 0.42, which according to table 13 or fig. 23 corresponds to an increase in the temperature level of 1.5 °C, the predicted mean vote for the whole room becomes zero. The corresponding PPD values for each point are determined from fig. 27 and the mean value gives the LPPD ($= 7.6\%$). The thermal variability in the room thus means that half as many again decidedly dissatisfied can be expected than in a uniform room. This value seems to be unacceptable, and one must therefore analyse how the conditions can be improved. In fig. 28, iso-PMV-curves are drawn which show that it is on the left side and especially

Table 16. Calculation of PMV, PPD and LPPD in a Room (Example 10)

Measuring Point	Air Temp. t_a °C	Relative Velocity v m/s	PMV_{air} for $t_{mrt}=t_a$ (table 13)	$\Delta t = t_{mrt}-t_a$ °C	$\frac{\delta(PMV)}{\delta t_{mrt}}$ (Fig. 24) °C⁻¹	$\Delta(PMV) = \Delta t \cdot \frac{\delta(PMV)}{\delta t_{mrt}}$	$PMV = PMV_{air} + \Delta(PMV)$	PPD (Fig. 27) %	$PMV + 0.42$ (1.5°C Higher Temp. Level)	LPPD (Fig. 27) %
A1	21.3	0.15	−0.65	−1.0	0.11	−0.11	−0.76	17.5	−0.34	7.4
A2	21.0	0.12	−0.65	−1.6	0.11	−0.18	−0.83	20.0	−0.41	8.5
A3	21.5	0.20	−0.70	−2.0	0.10	−0.20	−0.90	23.0	−0.48	9.7
A4	21.0	0.22	−0.87	−1.9	0.10	−0.19	−1.06	30.0	−0.64	13.9
A5	21.2	0.34	−0.98	−2.3	0.10	−0.23	−1.21	37.5	−0.79	18.8
A6	21.2	0.25	−0.86	−2.5	0.10	−0.25	−1.11	32.5	−0.69	15.5
B1	21.9	0.07	−0.33	−0.2	0.12	−0.02	−0.35	7.5	+0.07	5.2
B2	21.8	0.04	−0.35	−0.1	0.12	−0.01	−0.36	7.7	+0.08	5.2
B3	22.1	0.09	−0.27	−0.2	0.12	−0.02	−0.29	6.7	+0.13	5.4
B4	22.0	0.15	−0.46	−0.6	0.11	−0.07	−0.53	10.6	−0.11	5.3
B5	22.0	0.24	−0.61	−1.2	0.10	−0.12	−0.73	16.5	−0.31	6.8
B6	21.5	0.20	−0.70	−1.5	0.10	−0.15	−0.85	21.0	−0.43	8 7
C1	22.1	0.06	−0.27	+0.3	0.12	+0.04	−0.24	6.2	+0.18	5.7
C2	21.9	0.08	−0.33	+1.4	0.12	+0.17	−0.16	5.6	+0.26	6.4
C3	21.7	0.06	−0.38	+1.3	0.12	+0.16	−0.22	6.0	+0.20	5.8
C4	22.0	0.15	−0.46	+2.0	0.11	+0.22	−0.24	6.2	+0.18	5.7
C5	21.9	0.10	−0.36	+0.1	0.12	+0.01	−0.35	7.5	+0.07	5.2
C6	21.4	0.09	−0.46	−0.9	0.12	−0.11	−0.57	12.0	−0.15	5.5
D1	22.5	0.06	−0.16	+0.2	0.12	+0.03	−0.13	5.3	+0.29	6.7
D2	22.9	0.05	−0.05	+1.0	0.12	+0.12	+0.07	5.2	+0.49	10.0
D3	22.7	0.08	−0.11	+1.8	0.12	+0.21	+0.10	5.3	+0.52	10.8
D4	22.5	0.15	−0.32	+2.1	0.11	+0.21	−0.08	5.2	+0.34	7.4
D5	21.8	0.10	−0.39	+1.0	0.12	+0.12	−0.27	6.5	+0.15	5.5
D6	22.2	0.15	−0.40	−0.3	0.11	−0.03	−0.43	8.7	−0.01	5.0
E1	22.6	0.08	−0.13	+0.9	0.12	+0.11	−0.02	5.1	+0.40	8.3
E2	22.4	0.12	−0.28	+1.3	0.11	+0.14	−0.14	5.4	+0.28	6.7
E3	22.0	0.11	−0.35	+1.6	0.11	+0.17	−0.18	5.7	+0.24	6.2
E4	22.0	0.12	−0.38	+2.0	0.11	+0.22	−0.16	5.6	+0.26	6.4
E5	22.5	0.18	−0.37	+1.2	0.12	+0.14	−0.23	6.1	+0.19	5.8
E6	22.0	0.09	−0.30	+0.5	0.12	+0.06	−0.24	6.2	+0.18	5.7
Mean Value...							−0.42	11.3%	0.00	7.64%

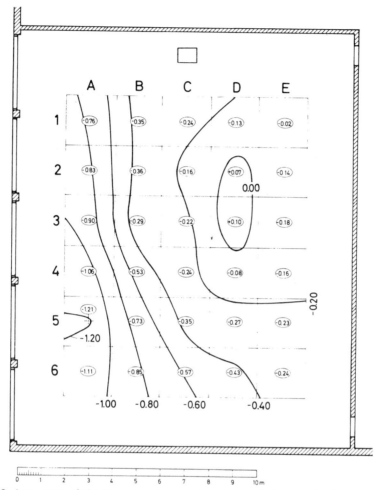

Fig. 28. Assessment of the thermal environment in a lecture hall (example 10). A square grid is constructed covering the seating area (the occupied zone). Measurements are taken in the centre of each square and the corresponding PMV-values are entered in the figure. Iso-PMV curves have been plotted in the occupied zone. The PMV is lowest near the window wall and the back wall which is also an outer one.

in the bottom left corner, where something is wrong. The air velocities are greatest here and the mean radiant temperature is lowest. One must therefore examine how, in the actual case, one can remedy the error by the application of suitable design changes.

METHODS OF MEASUREMENT

In the present section a concise summary will be given of those methods for measuring the environmental variables which are important in the practical assessment of thermal environments.

This concerns the measuring of air temperature, air velocity, mean radiant temperature and air humidity. Only specific methods and problems connected with the measuring of these factors in a space will be discussed here. General principles for the measuring of temperature, velocity and humidity are described in detail in standard handbooks (133, 330, 112, 65, 5).

Air Temperature

Air temperature can be measured by a mercury thermometer, a thermocouple or an electrical resistance sensor (including a thermistor). If the sensor is placed in a room, it will register a temperature between air temperature and mean radiant temperature. The simplest way to reduce the radiant error is to make the sensor as small as possible as the convective heat transfer coefficient rises with decreasing size, while the radiant heat transfer coefficient is constant. A small dimension of the sensor also provides a favourably low time constant. However, the radiant error can also be reduced by the use of a shield (an open, polished aluminium cylinder) around the sensor, or by the use of a sensor with a low-emittance surface, or by artificially increasing the air velocity around the sensor (aspirating air through a tube in which the sensor is placed).

Air Velocity

The instrument most commonly used is the thermal anemometer of a type suitable for measuring the small velocities which normally occur in rooms (0–0.5 m/s). The heated probe can either be relatively large (e.g a 3–6 mm sphere (307, 236, 251)) which thus averages the velocity fluctuations with time so that a mean value is measured, or it can be quite small (e.g., a 5 μ hot wire (64)) in which case it measures the instantaneous velocity. In all cases measurements should be taken over a suitable period, e.g., 3–5 min. in order to obtain a reasonable mean value. If a probe is used with a small time constant, the mean value is determined from a series of individual readings, e.g., every 5 seconds, or a recorder can be used, or an electronic integrator, so that the mean velocity can be determined afterwards.

Some sensors are not omni-directional and therefore require at least that the main direction of the velocity at the particular point is determined, e.g., by a smoke test.

A silvered kata-thermometer (22) can also be used, as the mean velocity in the measuring period can be calculated by the kata-value and the air temperature.

For less exact measurements the smoke technique can be used, timing the movement of a smoke puff. Smoke ampoules, available in various types, are most applicable for this purpose.

Mean Radiant Temperature

The mean radiant temperature refers to the shape of the human body and for this reason alone, is a factor which is difficult to measure precisely.

One method is to measure the surface temperature of ceiling, walls, floor, etc., e.g., with thermocouples, or more easily with a thermoradiometer (221, 305, 304) and then calculate the mean radiant temperature (see chapter 5) at the different locations by the use of the angle factor diagrams, presented in chapter six. The method is accurate, but requires a considerable amount of calculation work after the measurements are determined.

In the literature, several instruments are described for the direct measurement of mean radiant temperature in relation to spheres, which in many cases will give a reasonable approximation (Benzinger and Kitzinger (25), Richards et al. (272), Sutton and McNall (309), Aagard (1), Schüle and Lutz (296), Braun and McNall (39), Gagge et al. (99), Lidwell and Wyon (188)). Other instruments measure "directional" radiant temperatures (Korsgaard (173, 174), Pedersen (255, 256), Houghten and Brewer (150), Heidtkamp (130), Uldall-Jørgensen (318)). However, none of these instruments seem to be available on the market.

Because of its simplicity, the globe thermometer (320, 321, 322, 131, 20, 17, 216, 177, 178, 159) has been the instrument most used for the determination of the mean radiant temperature in practice. It consists of a black spherical shell in the centre of which is placed a thermal sensor (mercury in glass bulb, thermocouple, thermistor) which will take on the mean temperature of the globe. From the globe temperature, the air temperature and the air velocity, the mean radiant temperature can then be calculated. Spherical diameters of varying sizes have been used but the most common are Vernon's (d = 15.2 cm) and Missenard's (d = 9 cm). In theory, any diameter can be used, so long as a calibration is made, but a large sphere gives the greatest accuracy since the convective heat transfer coefficient is then lowest. Earlier, spherical shells of copper were used but these have an undesirably high time constant. It is suggested instead to use a thin plastic bubble or balloon (45, 177). These spheres can be blackened by using a new type of paint with an emittance very close to unity, which is available in aerosol containers.[1])

Air Humidity

The vapour pressure will normally be the same over the whole room, and it is therefore sufficient to measure the humidity at one location only. The measurement can be taken with a psychrometer, dew-point apparatus, hair hygrometer or electrolytic hygrometer. With regard to the determination of the predicted mean vote, a rough measurement is sufficient, but for other reasons it can of course be required to measure the humidity with greater accuracy.

Integrating Instruments

Several of the previously mentioned instruments (p. 109) which integrate the effect of at least two of the variables, might also be used in the determination of PMV, suitable calibration, however, being necessary. The precision naturally depends on the ability of the instrument to simulate the combined effect of the variables on the human body. Measurements with a suitable instrument can, in this way, be made quicker than by measuring all the variables, but if a particular room climate is found to be unsatisfactory, it can be more difficult to assess what steps should be taken to bring about an improvement. If, for example, the PMV values at one end of a room are too low, it is necessary to know whether this is due in particular to a lower air temperature or mean radiant temperature, or to a higher velocity than in the rest of the room, so that appropriate design changes may be made.

---

[1] 3 M Comp.: Velvet Coating, 101–C10 Black.

Chapter 5.

CALCULATION OF MEAN RADIANT TEMPERATURE

Since the mean radiant temperature has a considerable influence on man's heat loss and thus on his state of comfort, its calculation is important in the detailed thermal analysis of a room, which will be dealt with in a later chapter. The mean radiant temperature is easy to define but quite complicated to calculate or measure in practice. Therefore, we will deal with the mean radiant temperature separately in this chapter.

The exact definition of the mean radiant temperature will first be discussed, after which the necessary equations for the calculation of the mean radiant temperature will be derived so that they may be used later in the thermal analysis of a space.

For persons exposed to irradiation from high-intensity infrared heaters, formulae and a diagram are given for the determination of the mean radiant temperature in this case. In addition, a new and rational method for the calculation of high-intensity beam heating systems is given.

DEFINITION

The mean radiant temperature in relation to a person in a given body posture and clothing placed at a given point in a room, is defined as that uniform temperature of black surroundings which will give the same radiant heat loss from the person as the actual case under study.

As a mean radiant temperature can naturally be defined in relation to any body or surface, e.g., in relation to a sphere or a cube, it is important to specify that it is the mean radiant temperature in relation to a person which is of interest here. The body posture plays a certain role; the mean radiant temperature in relation to a standing person need not be the same as in relation to a seated one. Likewise, the person's location and orientation in the room must be known, since the mean radiant temperature will often vary from point to point and for the same point also, with the azimuthal orientation of the body.

143

When speaking of shortwave irradiation of the body (e.g. from the sun and some types of high-intensity infrared heaters), the absorptance of the outer surface of the clothed body (clothing and exposed skin) will also influence the mean radiant temperature. For a person receiving solar radiation the mean radiant temperature will be much higher if he is clothed in black than if he wears white clothing, and the mean radiant temperature will be higher in relation to a darkly pigmented person than in relation to a white person.

For normal longwave (low temperature) radiation, the absorptance is equal to the emittance which, as mentioned before, for the skin and all normal textiles is close to unity. However, the emittance of the person has no influence on the mean radiant temperature, which will be the same in relation to a man clothed in an aluminium suit as in relation to a man clothed in a normal textile suit. But in calculating the radiant heat exchange with the surroundings, naturally one must, for the aluminium suit, use a much lower emittance than the 0.97 which as a good approximation for skin and all normal textiles, is used in the comfort equation and in the PMV index.

It will thus be seen that the mean radiant temperature is an ambiguous concept unless it is specifically stated to what it refers. This should, of course, always be defined so there can be no doubt as to which mean radiant temperature is meant.

EMITTANCE OF SURROUNDING SURFACES

The emittance of the surfaces (floor, walls, ceiling, etc.) in a room have, according to the definition, a certain influence on the mean radiant temperature. The magnitude of this influence will be discussed in the present section.

Let us first, as a theoretical case, consider a room where all surfaces are perfect emitters ($\varepsilon = 1$), and all have a uniform temperature, e.g., 15 °C. According to the definition, the mean radiant temperature in this case is simply equal to 15 °C.

Let us now, as another extreme case, suppose that the surfaces in the same room are perfect reflectors ($\varepsilon = 0$), but with the same uniform temperature of 15 °C. In this case no radiant heat exchange between person and surroundings will occur. All radiation emitted from the outer surface of the person will be reflected from the surrounding surfaces, until it strikes the person again. The person "sees" himself in all directions and the mean radiant temperature will therefore be equal to the person's outer surface temperature, which for example is about 28 °C. The room will thus be felt to be warmer when the surfaces are perfect reflectors than when they are perfect emitters, even though the surface temperature is the same.

From this extreme case one may think at first that the use of reflecting materials on the walls would be a simple method of reducing the necessary air temperature and thus the capacity of the heating system. However, in practice, there are no materials which are perfect reflectors. And even by using those materials which have the highest known reflectances (highly polished Al, Cu and Au) the mean radiant temperature for a normal-sized room will be very near the actual temperature of the surfaces. This phenomenon stems from the fact that the radiation emitted from the person will be reflected (and each time partly absorbed) a great many times before striking the person again. When a small body (the human body) is situated in a large enclosure, the relationship between the areas will mean that the influence of low emittance walls on the radiant heat exchange will be insignificant. Disregarding extremely small rooms, it will be only the emittance for the small body which will be of significance.

For rooms in which all surfaces have a uniform temperature, the emittance has therefore no influence on the mean radiant temperature. If, on the other hand, there are significant temperature differences, the emittances will affect the relative influence on the mean radiant temperature of the various surfaces in the room.

EVALUATION OF THE MEAN RADIANT TEMPERATURE

A method for evaluating the mean radiant temperature will be given for a person placed in an enclosure consisting of N surfaces, which each are isothermal and have temperatures T_1, T_2, ... T_N (°K). The corresponding emittances are ε_1, ε_2, ... ε_N, and the angle factors between the person and the surfaces are F_{P-1}, F_{P-2} .... F_{P-N}.

If a given physical surface is found not to be isothermal, it should be subdivided into smaller surfaces, each of which is essentially isothermal. Each surface is assumed to be grey, that is emittance = absorptance, and furthermore it is assumed that the radiation emitted and reflected from any surface is diffusely distributed (i.e., Lambert's Cosine Law is obeyed). This assumption, which is a good approximation for all normal non-metallic surfaces, means that the emitted and reflected radiation from a surface are directionally indistinguishable, and it is thus sufficient in the analysis to deal with their sum, the radiosity B, defined by

$$B = \varepsilon\sigma T^4 + \rho H \qquad (42)$$

where H is the incident radiant energy arriving at a surface per unit time and unit area, and ρ is the reflectance, which for a grey body is equal to $1-\varepsilon$.

The radiosity is the rate at which radiant energy streams away from a surface, the first term on the right in eq. (42) representing the radiation emitted by the surface and the second term representing the reflected radiation.

In accordance with the foregoing assumptions, B is also diffusely distributed and customary angle factors can therefore be used in heat exchange calculations involving radiosities.

Assuming that the N surfaces in the enclosure in question have radiosities B_1, B_2 .... B_N respectively, we obtain, from the definition of the mean radiant temperature, the following equation:

$$\varepsilon_p\sigma(T_{mrt}^4 - T_{cl}^4) = \varepsilon_p [B_1F_{P-1} + B_2F_{P-2} + ...$$

$$...+ B_NF_{P-N}] - \varepsilon_p\sigma T_{cl}^4 \qquad (43)$$

where ε_p is the emittance of the person and T_{cl} is the outer temperature of the person.

Equation (43) expresses that the radiant heat transfer at the surface of the subject originating from an imaginary black enclosure at a uniform temperature (mean radiant temperature, T_{mrt}) must be equal to the absorbed part of all the actual incident radiation from the N surfaces minus the emitted radiation from the human body.

From eq. (43) we thus obtain the following formula for the determination of T_{mrt}

$$T_{mrt}^4 = \frac{1}{\sigma}(B_1F_{P-1} + B_2F_{P-2} + ... + B_NF_{P-N}) \qquad (44)$$

It will be noted that T_{cl} has no influence on the mean radiant temperature.

The problem now is to determine the unknown radiosities B_1, B_2 .... B_N. As can be seen from eq. (42) the radiosity of a given surface is not merely a function of temperature and emittance of the surface concerned, but is also dependent on the incident radiation from all the other surfaces. The radiosities must therefore be calculated by a total analysis of the radiant field; this will be dealt with in chapter seven, where also the radiosity concept itself will be discussed further. Here it will simply be pointed out that the radiosity for all surfaces in an enclosure can be calculated when the emittance and the temperature for each surface is known.

As mentioned earlier, most building materials have a high emittance, and for the calculation it will thus often be an acceptable approximation to disregard the reflections, i.e., to assume that all the surfaces in the room are black.

Eq. (44) is thus simplified to:

$$T_{mrt}^4 = T_1^4 F_{P-1} + T_2^4 F_{P-2} + \ldots + T_N^4 F_{P-N} \tag{45}$$

As the sum of the angle factors is unity, the fourth power of the mean radiant temperature will be seen to be equal to the mean value of the surrounding surface temperatures in the fourth power, weighted according to the size of the respective angle factors.

If there are only relatively small temperature differences between the surfaces of the enclosure, eq. (45) can be further simplified by linearizing:

$$T_{mrt} = T_1 F_{P-1} + T_2 F_{P-2} + \ldots + T_N F_{P-N} \tag{46}$$

In other words, the mean radiant temperature is calculated as the mean value of the surrounding temperatures weighted according to the magnitude of the respective angle factors.

Eq. (46) will always give a slightly lower mean radiant temperature than eq. (45), but in many cases the difference is small. If, for example, half of the surroundings (angle factor = 0.5) has a temperature which is $10\,°C$ higher than the other half, the difference between the calculated mean radiant temperatures according to eq. (45) and eq. (46) will thus be only $0.2\,°C$. If, however, there are large differences in temperature between the surfaces, the error by using eq. (46) can be considerable. If, for example, taking a surface of $100\,°C$ with the angle factor 0.1, according to formula (46), the mean radiant temperature will be calculated approximately $3\,°C$ too low.

In calculating the mean radiant temperature according to formulae (44), (45) or (46), it is necessary to know the angle factors between the person and the different surfaces. Up to now, however, data for angle factors between persons and typical surfaces have been inadequate. It has therefore been necessary to use rough approximations, e.g., by calculating the mean radiant temperature as the mean temperature of all the surface areas A_1, $A_2 \ldots A_N$ in the enclosure:

$$T_{mrt} = \frac{T_1 A_1 + T_2 A_2 + ... + T_N A_N}{A_1 + A_2 + ... + A_N} \tag{47}$$

Although equation (47) has been widely used in practical engineering, it is of highly questionable accuracy and can under many conditions lead to serious errors and directly misleading results. If, for example, we consider a floor-heated room, where the floor has one temperature and the ceiling and all walls have a uniform lower temperature, the mean radiant temperature will naturally be independent of the height of the ceiling. But according to formula (47), the mean radiant tenperature will approach the ceiling and wall temperature as the ceiling height is increased. It will also be seen that the mean radiant temperature calculated according to eq. (47) has only one value for a given room, independent of the body posture and location of the person: for example, independent of whether the person is seated close to or far from a heating panel. Formula (47) must therefore be used with care and normally should be used only for rough calculations.

In order to be able to use the more exact formulae (44), (45) or (46) in practice, it is necessary to know the angle factors between the human body and typical surrounding surfaces. In the present study angle factors necessary for practical use have been determined by extensive experiments which will be described in the next chapter. The results are presented in diagrams from which the necessary angle factors can be read directly for use in the calculation of the mean radiant temperature (p.176–194).

IRRADIATION FROM HIGH-INTENSITY RADIANT SOURCES

In the foregoing, formulae have been derived for determining the mean radiant temperature in normal low temperature surroundings.

In this section we will consider the special case in which a person is exposed to a strongly directional irradiation from a high-intensity radiant source. This type of heating is normally called beam or spot heating, and the source normally a high-intensity infrared heater. For outdoor use it is of interest to note that the sun is also a typical beam heater. High-intensity infrared heaters are characterized by the following: they take up a small area, they have a high temperature (up to 3000 °C), and they emit radiation which, by the use of suitable reflectors, is highly directional. Because of the high temperature, the radiant exchange with the surroundings is more or less independent of the temperature of the surroundings. In the following, formulae and a diagram are given for the determination of mean radiant temperatures for a person exposed to beam heating, and a new and rational procedure is outlined for the practical design of beam heating systems.

Let us consider a person in a low temperature enclosure, exposed to irradiation from a high-intensity infrared heater. First the mean radiant temperature in relation to the unirradiated person must be determined; this temperature, T_{umrt} (unirradiated mrt), is the hypothetical mean radiant temperature in relation to the person if he was not exposed to direct radiation from the heater. T_{umrt} is dependent on the temperature of the surrounding low-temperature surfaces, and an exact calculation can be made according to the formulae set forth in the previous section. It must be considered, however, that the temperature (and the radiosity) of some of the surrounding surfaces can perhaps be affected by the irradiation from the high-intensity radiant source, which must therefore be included in a total thermal analysis, to be discussed in chapter seven.

In many practical cases, however, one can assume T_{umrt} to be equal with the air temperature or perhaps a degree or two higher in consideration of the reflection from the floor and eventual reradiation, if the floor is heated significantly by the IR-heater.

The radiation from the IR-heater can be characterized by the intensity (i.e., radiant heat flux per unit solid angle) as a function of the direction, or by the radiant flux density, q_{ir}, as a function of the axial distance from the heater and the angle from the axis (analogous with the specification of illumination power for lighting fixtures). As an aid in the selection and application of products, the above-mentioned data are given (or ought to be given) by the manufacturer of the IR-heater.

Suppose that the person is irradiated with a mean radiant flux density q_{ir} from the heater. If the area of the person, projected on to a plane perpendicular to the direction to the heater, is called A_p, the irradiation which strikes the person will be equal to $q_{ir} A_p$. Of this, $\alpha_{ir} q_{ir} A_p$ will be absorbed, where α_{ir} is the absorptance of the outer surface of the person at the actual mean wavelength of the irradiation. The following equation can then be derived for the determination of the mean radiant temperature for the irradiated person:

$$\varepsilon_p \sigma A_{eff}(T_{cl}^4 - T_{mrt}^4) = \varepsilon_p \sigma A_{eff}(T_{cl}^4 - T_{umrt}^4) - A_p \alpha_{ir} q_{ir} \qquad (48)$$

Equation (48) expresses that the radiant heat loss from the human body to a black enclosure with uniform temperature (mean radiant temperature)

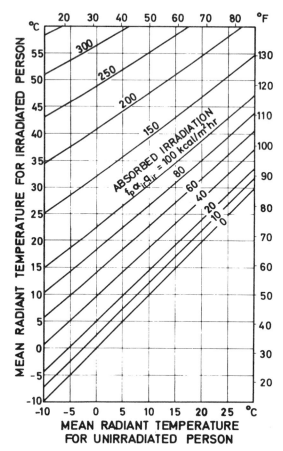

Fig. 29. Diagram for determination of mean radiant temperature for a person exposed to irradiation from a high-intensity radiant source.

must be equal to the radiant heat loss to the low temperature enclosure (unirradiated mean radiant temperature) minus the absorbed portion of the irradiation from the heater.

Rearranging eq. (48) one obtains

$$T_{mrt} = \left[T_{umrt}^4 + \frac{A_p\,\alpha_{ir}\,q_{ir}}{A_{eff}\,\varepsilon_p\sigma} \right]^{0.25} \tag{49}$$

In order to make the calculation independent of the size of the actual person, the relationship between the projected area and the effective radiation area is introduced:

150

$$f_p = \frac{A_p}{A_{eff}} \tag{50}$$

f_p is called the projected area factor and is a function of the irradiation direction and of the body posture.

When the values for the Stephan-Boltzmann constant and the emittance of the subject (= 0.97) are inserted in eq. (49), one obtains

$$T_{mrt} = (T_{umrt}^4 + 0.208 \cdot 10^8 \, f_p \, \alpha_{ir} \, q_{ir})^{0.25} \qquad (^\circ K) \tag{51}$$

In fig. 29 eq. (51) is shown graphically, the mean radiant temperature for the irradiated person, T_{mrt}, being given as a function of the mean radiant temperature for the unirradiated person, T_{umrt}, with $f_p \, \alpha_{ir} \, q_{ir}$ as parameter. The term $f_p \, \alpha_{ir} \, q_{ir}$ is the radiation absorbed by the person per unit effective radiation area.

To be able to determine the mean radiant temperature for a person exposed to an irradiation flux density q_{ir} from an infrared heater, it is therefore necessary to know, besides the temperature of the surroundings, the projected area factor, f_p, for the actual irradiation direction, and the absorptance α_{ir}.

In the present study the projected area factor has been experimentally determined as a function of the direction for seated and standing body posture. The experiments and the results (figs. 39 and 41) are dealt with in the following chapter.

The skin-clothing mean absorptance of man for radiation from IR-sources having colour temperatures of 2500°K (T–3 quartz lamps) and 1200°K (atmospheric gas-fired heaters) have been measured over the wavelength 0.3 to 9 μ (125, 126, 129, 270) and from these data Rapp (266, 267) recommends the values of α_{ir} (caucasians) given in table 17 for use in design.

Table 17. *Mean Absorptances for the Human Body (266, 267)*

	Colour Temperature	
	1200°K	2500°K
Clothed (medium grey).	0.9	0.8
Nude...............	0.95	0.65

The suggested, rational procedure for the calculation of IR-heaters is now the following.

1. Activity level and clo-value are determined from tables 1 and 2 with due consideration to location, season, etc. The relative air velocity and the air temperature are also determined.
2. The mean radiant temperature, T_{mrt}, which is necessary for comfort, is found from the diagrams in figs. 8 to 11.
3. The mean radiant temperature for an unirradiated person, T_{umrt}, is set equal to the air temperature, or perhaps one or two degrees higher considering the reflected radiation from the floor and the reradiation from the heated floor. (T_{umrt} can be calculated from eq. (44) if the temperatures, etc. are known.)
4. From fig. 29 the value of $f_p \alpha_{ir} q_{ir}$ which is necessary to create the desired mean radiant temperature for the irradiated person, can be determined.
5. The absorptance α_{ir} can be found from table 17, and the projected area factor f_p for the actual irradiation direction can be found from fig. 39 or fig. 41. Then the necessary mean radiant flux density q_{ir} can be determined.
6. An IR-heater should be chosen which, at the given direction and distance, can produce the necessary q_{ir}-value.

Example 11. In a large unheated storeroom ($t_a = 5^\circ$ C) a seated person works with medium activity ($M/A_{Du} = 100$ kcal/m²hr) at an assembly line. Because of the body movements required in connection with the work, he cannot clothe himself to more than $I_{cl} = 1.5$ clo. It would be uneconomical to heat the whole storeroom and it is therefore decided to create thermal comfort for the person by placing one IR-heater (1200°K) at each side of his workplace as shown in fig. 30. The relative velocity is assessed at $v = 0.3$ m/s.

From fig. 11 the mean radiant temperature necessary for thermal comfort is found to be 26°C.

The mean radiant temperature for the unirradiated person is assumed equal to the air temperature ($= 5°C$). The necessary absorbed irradiation is then determined from fig. 29: $f_p \alpha_{ir} q_{ir} = 100$ kcal/m²hr.

For the irradiation direction shown, f_p, according to fig. 39 is equal to 0.24, and according to table 17 is $\alpha_{ir} = 0.9$.

The necessary radiant flux density therefore becomes

$$q_{ir} = \frac{100}{0.24 \cdot 0.9} = 460 \text{ kcal/m}^2\text{hr}$$

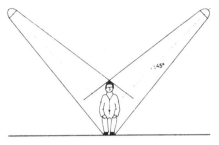

Fig. 30. Placement of IR-heaters (ex. 11).

Since two symmetrical IR-heaters have been chosen, as shown in fig. 30 each heater should therefore produce a radiant flux density equal to 230 kcal/m²hr in a plane through the centre of the person, perpendicular to the direction to the heater.

Under steady-state conditions the floor around the person will attain a temperature above air temperature and reradiation from the floor will raise T_{umrt}.

Assume a floor area of 3×3 m² around the person is irradiated with a mean flux of 150 kcal/hr m² floor area, and $\varepsilon = \alpha = 0.9$ for the floor. Assume that conduction through the floor can be neglected in steady-state. The following heat balance for the floor is then obtained for the determination of ΔT, the difference between floor and air temperature.

Absorbed irradiation = heat loss by longwave radiation + convection.

$$150 \cdot 0.9 = 0.9 \cdot 4.96 \cdot 0.9 \, \Delta T + 2.08 \, \Delta T^{1.31} \cdot 3^{-0.08}$$

The convective heat transfer coefficient was determined by formula (89).

From the equation is obtained $\Delta T = 16\,°C$, i.e. the floor temperature, $T_{fl} = 5 + 16 = 21\,°C$. From fig. 50 the angle factor between the person and the floor area $F_{P-A} = 4 \cdot 0.075 = 0.30$.

From eq. (46)

$$T_{umrt} = 0.30 \cdot 21 + 0.70 \cdot 5 = 10\,°C$$

From fig. 29 $f_p \, \alpha_{ir} \, q_{ir} = 80$ kcal/m²hr, and $q_{ir} = 370$ kcal/m²hr, i.e., 185 kcal/m²hr per heater.

When the irradiation from the floor is taken into consideration in the calculation, the radiant flux density obtained can thus be reduced by approx. 20%.

Example 12. Above the spectator area in a grandstand at an open-air stadium, it is proposed to place IR-heaters (1200°K) so that the seated spectators (M/A_{Du} = 50 kcal/m²hr) can be kept in thermal comfort at an outdoor temperature of 12°C. By suitable wind-breaks the air velocity is kept down to 0.3 m/s. I_{cl} = 1.5 clo (normal business suit + light coat).

From fig. 11 the necessary mean radiant temperature is found by extrapolation to be 40°C. The unirradiated mean radiant temperature is estimated to be 2 degrees higher than the air temperature (reciprocal radiation between the persons) i.e., T_{umrt} = 14°C. From fig. 29 we thus obtain the necessary absorbed irradiation $f_p \, \alpha_{ir} \, q_{ir}$ = 140 kcal/m² hr.

The irradiation direction being mainly vertical, from fig. 39 one obtain $f_p \backsim 0.19$. From table 17 is found α_{ir} = 0.9.

Thus

$$q_{ir} = \frac{140}{0.19 \cdot 0.9} = 820 \text{ kcal/m}^2\text{hr}$$

The IR-heaters must be chosen and located in relation to each other so that the irradiation flux density found is obtained over the whole of the spectator area.

Example 13. A hotel terrace (10 × 10 m²) is arranged for sunbathing, the wind velocity being maintained under 0.3 m/s by suitable wind-breaks. It is desired to determine what fraction of the year the terrace can be utilized, i.e., at how low an air temperature the terrace can be used for sunbathing by seated, almost nude persons (I_{cl} = 0).

The solar flux density available is assumed to be q_{ir} = 700 kcal/m²hr. At a sun height of β = 30–45°, f_p = 0.30 (fig. 39), the person being seated and facing the sun (azimuth α = 0). Also assuming an absorptance α_{ir} equal to 0.6, we obtain $f_p \, \alpha_{ir} \, q_{ir}$ = 0.30 · 0.6 · 700 = 130 kcal/m²hr. T_{umrt} was first estimated as 10°C. We obtain from fig. 29 T_{mrt} = 37°C, i.e., $T_{mrt} - T_{umrt}$ = 27°C. Note that $T_{mrt} - T_{umrt}$ is dependent on the introductory estimate of T_{umrt} only to a slight degree.

The person also receives diffusely reflected solar radiation from the floor. The reflectance of the floor is estimated at 0.6 (light grey) and the short-wave radiosity of the floor is therefore approximately $700 \, \frac{\sqrt{2}}{2} \cdot 0.6 = 300$ kcal/m²hr.

According to fig. 49, the angle factor between the person and the floor is 4 · 0.11 = 0.44.

When the temperature of the surroundings is set equal to the air temperature T_a (disregarding diffuse sky radiation and heating of the floor), we
obtain

$$T_{umrt}^4 = \frac{1}{\sigma} (\sigma T_a^4 + 300 \cdot 0.44 \cdot 0.6)$$

which linearized, gives $T_{umrt} = T_a + \dfrac{300 \cdot 0.44 \cdot 0.6}{4.96} = T_a + 16 \qquad (^{\circ}K)$

or $T_{mrt} = T_{umrt} + 27 = T_a + 43 \qquad (^{\circ}K)$

By extrapolation of fig. 8 we find that $t_a = 12\,^{\circ}C$ (and $t_{mrt} = 55\,^{\circ}C$)
will give thermal comfort. Sunbathing will thus be possible when the air
temperature is over $10\,^{\circ}C$. The mean radiant temperature here is $43\,^{\circ}C$
higher than the air temperature. It should be noted that the reflected solar
radiation has a considerable effect, namely approximately 50% of the direct
solar radiation.

Under steady-state conditions the floor will, of course, become heated
and therefore also increase the mean radiant temperature. The effect of this
on T_{mrt} can be calculated as in ex. 11.

Chapter 6.

RADIATION DATA
FOR THE HUMAN BODY

For the calculation of mean radiant temperature and of radiant heat exchange between the human body and its surroundings, including irradiation from high-intensity radiant sources, it is important to have reliable radiation data for the human body.

Values for emittance and absorptance of the human skin and different textiles at different wave lengths are well documented, while for many practical engineering applications sufficient geometrical radiation data for the human body do not exist.

The geometrical data needed are mean values, for a suitably large number of persons (seated and standing, nude and clothed), for the following:

(a) effective radiation area factor $f_{eff} = \dfrac{A_{eff}}{A_{Du}}$

(b) projected area factors, $f_p = \dfrac{A_p}{A_{eff}}$, as a function of the direction of irradiation,

(c) angle factors between the human body and any horizontal or vertical rectangle.

The effective radiation area factor has been experimentally determined by various research workers (35, 18, 123, 335, 243, 116), for both standing and seated subjects, by a series of varying methods, but with rather divergent results.

Projected area factors have been determined by Guibert and Taylor (116), but only for one individual nude person and only for relatively few angles. Underwood (319) has made similar investigations, but only for standing, nude persons.

Angle factors were first measured by Raber and Hutchinson (263, 264) and their results have been the only available data in the literature for many years. Using charts, angle factors can be determined for seated persons, but only in relation to a ceiling, and only for three fixed ceiling heights, while for standing persons, also, in relation to walls at fixed distances. The results of these measurements, taken with a clothed dummy, were shown by Dunkle (72) to contain serious errors in some cases, and, in addition, point angle factors were used which are rather difficult to apply in practice. Dunkle then simulated the human body with a sphere whose diameter varied with the angle of radiation exposure and gives simple approximate formulae for the diameter for seated and standing posture. The results are based on measurements for one clothed subject. Configuration factor diagrams are given, but only for a standing, clothed person.

Since the existing radiation data are incomplete in that they do not cover all the relevant cases and are often based on rather scanty test material, it was decided to carry out a detailed experimental determination of all the above-mentioned radiation data. It included standing and seated persons, nude and clothed, and used a reasonably large number of male and female subjects (twenty in all).

In the following sections, an explanation is given of the experimental methods employed, the analytical basis for the treatment of the experimental data, and the results, which are illustrated by diagrams for direct practical use in engineering. Finally, the results will be discussed and compared with earlier data.

METHODS

Several experimental techniques for determining geometrical radiant data for the human body have been presented in the literature; Raber and Hutchinson (263, 264) and Dunkle (72) employed the mechanical integrator, utilizing the unit sphere concept, while Guibert and Taylor (116) and Underwood (319) used a projected area technique. In the present investigation a photographic method was chosen which, in principle, was the same as that used by Guibert and Taylor and Underwood, but which was technically improved so that the measurements could be taken quickly and easily. The method consisted of photographing the subject from many directions. Each photograph then provides the projected area of the body for a given viewing angle. When the projected area of the body is known for an adequately large number of angles, all the desired radiation data for the human body can be calculated according to formulae which will be described in a subsequent section.

Table 18. *Anthropometric Data for the Subjects*

Subjects	Number of Subjects	Height m	Weight kg	DuBois Area m²	Ponderal Index kg⁰·³³/m
Females..........	10	1.66 ± 0.04[1]	55.7 ± 2.9	1.61 ± 0.05	2.27 ± 0.05
Males.............	10	1.78 ± 0.07	68.7 ± 6.6	1.86 ± 0.11	2.26 ± 0.09
Females + Males....	20	1.72 ± 0.09	62.2 ± 8.3	1.74 ± 0.13	2.27 ± 0.07

[1] Standard deviation.

Subjects

Ten male and ten female subjects were studied. In table 18, mean values for anthropometric data for the subjects are listed. The height and weight of each person were measured and the DuBois-area and ponderal index were calculated. The value of the Ponderal index (42) is an indication of the fatness of the body. There is general agreement between data in table 18 and results from extensive statistical investigations of anthropometric data of American (326) and Scandinavian (42) persons; thus the test persons used can be regarded as a fair sample of the adult population. For each subject two postures were thoroughly investigated: (a) standing, relaxed, arms at sides, (b) seated, relaxed, hands on thighs (an angle of approx. 90° between trunk and thighs).

These body positions can, with reasonable approximation, be assumed to simulate normal working postures in practice, e.g., for standing or walking persons in workshops, stores, laboratories and kitchens, and seated persons at assembly lines, work-benches or office machines. Data for the erect posture can also be applied to recumbent persons. For each body position the subject was measured nude as well as clothed in a standard clothing ensemble (∽KSU-uniform), which closely simulates most typical indoor clothings, for instance a common business suit.

Experimental Procedure

The experimental set-up is shown in fig. 31. The subject is placed on a platform which can be pivoted around a vertical axis as well as elevated. Mounted around the test person is a system of optical mirrors, consisting

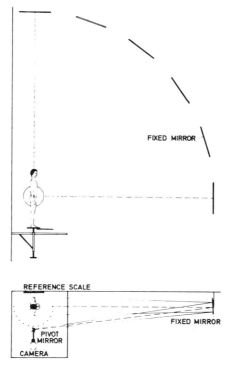

Fig. 31. Plan and elevation of the experimental set-up for radiation studies.

of a small, plane precision mirror which is pivoted around a horizontal axis, and six large fixed plane mirrors placed in a vertical quarter circle, with the subject in the centre. By turning the small mirror, the test person can be viewed and photographed with a fixed camera, from six different angles (altitudes β) on a vertical plane. The reflection of the light rays in the mirrors is diagrammatically shown in fig. 31. A circular reference-scale with its axis through the centre of the quarter circle is placed beside the person and appears in each photograph as a measure of the scale relationship. For each person the platform was moved in a vertical direction, so that the centre of the waist line of each subject was coincident with the centre of the quarter circle. By turning the platform 15° at a time, a total of 13 horizontal angles (azimuth α), can be obtained, or $13 \times 6 = 78$ exposures within a quarter sphere. A quarter sphere measurement is sufficient because of the right/left symmetry of the body, and because the projected area from any two opposite directions is the same.

The mirror system shown, which makes possible the fixed camera position, provides a quick experimental procedure: 78 exposures of a subject for one specific posture-clothing combination can be taken in only 10 minutes.

The photographs were produced with a 16 mm BOLEX mirror reflex camera with a Cannon-zoom lens, focus 25–100 mm. The optical distance between the camera and the reference-scale (subject) was 7 m. The film used was of fine grain structure (Kodak Plus X positive film, 17 DIN), which, together with the artificial lighting arrangement used to emphasize the contrast between the subject and the background, yielded negatives of good quality.

By using a projector and a mirror arrangement, the negatives were projected upward to a table with a matt glass top in a size corresponding to approx. 1:5 in relation to natural size. The projected areas were then measured by double planimetering. From the reference-scale recorded on the photographs, the exact factor converting the planimetered areas to the actual projected areas could be determined. The projected areas determined in the above manner were subject to minor errors due to differences in the distance to the different parts of the body in relation to the reference-scale distance. By an initial detailed examination of this phenomenon, the corrections were determined for a single person for all angles, and these percentage corrections (up to 2%) were used for all subjects.

For each person, 312 photographs (4 × 78) were taken and planimetered, giving, for 20 persons, a total of 6240 photographs. In addition, for one test person (seated) a more detailed analysis was made, in which, with a special tilting arrangement, he was photographed from 273 angles within a quarter sphere instead of the usual 78 angles. This series of measurements was carried out in order to examine and improve the basis for the interpolation formulae which it is necessary to set up in connection with the numerical integrations decribed in the next section. Thus, in all, approx. 7000 photographs were exposed and planimetered.

ANALYTICAL BASIS FOR THE TREATMENT OF THE EXPERIMENTAL DATA

Effective Radiation Area Factor

Consider a person located in the centre of a spherical coordinate system, where any direction in relation to the person is defined by the azimuth angle α and the altitude angle β (see fig. 32).

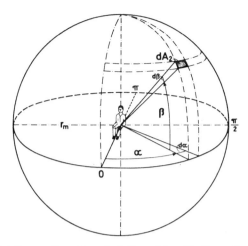

Fig. 32. Notation pertinent to calculation of the effective radiation area.

If the surroundings are considered as a large sphere A_2 with a radius r_m, the reciprocity theorem for angle factors for the area of the sphere and the person can be used, assuming that the angular distributions of the radiant fluxes leaving the surfaces are diffuse:

$$A_{eff} \, F_{P-A_2} = A_2 \, F_{A_2-P} \tag{52}$$

where

A_{eff} is the effective radiation area of the subject
F_{P-A_2} is the angle factor between the person and the sphere (A_2).
$A_2 = 4\pi r_m^2$ is the area of the sphere
F_{A_2-P} is the angle factor between the sphere and the person.

As the angle factor F_{P-A_2} designates the fraction of the radiation leaving the person (P) that arrives at A_2, it is obvious that F_{P-A_2} is unity.

Thus, eq. (52) can be written

$$A_{eff} = 4\pi r_m^2 \, F_{A_2-P} \tag{52a}$$

The angle factor F_{A_2-P} cannot be directly determined, but must be found by integration. Consider a differential surface element dA_2 on the sphere with the angle coordinates (α, β), see fig. 32. The angle factor F_{dA_2-P} between dA_2 and the person then becomes

$$F_{dA_2-P} = \frac{A_p}{\pi r_m^2}$$

where A_p is the person's projected area on a plane perpendicular to the direction to dA_2. The angle factor between the whole sphere and the person thus becomes:

$$F_{A_2-P} = \frac{1}{A_2} \int_{A_2} \frac{A_p}{\pi r_m^2} \, dA_2 \tag{53}$$

When $dA_2 = r_m \, d\alpha \cos\beta \, r_m \, d\beta$
and $A_2 = 4\pi r_m^2$

$$F_{A_2-P} = \frac{1}{4\pi^2 r_m^2} \int_{\alpha=0}^{\alpha=2\pi} \int_{\beta=-\frac{\pi}{2}}^{\beta=\frac{\pi}{2}} A_p \cos\beta \, d\alpha \, d\beta \tag{54}$$

Since the human body is symmetrical, and since A_p is the same for any two opposite directions, the value of the double integral in (54) for the whole sphere will be equal to four times the value for a quarter sphere:

$$F_{A_2-P} = \frac{1}{\pi^2 r_m^2} \int_{\alpha=0}^{\alpha=\pi} \int_{\beta=0}^{\beta=\frac{\pi}{2}} A_p \cos\beta \, d\alpha \, d\beta \tag{54a}$$

Substituting (54a) in (52a):

$$A_{eff} = \frac{4}{\pi} \int_{\alpha=0}^{\alpha=\pi} \int_{\beta=0}^{\beta=\frac{\pi}{2}} A_p \cos\beta \, d\alpha \, d\beta \tag{55}$$

A_{eff} is calculated for the four posture-clothing combinations for each subject, by numerical integration of the double integral on the basis of the experimentally determined A_p-values for 78 angles within a quarter sphere. Interpolation formulae for A_p between the observed values were, for the seated position, deduced on the basis of a detailed examination of a single subject, where, in all, 273 A_p-values were determined.

For a nude person, f_{eff} can thus be determined by

$$f_{eff} = \frac{A_{eff}}{A_{Du}} \tag{56}$$

when the DuBois-area A_{Du} is calculated as

$$A_{Du} = 0.203 \, W^{0.425} \, H^{0.725} \qquad (m^2) \tag{57}$$

where W is the weight (kg) and
H is the height (m) of the subject.

Moreover, the clothing area factor f_{cl} can be calculated as the relation between the A_{eff} values for clothed and nude subjects.

Projected Area Factors

After calculation of the effective radiation area factor for each subject-posture-clothing combination, the desired f_p-values as functions of (α, β) can be found from the experimentally determined A_p-values with the formula

$$f_p = \frac{A_p}{A_{eff}} \tag{58}$$

Angle Factors

The enclosure surfaces which are found most often in a normal room are rectangular in form (walls, floors, ceilings, windows, heating and cooling panels, etc.), and it is therefore the angle factors between a person and ver-

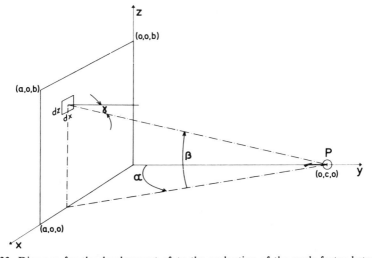

Fig. 33. Diagram for the development of to the evaluation of the angle factor between a person (centre in P and facing towards the centre of the coordinate system) and a rectangle (a × b) in the x−z plane.

tical and horizontal rectangles which are of primary interest in the calculation of mean radiant temperature and radiant exchange between a person and his practical surroundings.

First consider a person located in the orthogonal coordinate system (x, y, z) shown in fig. 33. The person (P) faces towards the system's zero point with his centre having the coordinates (o, c, o). The angle factor F_{P-A} between the person and the rectangle A (a × b) shown in the xz-plane will now be determined.

In considering first a differential area element dA = dx dz situated in the xz-plane with the coordinates (x, o, z) one obtains, according to the reciprocity theorem,

$$A_{eff}\, dF_{P-dA} = dA\, F_{dA-P} \tag{59}$$

where dF_{P-dA} is the differential angle factor between the person (P) and dA and F_{dA-P} is the angle factor between dA and the person.
Since

$$F_{dA-P} = \frac{1}{\pi} \frac{A_p}{x^2 + y^2 + z^2} \cos\gamma \tag{60}$$

and

$$\cos\gamma = \frac{y}{\sqrt{x^2 + y^2 + z^2}} \tag{61}$$

$$dF_{P-dA} = \frac{1}{\pi} \frac{A_p}{A_{eff}} \frac{y}{(x^2 + y^2 + z^2)^{\frac{3}{2}}}\, dx\, dz \tag{62}$$

The angle factor F_{P-A} between the person and the whole rectangle (a × b) is:

$$F_{P-A} = \frac{1}{\pi} \int_{x=0}^{x=a} \int_{z=0}^{z=b} \frac{f_p\, y}{(x^2 + y^2 + z^2)^{\frac{3}{2}}}\, dx\, dz$$

$$= \frac{1}{\pi} \int_{\frac{x}{y}=0}^{\frac{x}{y}=\frac{a}{c}} \int_{\frac{z}{y}=0}^{\frac{z}{y}=\frac{b}{c}} \frac{f_p}{\left[1 + \left(\frac{x}{y}\right)^2 + \left(\frac{z}{y}\right)^2\right]^{\frac{3}{2}}}\, d\left(\frac{x}{y}\right) d\left(\frac{z}{y}\right) \tag{63}$$

In equation (58), f_p is determined as a function of (α, β). Since the correlation between the angles and the orthogonal coordinates is given in the following terms

$$\alpha = \tan^{-1}\left(\frac{x}{y}\right) \tag{64}$$

$$\beta = \tan^{-1}\frac{\dfrac{z}{y}}{\sqrt{\left(\dfrac{x}{y}\right)^2 + 1}} \tag{65}$$

F_{P-A} can thus be determined from equation (63) by numerical integration. It is clear from eq. (63) that F_{P-A} is a function of the dimensionless relationship a/c and b/c. A simple diagram showing this functional connection can therefore be used for rectangles of any size, placed as shown in fig. 33 with the normal at the corner point passing through the centre of the person. This particular placing enables a dimensionless calculation and diagram to be made.

The angle factor between a person and a vertical rectangle A located anywhere in the xz-plane (see fig. 34) can be calculated by simple angle factor algebra:

$$F_{P-A} = F_{P-ABCD} - F_{P-BC} - F_{P-CD} + F_{P-C} \tag{66}$$

as the four angle factors at the right of equation (66) are determined by the above-mentioned diagram.

Equation (63) and the associated figure (fig. 33) apply only to the angle factor between a person and a vertical rectangle in front of and above his centre, through which the normal at the corner point passes. As the projected area of a person is equal from two opposite directions, it is obvious

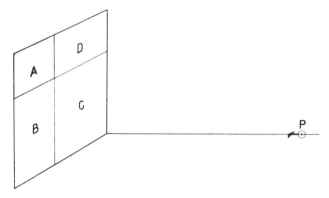

Fig. 34. Angle factor algebra.

that the same diagram can be used for a rectangle behind and below the centre of a person.

In calculating angle factors for all surfaces in a room, where a person is directly facing one wall, it will be seen from fig. 35 that dimensionless representation necessitates the division of each of the surrounding surfaces into four rectangles, and that an angle factor diagram must therefore be drawn for each of the following six cases:

Case 1: Vertical rectangle in front of the person and above his centre, or behind him and below his centre.

Case 2: Vertical rectangle in front of the person and below his centre, or behind him and above his centre.

Case 3: Vertical rectangle on the side wall, above and forward of his centre, or below and behind his centre.

Case 4: Vertical rectangle on the side wall, below and forward of his centre, or above and behind his centre.

Case 5: Horizontal rectangle in the ceiling and forward of his centre, or on the floor and behind his centre.

Case 6: Horizontal rectangle in the ceiling and behind his centre, or on the floor and forward of his centre.

In all six cases, the normal in one corner point of the rectangle passes through the centre of the person. Case 1 corresponds to formula (63) derived earlier, but similar formulae can be derived as a basis for the diagrams for the other five cases.

In cases where the location of the person in the room (the coordinates of his centre) is known, but not his orientation (the azimuth α), it will be natural to calculate a mean value of the angle factor for $0 < \alpha < 2\pi$, which, for a vertical rectangle, would be

$$\bar{F}_{P-A} = \frac{1}{2\pi^2} \int\limits_{\frac{x}{y}=0}^{\frac{x}{y}=\frac{a}{c}} \int\limits_{\frac{z}{y}=0}^{\frac{z}{y}=\frac{b}{c}} \int\limits_{\alpha=0}^{\alpha=2\pi} \frac{f_p}{\left[1 + \left(\frac{x}{y}\right)^2 + \left(\frac{z}{y}\right)^2\right]^{\frac{3}{2}}} \, d\left(\frac{x}{y}\right) d\left(\frac{z}{y}\right) d\alpha \qquad (67)$$

$\bar{F}_{P-A}$ represents the mean value of the angle factor between person and rectangle, when the person rotates around a vertical axis.

To determine mean angle factors in a room, it can immediately be seen that in this case it is sufficient to draw two diagrams: one for vertical rectangles (above or below the centre) and one for horizontal rectangles (forward or behind the centre).

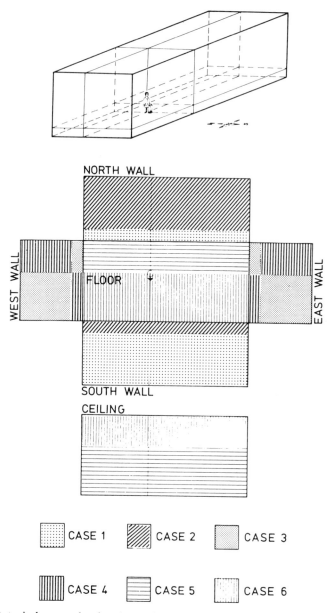

Fig. 35. A typical space, showing the method of dividing the surface areas so that angle factors may be calculated using dimensionless parameters. The lowest figure shows the necessary partitioning of the surfaces in the six cases.

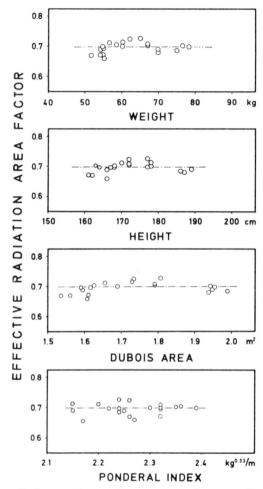

Fig. 36. Effective radiation area factors for twenty seated persons plotted as a function of weight, height, DuBois area, and ponderal index. The line indicated shows the mean value = 0.696.

RESULTS

All the calculations have been performed by a digital computer using the experimentally determined data and the necessary programmes, according to the formulae derived earlier; all the diagrams have been plotted directly by the computer equipment.

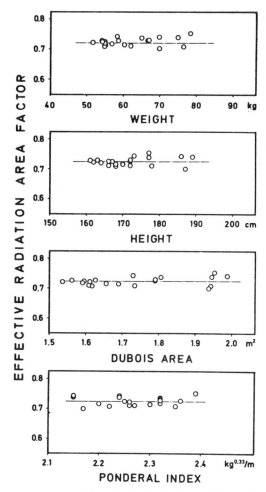

Fig. 37. Effective radiation area factors for twenty standing subjects plotted as a function of weight, height, DuBois area and ponderal index. The line indicated shows the mean value = 0.725.

Effective Radiation Area Factor

Table 19 shows the calculated mean values and their standard deviations for the effective radiation area factor for the two body positions, and for females and males separately and combined. It will be seen that there is no sex-related difference between the f_{eff}-values found; in addition, the standard deviations are remarkably small.

Table 19. *Effective Radiation Area Factors*

Group	Eff. Radiation Area Factor f_{eff}
Seated Females......................	0.692 ± 0.019[1]
Seated Males........................	0.700 ± 0.013
Seated Females and Males............	0.696 ± 0.017
Standing Females....................	0.725 ± 0.014
Standing Males......................	0.725 ± 0.013
Standing Females and Males..........	0.725 ± 0.013

[1] Standard deviation

In fig. 36, the f_{eff} for each individual subject has been plotted against weight, height, DuBois area and ponderal index, for the seated posture. Similar data for the standing posture are plotted in fig. 37. It will be seen that f_{eff} is apparently independent of each of these factors, i.e., that the mean values for the effective radiation area factor for seated persons, and for standing persons, can be used independently of the person's sex, weight, height, surface area and body type. The clothing area factor f_{cl} for the uniform was determined as 1.11 ± 0.03 for seated persons and 1.19 ± 0.03 for standing persons.

Projected Area Factors

For each individual subject the projected area factor has been calculated as a function of (α, β), for the four posture-clothing combinations. Mean values for each of the combinations were calculated for females only, males only and for females and males combined.

In fig. 38, diagrams for seated persons are presented, showing the projected area factor as a function of the azimuth angle α with the altitude angle β as a parameter. The upper two diagrams are for nude females and nude males repectively. Comparison shows no significant difference between the diagrams for the two sexes, and they are therefore shown in one diagram for nude females and males combined, at the bottom left in fig. 38. In the diagram at the bottom right of this figure, the results for clothed females and males combined are shown. It will be seen that the clothing has

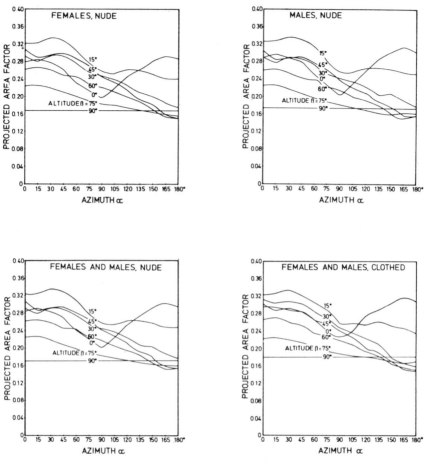

Fig. 38. Projected area factor for seated persons as a function of the azimuth with the altitude as a parameter, for four different combinations of sex and clothing.

surprisingly little effect on the f_p-values, i.e. the increments of A_p and A_{eff} due to the clothing are reasonably equal, and there seems therefore no good reason to treat nude and clothed persons separately. In fig. 39, all the f_p data for seated persons have been combined, i.e., data for females and males, nude and clothed. Each point plotted in the diagram represents a mean value of 40 f_p-values. This diagram can be used in practice for seated persons independent of the size and sex of the person, and independent of whether he is nude or clothed.

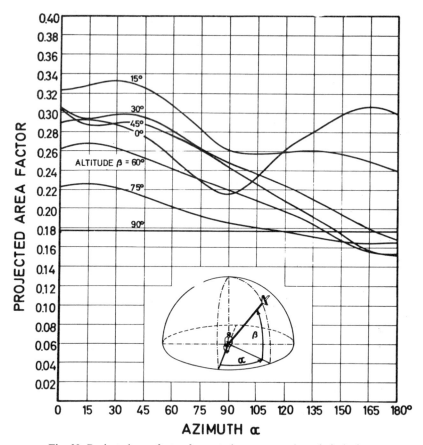

Fig. 39. Projected area factor for seated persons, nude and clothed.

It will be seen from the diagram, that f_p is greatest (0.33) for $(\alpha, \beta) =$ (30°, 15°), and it is more than double the smallest value (0.15), which is given by $(\alpha, \beta) = $ (180°, 45°). $\beta = 90°$ is a horizontal line since it only represents one direction, namely the person seen from above. There is symmetry only for $\beta = 0$ with regard to $\alpha = 90°$. f_p is generally greater for frontal directions ($\alpha < 90°$) than for those from behind, owing to the asymmetry caused by the legs. The smallest difference between various altitudes occurs when the subject is viewed from the side, ($\alpha = 90°$).

With the use of beam heating it will be seen that irradiation from the front ($-60° < \alpha < 60°$) with an altitude 15–45° is most preferable. For

172

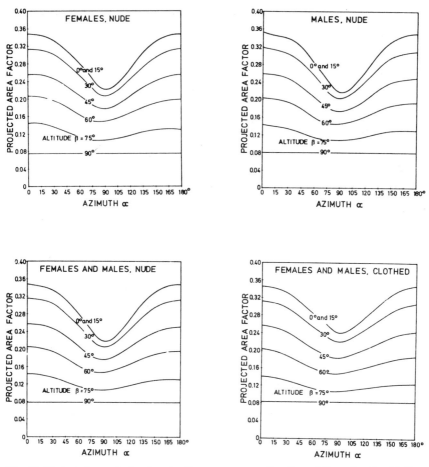

Fig. 40. Projected area factor for standing persons as a function of the azimuth with the altitude as a parameter, for four different combinations of sex and clothing.

irradiation from behind, use of the lowest altitudes practically possible gives the highest projected areas.

Fig. 40 shows projected area factor diagrams for standing persons. Diagrams for nude females, nude males, nude females and males combined and clothed females and males combined are shown. Just as for seated persons, there are only negligible differences between females and males and between nude and clothed subjects. Therefore all data have been combined in a single diagram (fig. 41) which can be used in practice independent

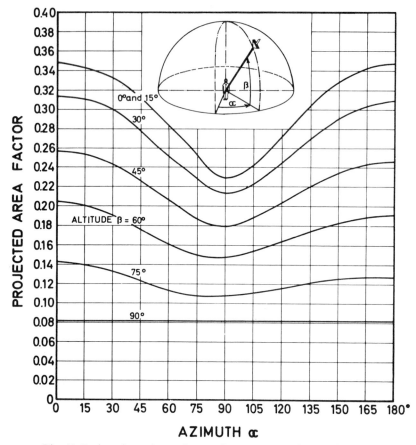

Fig. 41. Projected area factor for standing persons, nude and clothed.

of the size and sex of the person, and independent of whether he is nude or clothed.

It will be seen that f_p is greatest (0.35) for $(\alpha, \beta) = (0°, 0°)$ and it is more than four times greater than its smallest value, (0.08), given by $\beta = 90°$. Since the f_p-curve for $\beta = 15°$ lies very near the curve for $\beta = 0$, below it for $\alpha < 60°$ and $\alpha > 120°$, and even above it for $60° < \alpha < 120°$, (due to the protrusion of the feet) only one common curve for $\beta = 0°$ and $\beta = 15°$ has been drawn. For $\beta > 15°$ f_p falls uniformly as the values of β rise. The curves are nearly symmetrical about $\alpha = 90°$, where each β curve has its minimum. Nevertheless, f_p is usually a little lower for $\alpha > 90°$ because of the effect of the feet.

174

With the use of beam heating it will be seen, as anticipated, that vertical irradiation ($\beta = 90°$) will have a poor effect because of the small f_p-value; irradiation from the side ($\alpha = 90°$) is also unfavourable. The best results are obtained with irradiation, from the front or from behind ($\alpha = 0$ or $180°$), with an altitude angle as small as practically possible.

Angle Factors

The angle factors between a person and vértical or horizontal rectangles are calculated and plotted on the basis of the mean values of f_p shown in fig. 39 and fig. 41 for seated and standing subjects repectively. The plotted angle factors can therefore, like the f_p-diagrams, be used independently of sex and body size, and of whether the persons are nude or clothed.

Angle factor diagrams for seated persons are shown in figs. 42 to 47, corresponding to cases 1–6. Each diagram portrays dimensionlessly the angle factor as a function of the two length relationships b/c and a/c, where a and b are the side lengths in the rectangle and c is the normal distance between person (his centre) and rectangle. For each case, two angle factor diagrams have been worked out: a main diagram for $0 < b/c < 10$ and a detailed diagram which gives more accurate readings for small values of b/c (b/c < 2).

The diagrams apply for rectangles where the normal at one corner point passes through the centre of the person. For any other location, the angle factor can be found by means of simple angle factor algebra (see fig. 34 and eq. (66)).

By comparing case 1 (fig. 42) and case 2 (fig. 43) it will be seen that there are considerable differences in the size of the angle factor (up to 30%) due to the asymmetry caused by the legs. Also between cases 3 (fig. 44) and 4 (fig. 45) and cases 5 (fig. 46) and 6 (fig. 47) there are considerable differences which justify the detailed division into six cases for seated persons.

In the figures a normal centre height above the floor of 0.6 m has been inserted, corresponding to normal height in a sitting position. The establishment of this height is critical only in the determination of angle factors in relation to the floor and then only for small areas around the person. In special cases, for example if the person is placed on a platform or the like, another centre height can be used.

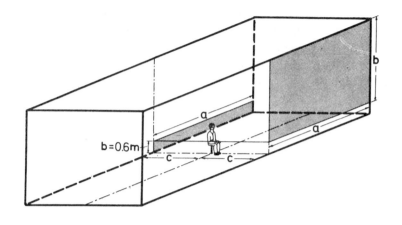

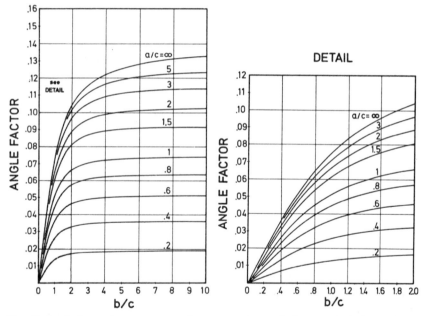

Fig. 42. Angle factor between a seated person and a vertical rectangle, in front of him and above his centre, or behind him and below his centre (case 1).

Example: a = 6m, b = 2m, c = 4m. b/c = 0.5, a/c = 1.5: F_{P-A} = 0.037.

176

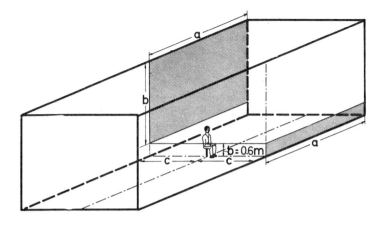

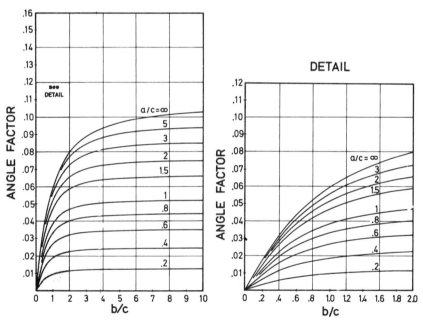

Fig. 43. Angle factor between a seated person and a vertical rectangle, in front of him and below his centre or behind him and above his centre (case 2).

Example: a = 6m, b = 0.6m, c = 2m. b/c = 0.3, a/c = 3.0: F_{P-A} = 0.023.

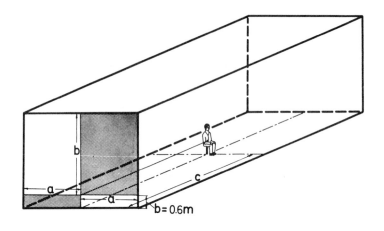

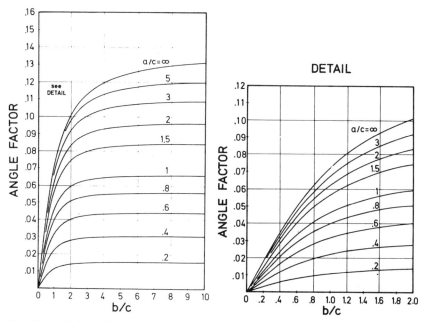

Fig. 44. Angle factor between a seated person and a rectangle on the side wall, above and forward of his centre, or below and behind his centre (case 3).

Example: a = 1.5m, b = 2m, c = 5m. b/c = 0.4, a/c = 0.3: F_{P-A} = 0.009.

178

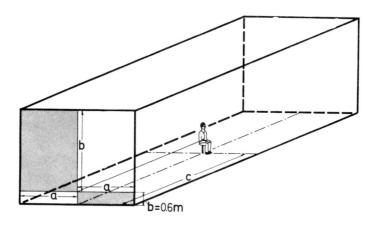

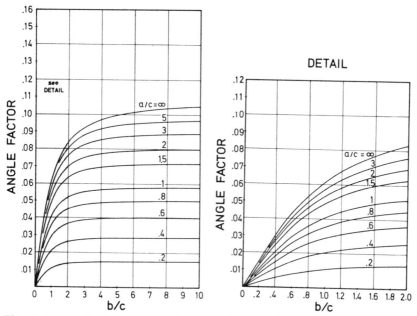

Fig. 45. Angle factor between a seated person and a rectangle on the side wall, below and forward of his centre, or above and behind his centre (case 4).

Example: a = 3m, b = 0.6m, c = 3m. b/c = 0.2, a/c = 1.0: F_{P-A} = 0.011.

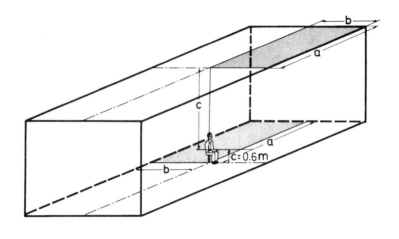

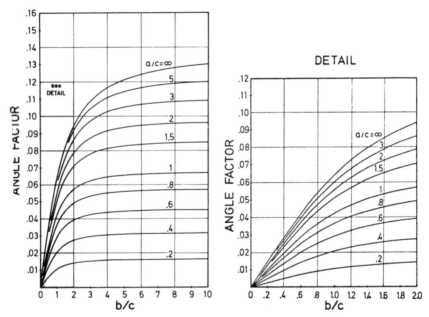

Fig. 46. Angle factor between a seated person and a rectangle on the ceiling and forward of his centre, or on the floor and behind his centre (case 5).

Example: a = 3m, b = 2.4m, c = 0.6m. b/c = 4.0, a/c = 5.0: F_{P-A} = 0.111.

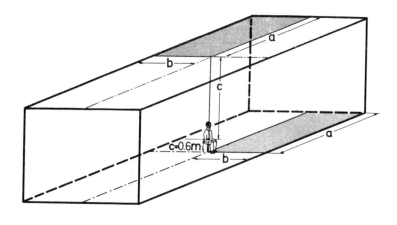

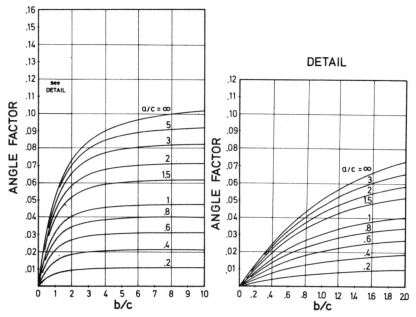

Fig. 47. Angle factor between a seated person and a rectangle on the ceiling and behind his centre or on the floor and forward of his centre (case 6).

Example: a = 3m, b = 1.8m, c = 0.6m. b/c = 3.0, a/c = 5.0: F_{P-A} = 0.080.

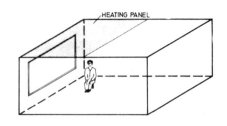

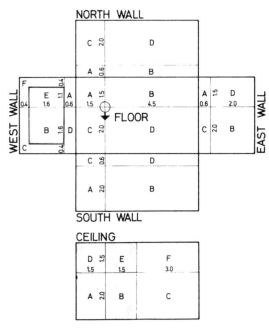

Fig. 48. Room dimensions and person placement, pertinent to ex. 14 and 15.

Example 14. All angle factors between the seated person oriented as shown in fig. 48 and all the room surfaces are to be determined. Each surface of the room is divided into rectangles as shown in the figure. The angle factors pertaining to each are determined from figs. 42–47. All the results are given in table 20.

As a check on the calculations, the sum of all the angle factors between the person and the surrounding surfaces should equal unity.

When the location of a seated person in a room is known but not his azimuthal orientation (in which direction he faces), the diagrams in figs.

182

Table 20. *Calculation of Angle Factors Pertinent to Example 14*

NORTH WALL	F_{P-ABCD} =	F_{P-A} + F_{P-B} + F_{P-C} + F_{P-D}		
	F_{P-A}	(fig. 42)	(b/c, a/c) = (0.40, 1.0): 0.026	
	+F_{P-B}	(fig. 42)	(0.40, 3.0): 0.035	
	+F_{P-C}	(fig. 43)	(1.3 , 1.0): 0.043	
	+F_{P-D}	(fig. 43)	(1.3 , 3.0): 0.063	0.167
EAST WALL	F_{P-ABCD} =	F_{P-A} + F_{P-B} + F_{P-C} + F_{P-D}		
	F_{P-A}	(fig. 44)	(b/c, a/c) = (0.13, 0.33): 0.003	
	+F_{P-B}	(fig. 44)	(0.44, 0.44): 0.015	
	+F_{P-C}	(fig. 45)	(0.13, 0.44): 0.005	
	+F_{P-D}	(fig. 45)	(0.44, 0.33): 0.010	0.033
SOUTH WALL	F_{P-ABCD} =	F_{P-A} + F_{P-B} + F_{P-C} + F_{P-D}		
	F_{P-A}	(fig. 42)	(b/c, a/c) = (1.0 , 0.75): 0.044	
	+F_{P-B}	(fig. 42)	(1.0 , 2.3): 0.069	
	+F_{P-C}	(fig. 43)	(0.30, 0.75): 0.015	
	+F_{P-D}	(fig. 43)	(0.30, 2.3): 0.024	0.152

WEST WALL Window: F_{P-BE} = F_{P-B} + F_{P-E}

	F_{P-B}	(fig. 44)	(b/c, a/c) = (1.1 , 1.1): 0.050	
	+F_{P-E}	(fig. 45)	(1.1 , 0.73): 0.035	0.085

Rest of the west wall: F_{P-ACDF} = F_{P-A} + F_{P-C} + F_{P-D} + F_{P-F} = F_{P-A} + F_{P-BC} − F_{P-B} + F_{P-D} + F_{P-EF} − F_{P-E}
= F_{P-A} + F_{P-BC} + F_{P-D} + F_{P-EF} − F_{P-BE}

	F_{P-A}	(fig. 44)	(b/c, a/c) = (0.40, 1.0): 0.024	
	+F_{P-BC}	(fig. 44)	(1.3 , 1.3): 0.060	
	+F_{P-D}	(fig. 45)	(0.40, 1.3): 0.025	
	+F_{P-EF}	(fig. 45)	(1.3 , 1.0): 0.046	
	−F_{P-BE}		: 0.085	0.070
FLOOR	F_{P-ABCD} =	F_{P-A} + F_{P-B} + F_{P-C} + F_{P-D}		
	F_{P-A}	(fig. 46)	(b/c, a/c) = (2.5 , 2.5): 0.089	
	+F_{P-B}	(fig. 46)	(2.5 , 7.5): 0.100	
	+F_{P-C}	(fig. 47)	(3.3 , 2.5): 0.070	
	+F_{P-D}	(fig. 47)	(3.3 , 7.5): 0.084	0.343

CEILING Heating panel: F_{P-ABDE} = F_{P-A} + F_{P-B} + F_{P-D} + F_{P-E}

	F_{P-A}	(fig. 46)	(b/c, a/c) = (1.0 , 0.75): 0.035	
	+F_{P-B}	(fig. 46)	(1.0 , 0.75): 0.035	
	+F_{P-D}	(fig. 47)	(0.75, 0.75): 0.021	
	+F_{P-E}	(fig. 47)	(0.75, 0.75): 0.021	0.112

Rest of the ceiling: = F_{P-CF} = F_{P-C} + F_{P-F}
= F_{P-BC} − F_{P-B} + F_{P-EF} − F_{P-E}

	F_{P-BC}	(fig. 46)	(b/c, a/c) = (1.0 , 2.3): 0.057	
	−F_{P-B}	(fig. 46)	(1.0 , 0.75): 0.035	
	+F_{P-EF}	(fig. 47)	(0.75, 2.3): 0.037	
	−F_{P-E}	(fig. 47)	(0.75, 0.75): 0.021	0.038
	$F_{Person - all surfaces}$			1.000

49 and 50 can be used. They give the mean value of the angle factor between the person and the rectangle when he rotates around a vertical axis through his centre.

It is obvious that in this instance there will be only two cases: angle factors in relation to a vertical rectangle, and in relation to a horizontal rectangle. Fig. 49 and fig. 50 show diagrams for these two cases for a seated person. It will often be sufficient to use these diagrams for approximate calculations, even when the person's orientation is known.

Example 15. Angle factors between the person and the surrounding surfaces mentioned in example 14 are to be determined, the location of the person being the same, but his orientation is unknown. In this case, figs. 49 and 50 should be used. The results are given in table 21.

Comparing tables 20 and 21 it will be seen that for certain surfaces, considerable differences can be found between the angle factors.

The sum of all the angle factors between the person and the surrounding surfaces is, also in this case, 1.00.

Angle factor diagrams for standing persons are shown in figs. 51 to 53. Due to the approximate anterior–posterior symmetry of a standing person, there were only differences of 2–3% between cases 1 and 2, and the results were pooled in one diagram (fig. 51), calculated from the mean values of the two cases. In the same way, the diagram in fig. 52 covers cases 3 and 4, and that in fig. 53 covers cases 5 and 6.

In all the figures, a centre height over the floor equal to 1.0 m has been inserted, corresponding to that of an average standing person. For special cases (for example if the person stands on a platform or the like), another centre height can be substituted. Just as for seated persons, the establishment of the centre height is critical only in the determination of angle factors in relation to the floor, and then only for small areas close to the person.

Example 16. Angle factors are to be determined between the surrounding surfaces and a person placed and oriented in a room as shown in fig. 54.

The dimensions of the room are divided into rectangles as shown in fig. 54, and the angle factors, found from figs. 51–53, are given in table 22. The sum of the angle factors is close to unity (equal to 0.99) and an adequate check is thus made of the accuracy of the calculations.

When the location of a person standing in a room is known but not his orientation (in which direction he faces) the diagrams in figs. 55 and 56 can

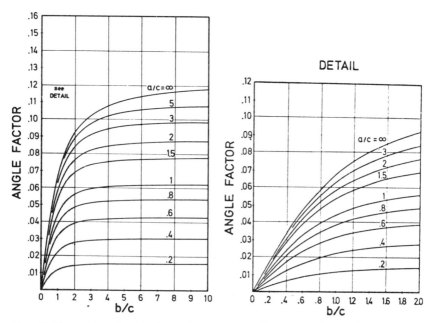

Fig. 49. Mean value of angle factor between a seated person and a vertical rectangle (above or below his centre) when the person is rotated around a vertical axis. To be used when the location but not the orientation of the person is known.

Example: a = 4m, b = 3m, c = 5m. b/c = 0.6, a/c = 0.8: F_{P-A} = 0.029.

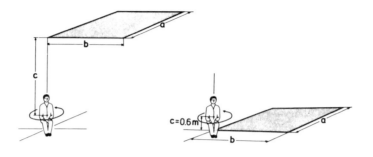

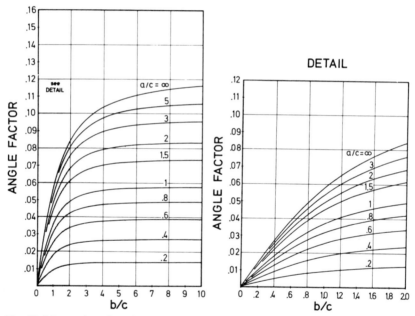

Fig. 50. Mean value of angle factor between a seated person and a horizontal rectangle (on the ceiling or on the floor) when the person is rotated around a vertical axis. To be used when the location but not the orientation of the person is known.

Example: a = 3m, b = 6m, c = 2m. b/c = 3.0, a/c = 1.5: F_{P-A} = 0.067.

186

Table 21. *Calculation of Angle Factors Pertinent to Example 15*

NORTH WALL	$F_{P-ABCD} = F_{P-A} + F_{P-B} + F_{P-C} + F_{P-D}$			
	F_{P-A}	(fig. 49)	(b/c, a/c) = (0.40, 1.0): 0.024	
	$+F_{P-B}$		(0.40, 3.0): 0.033	
	$+F_{P-C}$		(1.3 , 1.0): 0.50	
	$+F_{P-D}$		(1.3 , 3.0): 0.072	0.179
EAST WALL	$F_{P-ABCD} = F_{P-A} + F_{P-B} + F_{P-C} + F_{P-D}$			
	F_{P-A}	(fig. 49)	(b/c, a/c) = (0.13, 0.33): 0.004	
	$+F_{P-B}$		(0.44, 0.44): 0.015	
	$+F_{P-C}$		(0.13, 0.44): 0.005	
	$+F_{P-D}$		(0.44, 0.33): 0.011	0.035
SOUTH WALL	$F_{P-ABCD} = F_{P-A} + F_{P-B} + F_{P-C} + F_{P-D}$			
	F_{P+A}	(fig. 49)	(b/c, a/c) = (1.0 , 0.75): 0.037	
	$+F_{P+B}$		(1.0 , 2.3): 0.060	
	$+F_{P-C}$		(0.30, 0.75): 0.015	
	$+F_{P-D}$		(0.30, 2.3): 0.024	0.136
WEST WALL	Window: $F_{P-BE} = F_{P-B} + F_{P-E}$			
	F_{P-B}	(fig. 49)	(b/c, a/c) = (1.1 , 1.1): 0.049	
	$+F_{P-E}$		(1.1 , 0.73): 0.038	0.087

Rest of the wall: $F_{P-ACDF} = F_{P-A} + F_{P-C} + F_{P-D} + F_{P-F}$
$= F_{P-A} + F_{P-BC} - F_{P-B} + F_{P-D} + F_{P-EF} - F_{P-E}$
$= F_{P-A} + F_{P-BC} + F_{P-D} + F_{P-EF} - F_{P-BE}$

	F_{P-A}	(fig. 49)	(b/c, a/c) = (0.40, 1.0): 0.024	
	$+F_{P-BC}$		(1.3 , 1.3): 0.057	
	$+F_{P-D}$		(0.40, 1.3): 0.026	
	$+F_{P-EF}$		(1.3 , 1.0): 0.050	
	$-F_{P-BE}$		0.087	0.070
FLOOR	$F_{P-ABCD} = F_{P-A} + F_{P-B} + F_{P-C} + F_{P-D}$			
	F_{P-A}	(fig. 50)	(b/c, a/c) = (2.5 , 2.5): 0.078	
	$+F_{P-B}$		= (2.5 , 7.5): 0.090	
	$+F_{P-C}$		= (3.3 , 2.5): 0.082	
	$+F_{P-D}$		= (3.3 , 7.5): 0.095	0.345
CEILING	Heating panel: $F_{P-ABDE} = F_{P-A} + F_{P-B} + F_{P-D} + F_{P-E}$			
	F_{P-A}	(fig. 50)	(b/c, a/c) = (1.0 , 0.75): 0.030	
	$+F_{P-B}$		(1.0 , 0.75): 0.030	
	$+F_{P-D}$		(0.75, 0.75): 0.025	
	$+F_{P-E}$		(0.75, 0.75): 0.025	0.110

Rest of the ceiling: $F_{P-CF} = F_{P-C} + F_{P-F}$
$= F_{P-BC} - F_{P-B} + F_{P-EF} - F_{P-E}$

	F_{P-BC}	(fig. 50)	(b/c, a/c) = (1.0 , 2.3): 0.051	
	$-F_{P-B}$		(1.0 , 0.75): 0.030	
	$+F_{P-EF}$		(0.75, 2.3): 0.042	
	$-F_{P-E}$		(0.75, 0.75): 0.025	0.038
	$F_{Person - all surfaces}$			1.000

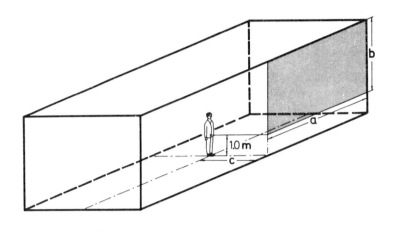

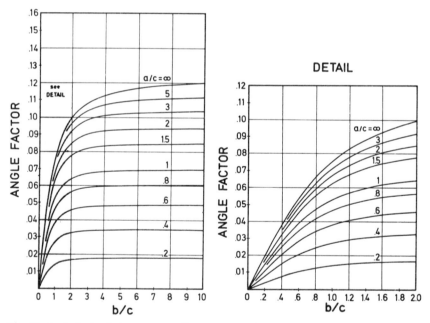

Fig. 51. Angle factor between a standing person and a vertical rectangle in front of him or behind him, above or below his centre (case 1 & 2).

Example: a = 6m, b = 4m, c = 4m. b/c = 1.0, a/c = 1.5: F_{P-A} = 0.063.

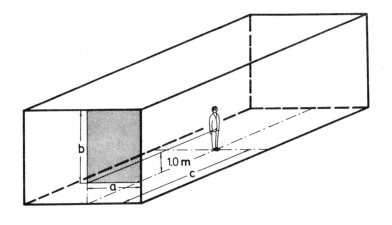

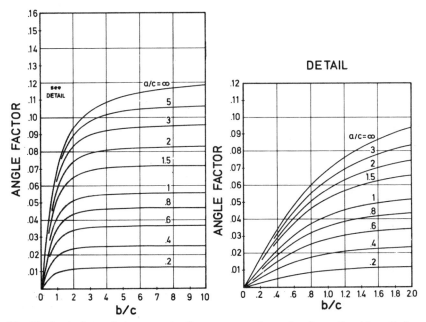

Fig. 52. Angle factor between a standing person and a rectangle on the side wall, forward or behind, above or below his centre (case 3 and 4).

Example: a = 1.5m, b = 4.5m, c = 1.5m. b/c = 3.0, a/c = 1.0: F_{P-A} = 0.054.

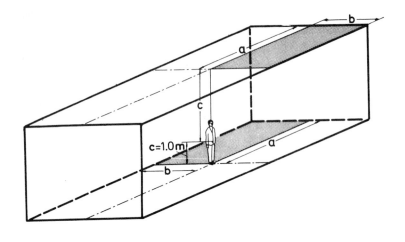

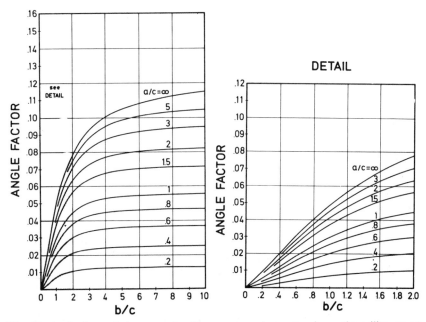

Fig. 53. Angle factor between a standing person and a rectangle on the ceiling or on the floor, forward of or behind his centre (case 5 and 6).

Example: a = 5m, b = 4m, c = 1.0m. b/c = 4.0, a/c = 5.0: F_{P-A} = 0.095.

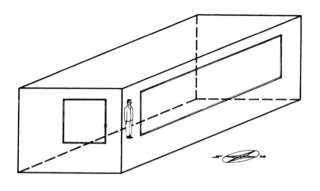

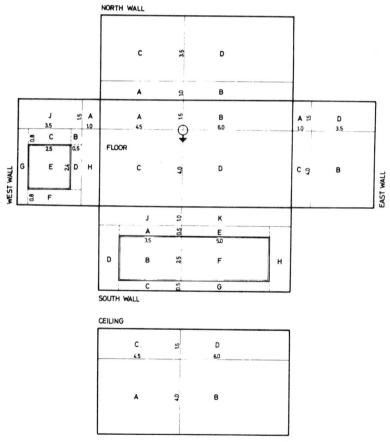

Fig. 54. Room dimensions and person placement, pertinent to ex. 16.

Table 22. *Calculation of Angle Factors Pertinent to Example 16*

NORTH WALL	$F_{P-ABCD} = F_{P-A} + F_{P-B} + F_{P-C} + F_{P-D}$			
	F_{P-A}	(fig. 51)	(b/c, a/c) = (0.67, 3.00): 0.056	
	$+F_{P-B}$	(fig. 51)	(0.67, 4.00): 0.057	
	$+F_{P-C}$	(fig. 51)	(2.33, 3.00): 0.094	
	$+F_{P-D}$	(fig. 51)	(2.33, 4.00): 0.097	0.304
EAST WALL	$F_{P-ABCD} = F_{P-A} + F_{P-B} + F_{P-C} + F_{P-D}$			
	F_{P-A}	(fig. 52)	(b/c, a/c) = (0.17, 0.25): 0.003	
	$+F_{P-B}$	(fig. 52)	(0.58, 0.67): 0.022	
	$+F_{P-C}$	(fig. 52)	(0.17, 0.67): 0.007	
	$+F_{P-D}$	(fig. 52)	(0.58, 0.25): 0.009	0.041
SOUTH WALL	Window: $F_{P-BF} = F_{P-EF} - F_{P-E} + F_{P-AB} - F_{P-A}$			
	F_{P-EF}	(fig. 51)	(b/c, a/c) = (0.75, 1.25): 0.049	
	$+F_{P-AB}$	(fig. 51)	(0.75, 0.88): 0.043	
	$-F_{P-E}$	(fig. 51)	(0.13, 1.25): 0.010	
	$-F_{P-A}$	(fig. 51)	(0.13, 0.88): 0.009	0.073
	Rest of the wall: $F_{P-ACDEGHJK} = F_{P-J} + F_{P-K} + F_{P-EFGH}$ $+ F_{P-ABCD} - F_{P-BF}$			
	F_{P-J}	(fig. 51)	(b/c, a/c) = (0.25, 1.13): 0.020	
	$+F_{P-K}$	(fig. 51)	(0.25, 1.50): 0.022	
	$+F_{P-EFGH}$	(fig. 51)	(0.88, 1.50): 0.059	
	$+F_{P-ABCD}$	(fig. 51)	(0.88, 1.13): 0.052	
	$-F_{P-BF}$		0.073	0.080
WEST WALL	Window: $F_{P-E} = F_{P-BCDE} + F_{P-B} - F_{P-BD} - F_{P-BC}$			
	F_{P-BCDE}	(fig. 52)	(b/c, a/c) = (0.67, 0.71): 0.026	
	$+F_{P-B}$	(fig. 52)	(0.11, 0.18): 0.001	
	$-F_{P-BD}$	(fig. 52)	(0.11, 0.71): 0.005	
	$-F_{P-BC}$	(fig. 52)	(0.67, 0.18): 0.007	0.015
	Rest of the wall: $F_{P-ABCDFGHJ} = F_{P-A} + F_{P-H} + F_{P-J} +$ $F_{P-BCDEFG} - F_{P-E}$			
	F_{P-A}	(fig. 52)	(b/c, a/c) = (0.22, 0.33): 0.005	
	$+F_{P-H}$	(fig. 52)	(0.22, 0.89): 0.012	
	$+F_{P-J}$	(fig. 52)	(0.78, 0.33): 0.014	
	$+F_{P-BCDEFG}$	(fig. 52)	(0.78, 0.89): 0.037	
	$-F_{P-E}$		0.015	0.053
FLOOR	$F_{P-ABCD} = F_{P-A} + F_{P-B} + F_{P-C} + F_{P-D}$			
	F_{P-A}	(fig. 53)	(b/c, a/c) = (1.50, 4.50): 0.063	
	$+F_{P-B}$	(fig. 53)	(1.50, 6.00): 0.065	
	$+F_{P-C}$	(fig. 53)	(4.00, 4.50): 0.092	
	$+F_{P-D}$	(fig. 53)	(4.00, 6.00): 0.091	0.311
CEILING	$F_{P-ABCD} = F_{P-A} + F_{P-B} + F_{P-C} + F_{P-D}$			
	F_{P-A}	(fig. 53)	(b/c, a/c) = (1.14, 1.29): 0.038	
	$+F_{P-B}$	(fig. 53)	(1.14, 1.71): 0.043	
	$+F_{P-C}$	(fig. 53)	(0.43, 1.29): 0.015	
	$+F_{P-D}$	(fig. 53)	(0.43, 1.71): 0.017	0.113
	$F_{Person - all surfaces}$			0.990

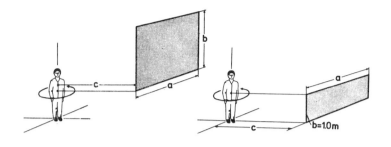

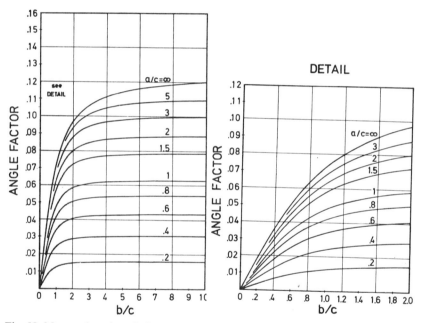

Fig. 55. Mean value of angle factor between a standing person and a vertical rectangle (above or below his centre) when the person is rotated around a vertical axis. To be used when the location but not the orientation of the person is known.

Example: a = 4.5m, b = 2.0m, c = 3.0m. b/c = 0.67, a/c = 1.5: F_{P-A} = 0.047.

193

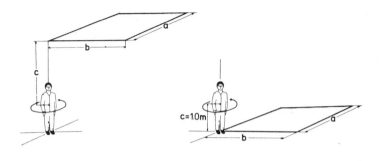

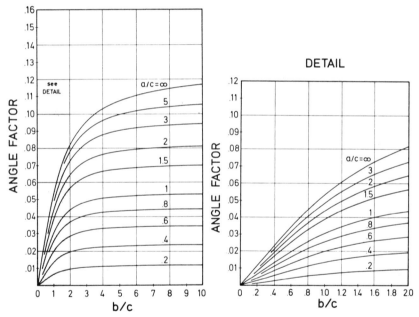

Fig. 56. Mean value of angle factor between a standing person and a horizontal rectangle (on the ceiling or on the floor) when the person is rotated around a vertical axis. To be used when the location but not the orientation of the person is known.

Example: a = 1.0m, b = 15m, c = 1.5m. b/c = 10, a/c = 0.67: F_{P-A} = 0.039.

194

be used. They give the mean value of the angle factor between person and rectangle when he rotates around a vertical axis through his centre. Just as for seated persons, there are in this case only two diagrams: angle factors in relation to a vertical rectangle, and in relation to a horizontal rectangle. Fig. 55 and fig. 56 show diagrams for these two cases for a standing person.

DISCUSSION

Effective Radiation Area Factor

The effective radiation area of the human body in different postures has been the subject of several investigations with the use of surprisingly varied experimental techniques. In comparing these with the present results it should be remembered that the majority of these experiments were made with a few subjects, sometimes only one. Considering different body types, some deviations may be expected from the present results, which are mean values of quite a large number of subjects.

Bohnenkamp et al. (35, 13), at the beginning of the 'thirties, measured effective radiation areas of a group of subjects differing in sex, age and body proportions, but all in the standing position. The experimental method consisted of measuring the electrical capacity of each subject. By analysis and measurement on physical models it was claimed that the electrical capacity was related to the effective radiation area. The mean value of f_{eff} found was 0.82, which is somewhat higher than the present results. However, the experimental technique employed has later been criticized by Deighton (63) and Guibert (116) among others, because the method does not seem to give reproduceable results. With subsequent measurements by this method, deviations of up to 9% were thus found, and in certain cases f_{eff}-values even greater than unity were obtained, an obvious impossibility.

Bedford (18) used a graphic construction technique, assuming ellipticity in the body silhouette. He found for two subjects an average f_{eff}-value equal to 0.82 for standing and 0.72 for crouched positions, but it seems quite clear that the method was highly approximate. Hardy and DuBois (123) used an envelope area method and found for two standing subjects an effective radiation area factor of 0.78.

Winslow, Gagge and Herrington (335) employed a thermal method in which radiant heat transfer was determined by the establishment of a heat balance for the human body. For two subjects in a "semi-reclining" position (mid-way between standing and sitting position) f_{eff}-values from 0.70 to 0.75 were found, which agrees well with the present results.

Nielsen and Pedersen (243) employed a similar method, but found somewhat lower values for a subject and a thermal manikin: 0.66 for the standing position and 0.60 for the seated position.

Guibert and Taylor (116) employed a photographic method which is similar to the present method, but measured from considerably fewer directions (16–22 within a quarter sphere). For three subjects with widely varying body size, they found mean values of 0.76 for a standing person and 0.70 for a seated person. In addition, for a single subject, an f_{eff}-value of 0.73 was found for a "semi-erect" and 0.65 for a crouched position. These data are in reasonable agreement with the present results. Guibert and Taylor also found that f_{eff} was independent of body size, which is in agreement with the present results.

Projected Area Factors

Guibert and Taylor (116) give as a secondary result in the determination of the effective radiation area factor, curves for the projected areas for a single subject, standing and seated, but as mentioned earlier, the results are based on measurements from comparatively few directions. Comparison is rather difficult since, among other things, a different system of coordinates was used.

For a standing person there is, in general, reasonable agreement between the results, although Guibert and Taylor's f_p values for the majority of (α, β)-values are somewhat higher (5–10%). For $(\alpha, \beta) = (90°, 0°)$, the f_p value found is, however, 25% less, and for $\beta = 90°$ it is 25% greater than the present results.

For a seated person the deviations for most angles were smaller than 10%, Guibert and Taylor's data in general being a little lower than the present results. However, for $(\alpha, \beta) = (90°, 0°)$ the f_p was 40% higher and for $\beta = 90°$ it was 20% lower than the present results.

Dunkle (72) used a mechanical shape factor integrator for the measurement of radiation data for a single test person. He does not give the direct investigation results, but instead gives approximate formulae for the radius of a sphere, which should be equivalent to the human body for radiation exchange. Dunkle states that the approximate formulae deviate up to 20% from the results of the investigation. By suitable conversion on the basis of his formulae and other data, it is possible to find the projected area factor as a function of direction, so that a comparison with the present results can be made.

For a standing person there is reasonable agreement for $\beta < 30°$, but for $\beta > 30°$ there is a steadily rising deviation up to $\beta = 90°$, where Dunkle's value is approximately 40% higher than that of the present study.

For seated persons there is only fair agreement for $\beta = 15°$. For $\alpha = 90°$, Dunkle's formula gives one constant value of f_p, independent of β, while f_p in the present investigation was found to be 50% higher for $\beta = 15°$ than for $\beta = 0°$.

Underwood and Ward (319) measured projected areas for a group of males and females using a photographic method, but only for the standing position and nude subjects. Measurements were made for 7 altitudes, but only for 3 azimuth values ($\alpha = 0°$, $45°$, $90°$). Using the effective radiation area factor determined in the present study a comparison is possible. For $\beta < 60°$ there is reasonable agreement between the two studies, while for $\beta > 60°$ there is a steadily rising deviation up to $\beta = 90°$ where Underwood's value is 25% lower than the present data.

Angle Factors

Investigations to determine angle factors in relation to the human body have been carried out earlier by Raber and Hutchinson (263, 264) and by Dunkle (72).

Raber and Hutchinson used a mechanical integrator to determine the angle factor of a clothed dummy, standing and seated, with respect to elemental areas in the ceiling. The results are given for each body posture as iso-shape factor curves in three diagrams, corresponding to three fixed ceiling heights (10, 12 and 15 ft.). The applicability of these diagrams is relatively limited, partly because they are valid only for the three above-mentioned heights, and partly because they comprise only the ceiling area quite close to the person (a/c and b/c < 2). Moreover, the diagrams are difficult to apply in practice, since for a given finite area one must first estimate a mean value for the whole of the relevant area of the angle factor, based on the iso-shape factor curves, after which the angle factor between the person and the area must be determined using the reciprocity theorem.

For a seated person, Raber and Hutchinson have only determined angle factors in relation to ceiling areas directly above the person, and this gives reasonable agreement with the present results, deviations of between -9% and $+14\%$ being found.

However, for a standing person in relation to the ceiling, Raber and Hutchinson's values are considerably higher than those of the present study, particularly for relatively small areas directly above the person. For a $3' \times 3'$ area directly above the person, their angle factor is 76% greater with a ceiling height of 8′, and 55% greater with a ceiling height of 12′. For a $12' \times 12'$ area and a ceiling height of 12′, a 16% greater angle factor was found compared to that of the present study. For angle factors between a standing person and vertical areas, Raber and Hutchinson give very little data, and a comparison shows large deviations: for side walls up to 90% and for end walls up to 200% greater values than those of the present study.

Dunkle (72) also used a mechanical integrator and worked out angle factor diagrams for a single subject, but only for a standing posture. Dunkle's diagrams include the surface area of the actual subject, and are therefore rather inconvenient to use in practice. For cases 1 and 2 there is reasonable agreement, Dunkle's data generally being around 5–10% lower than the data of the present study. For cases 3 and 4 there is good agreement, while for cases 5 and 6, Dunkle's data are up to 27% higher than the present results. These deviations are not surprising as he approximated the human body with a sphere, and this alone, according to Dunkle, can involve errors of up to 20%.

Chapter 7.

THERMAL ENVIRONMENTAL ANALYSIS

The purpose of heating or cooling enclosures to be occupied by human beings is to provide thermal comfort. A given system will be judged by the occupants according to its ability to satisfy this demand, and it is therefore obvious that a rational calculation of heating and air-conditioning systems must begin with the conditions for comfort, expressed here by the comfort equation.

The activity level and the thermal resistance of clothing are determined, depending on the purpose for which the space will be used, and the comfort equation gives all combinations of the environmental variables which will create optimal thermal comfort. Therefore there are many possiblities for satisfying the comfort demand. However, for a given room, the environmental system chosen, the thermal properties of the room and the outdoor conditions will jointly establish a certain dependance between the variables.

In the present chapter, a method will be proposed for conducting a detailed thermal analysis of a room, to provide a state of comfort. The procedure establishes comfort for a chosen characteristic location in the room, after which mean radiant isotherms and iso-PMV-curves can be calculated and plotted in the occupied zone. The LPPD-value for the room can also be calculated. Through the analysis one can find the necessary temperatures or areas of possible heating or cooling panels, the heat to be produced by possible convective heaters in the room, the temperature or flow rate of possible supply air, and the temperature of, and heat flow through, all surfaces.

By means of the analysis one obtains a detailed knowledge of the thermal conditions in the space (in particular the radiant field) and the engineering design of the heating/cooling system can be modified if necessary. The analysis can be performed for different systems, with a view to comparison and optimization.

The principle of the method requires that heat balance equations are derived for all surfaces in the room and for the air in the room. The comfort equation and one of the formulae for the mean radiant temperature derived earlier, are also employed. By a simultaneous solution of the equations, the desired factors can thus be determined.

Already at the end of the 'forties, a somewhat similar method was proposed by Raber and Hutchinson (264); however, they had neither modern comfort conditions at their disposal, nor sufficient information about angle factors between the human body and the surroundings. In addition they had to employ a series of gross simplifications in order to carry out the calculations at all, since digital computers were not then available.

THE COMFORT CONDITION

As a condition for comfort, one can use either the comfort equation directly or the formula for the PMV-index, with a predicted mean vote equal to zero. The two formulae in this case are identical. A characteristic location of a person in the room is established by judgement of the space use and the calculation is made for this location. Afterwards PMV-values can be determined for all other locations in the occupied zone, and the LPPD-value as an expression for the thermal variability, can be calculated for the room in question.

Considering the purpose for which the space will be used, the activity level and the clothing should then be estimated, using tables 1 and 2. The water vapour pressure in the space will normally be very uniform and this can be determined by writing a vapour balance equation for the room. However, as discussed previously, the humidity has only a small thermal influence, and a rough estimate will be sufficient in most cases.

The relative velocity should then be estimated considering body movements of the person (at higher activity levels) and air velocities in the occupied zone. Theoretical methods for the calculation of velocity distribution in a space do not exist at the present time. Field estimates are based partly on a knowledge of air currents generated by air outlets and warm or cold vertical surfaces (290, 78), and partly on various empirical rules for space air distribution (307, 308, 165, 271, 117, 192, 236, 212, 213, 169). Where air outlets are concerned, the calculations are normally based on the theory for free jets, which is experimentally well founded (15, 315, 249, 164, 248). In general one aims at the velocity in the jet being reduced to a small value before it reaches the occupied zone. In order to obtain a thermal field as uniform as possible in the occupied zone, velocities of less than ∞ 0.1 m/s are normally sought.

After including the above-mentioned values, the comfort equation then gives a relationship between air temperature and mean radiant temperature which must be satisfied in order to attain optimal thermal comfort. In some cases it can be predicted with certainty that the mean radiant temperature will be very close to the air temperature, and in this case $t_{mrt} = t_a$ can be determined direct from the comfort equation or, more easily, from the diagrams in figs. 3 to 7 (or from table 13 for PMV = 0). The comfort value of $t_{mrt} = t_a$ is then used directly in the following thermal analysis.

When t_a and t_{mrt} are not equal, instead of using the non-linear comfort equation direct, it is usually adequate to use the following linearized expression in showing the relationship between t_a and t_{mrt}:

$$t_{comf} = \frac{t_a + t_{mrt}\, \dfrac{\delta t_a}{\delta t_{mrt}}}{1 + \dfrac{\delta t_a}{\delta t_{mrt}}} \qquad (68)$$

where t_{comf} = that uniform value of air temperature and mean radiant temperature which, under the conditions stated, will give optimal thermal comfort,

$\dfrac{\delta t_a}{\delta t_{mrt}}$ = the partial differential coefficient in the comfort condition.

The magnitude of t_{comf} is most easily determined by one of the comfort diagrams in figs. 3 to 7. The value of $\delta t_a/\delta t_{mrt}$ can be found from fig. 12 for the actual combination of the variables. After including the values for t_{comf} and $\delta t_a/\delta t_{mrt}$, equation (68) thus gives the linear relationship between the variables t_a and t_{mrt}, necessary for optimal comfort.

HEAT BALANCE OF ROOM SURFACES

Each surface area A_i in the room will be in radiant exchange with all the other surfaces and will be in convective heat exchange with the air within the space. The sum of these two heat flows will, under steady-state conditions, be equal to the conductive heat flow through the surface:

$$q_r + q_c = q_{cd} \qquad (69)$$

In the following, each of the terms in the heat balance will be evaluated.

Radiant Heat Transfer

Suppose that the space consists of N isothermal surface areas A_1, A_2, ...

.... A_N. The corresponding absolute temperatures are T_1, T_2, ... T_N and the emittances are ε_1, ε_2, ... ε_N.

The calculations will be performed under the following assumptions:

1. The temperature (and the emittance) of a surface is the same over the entire surface (e.g., a wall can be divided into sections with different temperatures and emittances).
2. All radiation is emitted and reflected diffusely (obeying Lambert's Cosine Law). This will be a reasonable approximation for all usual non-metallic surfaces.
3. Each surface is grey, that is emittance equal to absorptance. This is a reasonable assumption where radiant exchange between surfaces with temperatures of the same magnitude is concerned.
4. The air in the room is a radiatively non-participating media, i.e., the air does not emit, absorb or scatter radiation. Water vapour is the only constituent in the air which is radiatively active, but with the small concentrations and space sizes occurring in practice, the significance of the water vapour is normally negligible.

The net rate of radiant heat loss from a typical surface A_i is the difference between the emitted radiation and the absorbed portion of the incident radiation. Thus, in general

$$q_i = \varepsilon_i \, \sigma T_i^4 - \alpha_i \, H_i \tag{70}$$

where q_i = radiant heat loss per unit time and area
ε_i = the emittance of surface i
α_i = the absorptance of surface i
T_i = the absolute temperature of surface i
H_i = the incident radiant energy arriving at the surface per unit time and unit'area.

The incident radiation H_i is made up partly of emitted radiation from the other surfaces and partly of radiation which has been reflected one or more times on the other surfaces. Due to these multiple reflections the calculation of the radiant interchange is therefore quite a complicated matter. However, the calculation can be simplified considerably by introducing,the radiosity concept (301). The radiosity B_i of a surface A_i is defined as the rate at which radiant energy streams away from the surface per unit time and unit area:

$$B_i = \varepsilon_i\, \sigma T_i^4 + \rho_i\, H_i \tag{71}$$

where ρ_i is the reflectance of A_i.

Since it is assumed that both the emitted and the reflected radiation is diffusely distributed, this will also be the case for the radiosity. It thus follows that angle factors can be used in the calculation of radiant interchange between surfaces with known radiosities.

The radiant flux H_i incident on surface i comes from the other surfaces of the enclosure. Consider the radiation coming from any other surface j. A radiant energy quantity

$$B_j A_j = (\varepsilon_j \sigma T_j^4 + \rho_j H_j) A_j \tag{72}$$

streams away from surface j.

Of this, an amount $B_j A_j F_{Aj-Ai}$, arrives at surface i (F_{Aj-Ai} = angle factor between A_j and A_i). By employing the reciprocity theorem it follows that the rate at which energy arrives per unit area of A_i from surface j is $B_j F_{Ai-Aj}$. Contributions such as this arrive at A_i from all the surfaces of the room. Thus H_i is expressible as a sum

$$H_i = \sum_{j=1}^{N} B_j F_{Ai-Aj} \tag{73}$$

and with this, equation (71) becomes

$$B_i = \varepsilon_i\, \sigma T_i^4 + (1 - \varepsilon_i) \sum_{j=1}^{N} B_j F_{Ai - Aj} \tag{74}$$

since $\rho_i = 1 - \varepsilon_i$.

Equations similar to (74) can be written for each of the N surfaces in the room and in this way the following N algebraic equations are generated:

$$B_1 = \varepsilon_1 \sigma T_1^4 + (1 - \varepsilon_1) \sum_{j=1}^{N} B_j F_{A1 - Aj}$$

$$B_2 = \varepsilon_2 \sigma T_2^4 + (1 - \varepsilon_2) \sum_{j=1}^{N} B_j F_{A2 - Aj} \tag{75}$$

$$\vdots$$

$$B_N = \varepsilon_N \sigma T_N^4 + (1 - \varepsilon_N) \sum_{j=1}^{N} B_j F_{AN - Aj}$$

For A_i the total radiant heat exchange can be determined by equations (70) and (71), with $\alpha_i = \varepsilon_i$ (grey body condition):

$$q_i = \frac{\varepsilon_i}{1 - \varepsilon_i} (\sigma T_i^4 - B_i) \tag{76}$$

When equations similar to (76) are written for each of the N surfaces in the room, the following N equations are obtained:

$$q_1 = \frac{\varepsilon_1}{1 - \varepsilon_1} (\sigma T_1^4 - B_1)$$

$$q_2 = \frac{\varepsilon_2}{1 - \varepsilon_2} (\sigma T_2^4 - B_2) \tag{77}$$

$$\vdots$$

$$q_N = \frac{\varepsilon_N}{1 - \varepsilon_N} (\sigma T_N^4 - B_N)$$

The equation systems (77) and (75) comprise in all 2 N equations for the determination of the radiant heat exchange at all the surfaces of the room. For most materials used in practice the emittances are rather high (around 0.9) and therefore it will be appropriate to disregard the reflections. Thus the necessary number of equations for the determination of the radiant heat exchange is reduced from 2N to N:

$$q_1 = \varepsilon_1 \sigma T_1^4 - \sum_{j=1}^{N} \varepsilon_j \sigma T_j^4 \, F_{A1 - Aj}$$

$$q_2 = \varepsilon_2 \sigma T_2^4 - \sum_{j=1}^{N} \varepsilon_j \sigma T_j^4 \, F_{A2 - Aj} \tag{78}$$

$$\vdots$$

$$q_N = \varepsilon_N \sigma T_N^4 - \sum_{j=1}^{N} \varepsilon_j \sigma T_j^4 \, F_{AN - Aj}$$

In the practical calculation it will be advantageous to linearize the equations (78). Since the emittances are nearly equal, the following equations result:

$$q_1 = \varepsilon_1 \sigma \sum_{j=1}^{N} \theta_{1j} (T_1 - T_j) F_{A1 - Aj}$$

$$q_2 = \varepsilon_2 \sigma \sum_{j=1}^{N} \theta_{2j} (T_2 - T_j) F_{A2 - Aj} \qquad (79)$$

$$\vdots$$

$$q_N = \varepsilon_N \sigma \sum_{j=1}^{N} \theta_{Nj} (T_N - T_j) F_{AN - Aj}$$

where $\theta_{ij} = \dfrac{T_i^4 - T_j^4}{T_i - T_j}$ $\qquad\qquad (80)$

The value of θ_{ij} varies only slightly with the temperature level (see table 23) and can therefore be determined when the temperatures are crudely estimated. If there are only small differences in temperature, one can with reasonable approximation set all θ values equal to one fixed value. If, for example, all temperatures range between $10°$ and $30°C$, θ can be established at $1.00 \cdot 10^8$ (errors of less than 10% are involved).

The angle factors in equations (75), (78) and (79) are available for many geometric surface arrangements in the literature, either expressed as equations or plots (167, 264, 301, 121, 313). Special computer programmes for the calculation of angle factors between rectangular surfaces in a room have been prepared by Brown (43) and Rubinstein (284).

Table 23. *Values of* $\theta_{ij} \times 10^{-8}$ *($°K^3$) at Different Temperatures*

t_j	t_i (°C)					
°C	0	10	20	30	50	100
0	0.81	0.86	0.91	0.96	1.07	1.38
10	0.86	0.91	0.96	1.01	1.12	1.44
20	0.91	0.96	1.00	1.06	1.17	1.50
30	0.96	1.01	1.06	1.11	1.23	1.56
50	1.07	1.12	1.17	1.23	1.35	1.70
100	1.38	1.44	1.50	1.56	1.70	2.08

Data for radiation properties (emittances, reflectances) for different surfaces can be found in standard textbooks and handbooks. The most comprehensive tables have been published by Gubareff et al. (115).

In the foregoing we have assumed that the surfaces are grey (emittance = absorptance). This condition is valid with reasonable accuracy when the surfaces have moderate temperatures, as is the case for normal indoor environments (longwave radiation).

If, however, shortwave radiation occurs in the room, e.g. arising from significant solar and sky radiation, from some types of high-intensity radiant heaters or from lighting systems with high illumination power, this assumption no longer holds. For shortwave radiation the absorptances for the surfaces have quite different, often much lower values, than for longwave radiation, and in such cases it can therefore be necessary to make separate calculations of the shortwave radiation.

The calculation of the shortwave radiation can be made independently of the longwave radiation, as the temperature of the wall surfaces has no influence on the shortwave radiant exchange.

Presupposing diffuse reflection, the concept of shortwave radiosity of a surface is introduced, defined as the rate at which shortwave radiant energy streams away from the surface per unit time and area.

Let us suppose that the surfaces in the room have the absorptances α_1^*, α_2^* ..... α_N^* in the actual shortwave region. The following equations can then be written for the shortwave radiosities B_1^*, B_2^* ..... B_N^*

$$B_1^* = (1 - \alpha_1^*) \sum_{j=1}^{N} B_j\, F_{A1-Aj}$$

$$B_2^* = (1 - \alpha_2^*) \sum_{j=1}^{N} B_j\, F_{A2-Aj} \qquad (81)$$

$$\vdots$$

$$B_N^* = (1 - \alpha_N^*) \sum_{j=1}^{N} B_j\, F_{AN-Aj}$$

One of the surfaces is designated as an "emitter" of shortwave radiation, and the corresponding equation in eqs. (81) is expanded by an extra term corresponding thereto. For solar radiation it can be either a window or possibly a directly irradiated wall, the transmitted solar and sky radiation being distributed over the surface concerned. Radiation from artificial lighting can, for example, be distributed over the ceiling area. Due to the low efficiency of artificial light sources, only a small part of the electrical power of the fixture is emitted as shortwave radiation (e.g., for fluorescent lamp fixtures only 5-10%).

The equations (81) can be solved independently of the longwave radiation equations and also of other heat transfer equations, since the shortwave radiosities are independent of the surface temperatures.

When the radiosities for each surface have been determined from eqs. (81), the absorbed shortwave radiation at each surface can then be calculated by

$$q_1^* = \alpha_1^* \sum_{j=1}^{N} B_j^* F_{A1-Aj}$$

$$q_2^* = \alpha_2^* \sum_{j=1}^{N} B_j^* F_{A2-Aj} \tag{82}$$

$$\vdots$$

$$q_N^* = \alpha_N^* \sum_{j=1}^{N} B_j^* F_{AN-Aj}$$

The heat transfer rates for shortwave radiation found from eqs. (82) can then be combined with the heat transfer rates for longwave radiation found earlier, and the total radiant heat transfer rates at each surface are thus:

$$q_{r1} = q_1 + q_1^*$$

$$q_{r2} = q_2 + q_2^* \tag{83}$$

$$\vdots$$

$$q_{rN} = q_N + q_N^*$$

Throughout the foregoing, diffuse reflection at the surfaces has been assumed. This is a reasonable assumption for all normal materials. In special cases, however, the question of the use of specular surfaces in a room can arise. In order to increase the effect of heating or cooling panels,

Bruun (46), Mills (214) and Lueder (193) suggested that the unheated (or uncooled) surfaces be covered with a special aluminium foil, possibly coated with a coloured plastic which is transparent for longwave radiation. Since this is not commonly done, the procedure for these special cases will not be dealt with here. The reader is referred to studies of Korsgaard (172) and Sparrow (301) among others, who have suggested a series of methods for the detailed analysis of enclosures involving specular surfaces.

Convective Heat Transfer

The surfaces in a space are in convective heat exchange with the air within the room. For any surface area A_i with the temperature T_i the convective heat loss from the surface per unit time and area will be

$$q_{c\,i} = h_{c\,i} (t_i - t_a) \tag{84}$$

where $h_{c\,i}$ = the convective heat transfer coefficient
t_a = the air temperature

In normal spaces with low air velocities, the heat transfer between surfaces and air will take place by free convection and the convective heat transfer coefficient can therefore be calculated from the usual formula for free convection

$$Nu = c\,(Gr\,Pr)^n \tag{85}$$

where Nu is the Nusselt number, Gr the Grashof number, Pr the Prandtl number, and c and n are constants.

Since the properties for air are reasonably constant at normal room temperatures, eq. (85) can be simplified to

$$h_c = c_1\,(\Delta t)^m\,L^s \tag{86}$$

where Δt = the difference between surface temperature and air temperature
L = a characteristic length
c_1, m, s = constants

Min et al. (215) have experimentally determined the constants in eq. (86). They suggest the following formulae:

Vertical surfaces: walls, windows, etc.:

$$h_c = 1.61\,(\Delta t)^{0.32}\,L^{-0.05} \tag{87}$$

Horizontal surfaces: warm ceiling or cold floor:

$$h_c = 0.173 \, (\Delta t)^{0.25} \, L^{-0.24} \tag{88}$$

cold ceiling or warm floor:

$$h_c = 2.08 \, (\Delta t)^{0.31} \, L^{-0.08} \tag{89}$$

In eq. (87), L = the height of the vertical surface, and in eqs. (88) and (89), L = the "hydraulic diameter" of the heated or cooled surface area, i.e., 4 times the area divided by the perimeter.

Conductive Heat Transfer

Under steady-state conditions the heat conduction per unit time and area through the surface i can be expressed by

$$q_{cd\,i} = C_i \, (t_i - t_o) \tag{90}$$

in which

$$C_i = \cfrac{1}{\cfrac{x_1}{k_1} + \ldots + \cfrac{1}{a_1} + \ldots + \cfrac{1}{h_o}} \tag{91}$$

where C_i = the overall wall conductance from the inside surface to the outside air

x = thickness of each homogeneous section of wall

k = conductivity of the material

a = conductance of each air space in the wall

h_o = coefficient of heat transfer by convection and radiation at the outside of the wall (surface conductance)

t_i = inside surface temperature

t_o = outside ambient temperature

C_i can be determined either direct from eq. (91) or it can be found from the overall coefficient of heat transmission U_i (air-to-air), which is listed in handbooks for many common types of building wall, floor and ceiling constructions:

$$\frac{1}{C_i} = \frac{1}{U} - \frac{1}{h_i} \tag{92}$$

where h_i is the standardized internal coefficient of heat transfer.

Where an outer element is concerned, t_o is the outdoor ambient temperature. Where an inner wall is concerned, t_o is the temperature of the adjoining space. For inner walls the temperature difference is often small and the conductive heat transfer can therefore be disregarded in many cases.

The above formulae apply, as mentioned, for steady state heat conduction. The present thermal analysis has been set up for this condition, but in principle, the calculations may also be made for transient conditions. The heat capacity of the materials is then also included in the calculations, which are based on Fourier's fundamental differential equation for heat conduction. In the literature several numerical methods have been discussed in detail.

HEAT BALANCE OF THE ROOM AIR

Heat can be introduced into the room by supply air (air flow G_v) heated or cooled to the temperature t_v and by infiltration air (air flow G_o) with the outdoor air temperature t_o. Heat is then removed from the room by the exhaust air (air flow $G_v + G_o$). In the room the air is in convective heat exchange with all the surfaces, and in addition, heat can be transferred to the air from people, heaters, lighting, etc. (Q_c).

We thus arrive at the following heat balance equation for the room air:

$$c_p (G_v t_v + G_o t_o) + Q_c = c_p (G_v + G_o) t_a +$$

$$\sum_{i=1}^{N} h_{c\,i} A_i (t_a - t_i) \tag{93}$$

where c_p = specific heat of air ($= 0.24 \text{ kcal/kg}°\text{C}$)

SIMULTANEOUS SOLUTION OF THE EQUATIONS

In the foregoing, the necessary equations have been set up with which to carry out the thermal analysis of a room. The number of equations depends on whether panel heating (cooling) or convective heating (cooling) is concerned.

For panel heating (cooling) there will be $N-1$ heat balance equation for surface elements, i.e., one equation for each of the N surface elements except for the heating (cooling) panel. In addition, a heat balance equation is obtained for the air, as well as the comfort equation (simplest in the linearized form, eq. (68)), and the definition equation for mean radiant temperature (simplest in the linearized form, eq. (46)). In all, $N + 2$ equations with $N + 2$ unknowns: N surface temperatures, air temperature and mean radiant temperature.

Thus, by solving the equations, the necessary temperature of the heating (cooling) panel can be obtained, as well as the corresponding temperatures of air and all the other surfaces, in order to create comfort for a person placed at the selected characteristic location in the room. The mean radiant temperature can then be calculated for every other location in the occupied zone, and mean radiant isotherms can be drawn. Also, for each point, the predicted mean vote can be calculated (see chapter four) and iso-PMV-curves can be drawn in the occupied zone. PMV will naturally be zero in the selected characteristic location for which the calculations have been made. Furthermore, LPPD can be calculated as an expression for the thermal variability in the occupied zone, but it must be remembered that in the calculation, it is only the mean radiant temperature which contributes to the variability, as the velocity and the air temperature are considered uniform. In practice, therefore, LPPD must be expected to be higher than that calculated, due to non-uniformities of air temperature and velocity.

With convective heating (cooling) there will be one heat balance equation for each of the N surface elements, and just as above, the heat balance equation for the air, the comfort equation, and the definition equation for mean radiant temperature. In all, $N + 3$ equations with $N + 3$ unknowns: N surface temperatures, the mean radiant temperature, the room air temperature and the temperature (or flow) of the heated (cooled) outlet air; if there are any convectors in the room, the last of the above-mentioned unknowns is replaced by the heat output from the convectors.

By solving the equations, the necessary outlet temperature for comfort is thus obtained (if the air flow is kept constant). If the outlet temperature is kept constant the necessary air flow is obtained. If there are any convective heaters in the room, the necessary heat output is given. In addition, all surface temperatures in the room are obtained, and the calculation of mean radiant isotherms, iso-PMV-curves and of LPPD can be made just as above for panel heating or cooling.

PRACTICAL PROCEDURE

The following practical procedure for performing the thermal environment analysis can now be set up

1. Activity level and clo-value are estimated, considering the intended use of the space. A characteristic location for a person is selected in the space, where the optimum thermal comfort is desired. Relative velocity in the occupied zone is estimated.
2. The outdoor temperature, the temperature in adjoining rooms, and the infiltration air flow are established.
3. The surrounding surfaces of the room are divided into a suitable number of surface elements N, and the corresponding conductances are determined.
4. If panel heating or cooling is involved, the size and location of the particular panels are chosen. If convective heating or cooling is involved, either the air flow or the outlet air temperature is selected.
5. The necessary angle factors between the surface elements themselves and between person and surface elements are then determined.
6. The equations are written and solved.
7. All the temperatures will be known from 6. above. The mean radiant temperature at each point in the occupied zone can then be determined and the corresponding values of PMV and PPD calculated. Also, LPPD for the space can be determined. If desired, mean radiant isotherms and iso-PMV-curves can be drawn.
8. The heat flow through each surface element and the total heat loss (positive or negative) can then be determined.

In practice the analysis will often be performed by using a digital computer. In this case the above procedure gives the logical sequence for programming.

Example 17. It is desired to carry out a thermal analysis of a room heated by a panel which completely covers the ceiling, as shown in fig. 57, for an outdoor temperature equal to 0°C. The room, which is symmetrical around the diagonal, has two outer surfaces, each consisting of a large window (double glass panes, $U = 3.0$ kcal/hr m² °C, $C_i = \left(\frac{1}{3.0} - 0.15\right)^{-1} = 5.6$ kcal/hr m² °C) and a small wall section ($U = 0.50$ kcal/hr m² °C, $C_i = \left(\frac{1}{0.50} - 0.15\right)^{-1} = 0.54$ kcal/hr m² °C). The heat flow through the other surfaces can be neglected.

The room is ventilated by air which has an outlet temperature equal to the air temperature of the room, the infiltration of outdoor air is one air

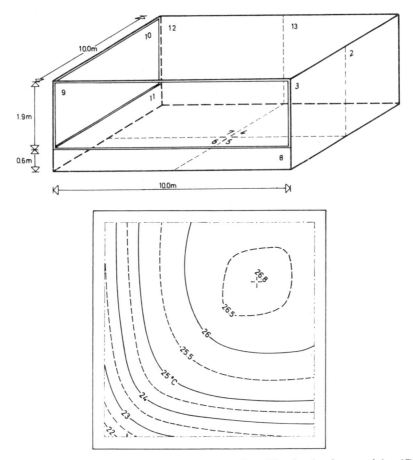

Fig. 57. Thermal analysis of a room where the entire ceiling is a heating panel (ex. 17).. The figure above shows the room dimensions. Below are plotted the calculated mean radiant isotherms (°C) in the occupied zone.

change per hour and the convective heat load from persons, etc. = 360 kcal/hr. No sun load.

The room is to be occupied by sedentary people clad at 1 clo; the air velocity < 0.1 m/s, and the rh = 50%.

From fig. 12 $\delta t_a/\delta t_{mrt} = 0.93$, and from fig. 7 $t_{comf} = 23.0°C$. The comfort condition, eq. (68) thus becomes

$$23.0 = \frac{t_a + 0.93\, t_{mrt}}{1 + 0.93}$$

The floor is divided into four identical squares and each of the two inner walls into two identical rectangles. This is assumed to be reasonable for this case. In all, 13 surface areas are obtained in the room (see fig. 57), but due to the symmetry it is sufficient to set up the heat balance equations for 7 surfaces (nos. 2, 3, 4, 5, 6, 8, 9 in fig. 57).

The mid-point of the room is chosen as a characteristic location, and the orientation of the person being unknown, the following angle factors between the person and ambient surfaces are obtained from figs. 49 and 50:

Surface	Angle Factor
i	F_{P-A_i}
1	0.308
2	0.029
3	0.029
4	0.110
5	0.110
6	0.110
7	0.110
8	0.012
9	0.046
10	0.046
11	0.012
12	0.029
13	0.029
Σ =	0.98

In all, seven surface heat balance equations are obtained, as well as one for the room air, the above-mentioned comfort condition and the definition equation for t_{mrt}. The resulting ten equations with ten unknowns are solved by iteration on a digital computer. The following results are obtained:

$$t_1 = 32.1 \,°C$$
$$t_2 = 24.9 \,°C = t_{13}$$
$$t_3 = 24.1 \,°C = t_{12}$$
$$t_4 = 26.0 \,°C$$
$$t_5 = 24.9 \,°C = t_7$$
$$t_6 = 24.4 \,°C$$
$$t_8 = 23.0 \,°C = t_{11}$$
$$t_9 = 14.1 \,°C = t_{10}$$
$$t_a = 20.5 \,°C$$
$$t_{mrt} = 26.1 \,°C$$

Heat loss: windows   = 3000 kcal/hr
           walls   = 150   –
           infiltration air = 1600 –
           _____
                            4750 kcal/hr

Heat gain: ceiling   = 4390 kcal/hr
           persons, etc. = 360   –
           _____
                            4750 kcal/hr

The mean radiant temperatures are then calculated for other locations in the occupied zone, and mean radiant isotherms are drawn as shown in fig. 57. It will be seen that there is considerable non-uniformity.

LPPD is calculated at 6.0%, i.e., the number of dissatisfied being 1/5 higher than the minimum value. However, LPPD can be expected to be even higher in practice. In the calculation only the mean radiant temperature contributes to the variability. In practice, air temperatures would also be lower in the outside corner. The non-uniformity may be reduced by refraining from heating the part of the ceiling area furthest away from the windows. Similar calculations can be made in order to determine the optimal placing of the heated area.

SUMMARY

The present book deals with the conditions for thermal comfort for man, the methods of assessing thermal environments, and the principles for performing theoretical thermal analyses of enclosures based on comfort criteria. Formatting the results and methods, so that they can be easily applied in practice, has been stressed. The applications are illustrated by numerous examples.

In chapter one the concept of thermal comfort is introduced, and its significance and applications are discussed.

In chapter two the comfort conditions are set forth, and the comfort equation, which has been presented earlier by the author, is reformulated and discussed. The comfort equation makes it possible, for the first time, to calculate those combinations of activity, clothing and the environmental variables (air temperature, mean radiant temperature, humidity and relative air velocity), which will create thermal comfort. For practical applications, a series of comfort diagrams (figs. 3–11, p. 44–54) is given, showing combinations of the variables which will provide thermal comfort. It is impossible to consider the effect of any of the physical factors influencing thermal comfort independently, as the effect of each of them depends on the level of the other factors. Therefore, emphasis has been placed on the combined influence and the interactions between the effects of the various factors (figs. 12–16, p. 59–65).

The comfort equation is based on experiments using North American students as subjects. In chapter three the application of the equation to other groups of people is discussed. Experiments have been carried out involving 128 Danish students (mean age 23 years) and 128 Danish elderly people (mean age 68 years). No significant difference was found in the comfort conditions between American and Danish students, between students and elderly people or between males and females (table 6, p. 78). It is therefore suggested that the comfort equation can be applied within the temperate climate zones for adults, independent of the sex.

217

Chapter three discusses also the significance of various other factors which possibly could have an influence on the thermal comfort conditions. Earlier experiments with subjects and theoretical analysis are employed to examine these factors, which include body build, menstrual cycle, ethnic differences, food, circadian rhythm, crowding, and colour. It is concluded that none of these factors seem to have an influence on the comfort conditions which is of any practical engineering significance. The effect of thermal transients is also discussed, as well as unilateral heating or cooling of the body (asymmetric radiant fields, draught, warm and cold floors) and the influence of air pressure.

In chapter four a rational method is introduced for the assessment of thermal environments in practice. A new thermal index is derived which establishes the "Predicted Mean Vote" (PMV) on a psycho-physical scale for a large group of persons, as a function of activity, clothing and the four environmental variables (p. 114). The new index is based on a theoretical model combined with the results from experiments with approx. 1300 subjects. The mathematical expression for PMV is rather complex, so a table (table 13, p. 115) is presented from which PMV can easily be determined when the environmental variables have been measured in practice.

In addition, a diagram is established to predict the number of "thermally dissatisfied" if the PMV is known (fig. 27, p. 131). The "Predicted Percentage of Dissatisfied" (PPD) of a large group of persons is an indication of the number who will be inclined to complain about the environment ("potential complainers"). PPD is therefore suggested as a meaningful "figure of merit" for rating the thermal quality of a given indoor environment.

The more non-uniform a thermal field in an enclosure, the greater the number of dissatisfied occupants. If measurements of the environmental variables are known for a large number of positions in a given space, it is possible to calculate the "Lowest Possible Percentage of Dissatisfied" (LPPD) which can be attained in the particular enclosure by adjusting the temperature level. LPPD is an expression for the non-uniformity of the thermal field, and it is suggested that it be used as a "figure of merit" to characterize the heating or air conditioning system and the overall architectural design of a particular space in practice.

Finally, this chapter contains a practical procedure for evaluating a given environment according to the new method (p. 135), as well as a short summary of suggested available methods for measuring the environmental variables.

As an important introduction to the theoretical thermal environmental analysis of an enclosure based on comfort criteria, chapter five discusses the calculation of the mean radiant temperature. Formulae are given for both longwave and shortwave radiation, and a rational method is introduced for the calculation of high-intensity radiant heating systems (p. 152).

The accurate calculation of mean radiant temperature and radiant heat exchange between man and his environment presupposes a detailed knowledge of man's radiant geometrical data, which so far have not been sufficiently examined. Chapter six describes comprehensive experiments which were designed to provide accurate engineering data. These experiments, involved 10 male and 10 female subjects, nude and clothed in a standard uniform, seated and standing, and the following geometrical radiation data were determined.

(a) The effective radiation area factor (that fraction of the body surface which is radiatively effective) was found to be 0.696 for seated persons and 0.725 for standing persons (table 19, p. 170). No influence of the body size or sex was observed (fig. 36–37, p. 168–169).

(b) The projected area factor (the area of the body projected on to a plane perpendicular to a given direction, in proportion to the total effective radiation area of the body) is shown in figs. 38–41, p. 171–174. No practical difference was observed in the results between nude and clothed subjects or between males and females (figs. 38 and 40, p. 171–173).

(c) The angle factor between the human body and any horizontal or vertical rectangle is shown in figs. 42–47, p. 176–181 for seated persons and in figs. 51–53, p. 188–190 for standing persons. When the orientation of the person in the space is unknown, figs. 49–50, p. 185–186 for seated persons and figs. 55–56, p. 193–194 for standing persons are suggested for practical approximation.

Chapter seven describes a general method for performing a detailed theoretical thermal environmental analysis of a controlled space, based on the comfort criteria. Man and his environment are considered as a whole, and the analysis is performed for the total system, thermal comfort being the objective. The comfort equation and heat balance equations for room surfaces and air are then solved simultaneously, and all desired temperatures and heat flows can be determined for practical environments.

NOMENCLATURE

a	Length
	Conductance of air space in wall
	Lower comfort limit for t_s
A_{Du}	DuBois area: body surface area of the human body
A_{eff}	Effective radiation area of the human body
A_p	Projected area of the human body
b	Length
	Upper comfort limit for t_s
B	Radiosity
c	Length
	Lower comfort limit for E_{sw}
c_p	Specific heat of air at constant pressure
cph	Cycles per hour
C	Heat loss by convection from the outer surface of the clothed body
C_i	Overall wall conductance from inside surface to outside air
d	Diameter
	Upper comfort limit for E_{sw}
E_d	Heat loss by water vapour diffusion through the skin
E_{re}	Latent respiration heat loss
E_{sw}	Heat loss by evaporation of sweat
f_{cl}	Ratio of the surface area of the clothed body to the surface area of the nude body (clothing area factor)
f_{eff}	Ratio of the effective radiation area of the human body to the total surface area of the body
f_p	Projected area factor
F	Angle factor
G_v	Air flow (supply air)
G_o	Air flow (infiltration air)
Gr	Grashof number
h_c	Convective heat transfer coefficient

H	Body height
	Incident radiant flux
	Internal heat production of the body
I_{cl}	Thermal resistance from skin to outer surface of the clothed body (clo)
k	Thermal conductivity
K	Dry heat transfer from the skin to outer surface of the clothed body
L	Characteristic length
	Dry respiration heat loss
	Thermal load
LPPD	Lowest Possible Percentage of Dissatisfied
m	Permeance coefficient
M	Metabolic rate
Nu	Nusselt number
p_a	Partial pressure of water vapour in ambient air
p_s	Saturated water vapour pressure at skin temperature
P	Barometric pressure
PI	Ponderal Index
PMV	Predicted Mean Vote
PPD	Predicted Percentage of Dissatisfied
Pr	Prandtl number
q	Heat flow rate per unit area
rh	Relative humidity
r_m	Radius
R	Heat loss by radiation from outer surface of the clothed body
R_{cl}	Thermal resistance from skin to outer surface of the clothed body
t_a	Air temperature
t_{cl}	Mean temperature of outer surface of clothed body
t_i	Internal body temperature
t_{mrt}	Mean radiant temperature
T_{mrt}	Mean radiant temperature (absolute)
T_{umrt}	Mean radiant temperature of unirradiated person (absolute)
t_o	Outdoor Air Temperature
t_s	Mean skin temperature
t_v	Supply Air Temperature
U	Overall coefficient of heat transmission
v	Relative air velocity
$\dot{V}$	Pulmonary ventilation
W	Body weight
	External mechanical power performed by the body
W_a	Humidity ratio of the inspiration air

W_{ex}	Humidity ratio of the expiration air
Y	Thermal vote
α	Azimuth
α_{ir}	Absorptance
β	Altitude
ε	Emittance
λ	Heat of vaporization
η	External mechanical efficiency of the body
ρ	Reflectance
σ	Stefan-Boltzmann constant

REFERENCES

1. AAGARD, R. L.: Convection-free instrument for measuring infrared radiation in the atmosphere. Rev. of Sci. Instruments, 29: 1011–1016, 1958.
2. ALLESCH, VON, G. J.: Die Aesthetische Erscheinungsweise der Farbe. Psychol. Forsch. 6: 1–91 and 6: 215–281, 1925.
3. AMBLER, H. R.: Notes on the climate of Nigeria with reference to personnel. Journ. of Tropical Medicine and Hygiene, 58: 99–112, 1955.
4. American Society of Heating, Refrigerating and Air-Conditioning Engineers: Thermal comfort conditions. ASHRAE Standard 55–66, New York, 1966.
5. American Society of Heating, Refrigerating and Air-Conditioning Engineers: Handbook of fundamentals. New York, 1967.
6. ANDERSEN, IB, and LUNDQUIST, G. R.: Indendørsklima i skoler (Indoor climate in schools). SBI-rapport 57, København, 1966.
7. ANDERSEN, J. J., and OLESEN, S.: MS-Thesis. Technical University of Denmark, 1968.
8. ANGUS, T. C., and BROWN, J. R.: Thermal comfort in the lecture room. JIHVE, 25: 175–182, 1957.
9. ANGUS, T. C.: The Control of Indoor Climate, Int. Series of Monographs in Heating, Ventilation and Refrigeration, Vol. 4, Pergamon Press, Oxford, 1968.
10. ASMUSSEN, E., and NIELSEN, M.: Studies on the regulation of respiration in heavy work. Acta Physiol. Scand. 12: 171–188, 1946.
11. ATWATER, W. O., and BENEDICT, F. G.: An experimental inquiry regarding the nutritive value of alcohol. Memoirs of the National Acad. of Sc. 8, 6: 231–237, Washington, 1902.
12. BALLANTYNE, E. R.; BARNED, J. R., and SPENCER, J. W.: Environment assessment of acclimatized caucasian subjects at Port Moresby, Papua. Proceedings of the Third Australian Building Research Congress, 1967.
13. BANDOW, FRITZ, und BOHNENKAMP, HELMUTH: Über die Bestimmung der Strahlungsfläche des Menschen aus seiner elektrischen Kapazität. Pflüger's Archiv für die gesamte Physiologie, 236: 427, 1935.
14. BARBER, NOEL: The Black Hole of Calcutta. Collins, London, 1965.
15. BECHER, P.: Om beregning af indblæsningsåbninger. (Calculation of jets and inlets in ventilation). Gjellerup, København, 1949.
16. BEDFORD, T., and WARNER, B.: The influence of radiant heat and air movement on the cooling of the kata-thermometer. J. Hyg. Camb. 33: 330, 1933.
17. BEDFORD, T., and WARNER, C. G.: The globe thermometer in studies of heating and ventilation. J. Hyg. Camb. 34: 458, 1934.
18. BEDFORD, T.: The effective radiating surface of the human body. J. Hyg. Camb. 35: 303–306, 1935.
19. BEDFORD, T.: Skin temperature in relation to the warmth of the environment. J. of Hygiene, 35: 307–317, 1935.
20. BEDFORD, T., and WARNER, C. G.: The globe thermometer in studies of heating and ventilating. J. of Hygiene, 35: 458, 1935.

21. BEDFORD, T.: The warmth factor in comfort at work. Rep. industr. Hlth. Res. Bd., No. 76, London, 1936.
22. BEDFORD, T.: Basic principles of ventilation and heating. H. K. Lewis & Co., Ltd., London, 1964.
23. BELDING, H. S., and HATCH, T. F.: Index for evaluating heat stress in terms of resulting physiological strains. Heat. Pip. and Air Cond. 27, II:129, 1955.
24. BELDING, H. S., and HATCH, T. F.: Index for evaluating heat stress in terms of resulting physiological strains. ASHAE Trans. 62: 213, 1956.
25. BENZINGER, T., and KITZINGER, C.: A 4π-radiometer. Rev. of Sci. Instruments, 21: 599–604, 1950.
26. BENZINGER, T. H.: Peripheral cold and central warm-reception, main origins of human thermal discomfort. Proc. of Nat. Academy of Science, Washington, 49: 832–839, 1963.
27. BERRY, PAUL C.: Effect of colored illumination upon perceived temperature. Journ. of Applied Psychology, 45: 248–250, 1961.
28. BIDLOT, R., and LEDENT, P.: Inst. d'Hygiène des Mines, Hasselt. Communication nr. 28, 1947.
29. BILLINGTON, N. S.: The warmth of floors – a physical study. J. Hygiene, 46: 445, 1948.
30. BILLINGTON, N. S.: Building Physics: Heat. Pergamon, 1967.
31. BISGAARD, N. F.: Om udførelse af resultanttermometre og indledende målinger med disse (Construction and measurements with resultant thermometers). Meddelelse fra Laboratoriet for Opvarminng og Ventilation, nr. 2, Gad, København, 1945.
32. BISGAARD, N. F.: Retningsbestemte termiske felter (Directional thermal fields). Meddelelse fra Laboratoriet for Opvarmning og Ventilation, nr. 16, Gad, København, 1952.
33. BLACK, FLORA A.: Desirable temperatures in offices. A study of occupant reaction to the heating provided. Inst. Heat. Vent. Engr. J. 22: 319–328, 1954–55.
34. BLACK, FLORA A., and MILROY, ELISABETH A.: Experience of air-conditioning in offices. JIHVE, 34: 188–196, 1966.
35. BOHNENKAMP, H., and PASQUAY, W.: Untersuchungen zu den Grundlagen des Energie- und Stoffwechsels. Pflüger's Archiv für die gesamte Physiologie, 228: 79, 1931.
36. BOOTHBY, W. M., and SANDIFORD, J.: Normal values of basal and standard metabolism. A modification of the DuBois standards. Amer. J. Physiol. 90: 290–291, 1929.
37. BORDES, H. J.: Behaaglijkheidsgevoel en behaaglijke klimaten. (Thermal sensations and comfortable climates). De Ingenieur, 72: G11, 1960.
38. BRADTKE, F., und LIESE, W.: Hilfsbuch für Raum- und aussenklimatische Messungen. Berlin, 1952.
39. BRAUN, DAVID L., and McNALL, P. E.: A radiometer for environmental applications. ASHRAE Trans. 75, part I, 1969.
40. BREBNER, D. F.; KERSLAKE, D. McK., and WADDELL, J. L.: The diffusion of water vapour through human skin. J. Physiol. 132: 225–231, 1956.
41. BRECHMANN, H. J.: Respirationsversuche nach Aufnahme von Fruchtzucker, Traubenzucker und Alcohol, sowohl während der Ruhe als auch während der Arbeit. Zt. f. Biol. 86: 447–466, 1927.
42. BROMAN, B.; DAHLBERG, G., and LICHTENSTEIN, A.: Height and weight during growth. Acta Pædiatrica, 30: 1–66, 1942.
43. BROWN, GÖSTA: Method för datamaskinberäkning av värme- och ljusstrålning i rum (A method for calculating heat and light radiation in rooms by digital computer). Svensk VVS, 34: 357–367 1963.

44. BRUCE, W.: Man and his thermal environment. Division of Building Research, Technical Paper No. 84, Ottawa, 1960.
45. BRUNCLAUS, J. H.: Messungen mit dem Globe-Thermometer. Die Messtechnik, 17: 6–9, 1941.
46. BRUUN, CARL: Undersøgelser udført i praksis vedrørende refleksvarmeanlæg (Practical studies concerning reflex heating plants). Boligopvarmningsudvalgets Meddelelse nr. 8, København, 1948.
47. BUETTNER, KONRAD J. K.: On the transfer function of human skin. University of Washington, Departments of Atmospheric Science and of Dermatology. Seattle, 1965.
48. BURTON, A. C., and EDHOLM, O. G.: Man in a cold environment. Arnold, London, 1955.
49. BØJE, OVE; NIELSEN, MARIUS, og OLESEN, JOHN: Undersøgelser over betydningen af ensidig strålingsafkøling (Studies on the effect of unilateral cooling by radiation). Boligopvarmningsudvalgets meddelelse, nr. 9, København, 1948.
50. CABANAC, MICHEL: Plaisir ou Déplaisir de la Sensation Thermique et Homeothermie. Physiology and Behaviour, 4: 359–364, 1969.
51. CADIERGUES, R.: État actuel de la technique francaise en chauffage par rayonnement des locaux non-industriels. Annales de l'Institut Technique du Bâtiment et des Travaux Publics, Equipem. technique, 28: 921, 1952.
52. CASSIE, A. B. D.: Fibres and fluids. J. Textile Inst. 53: 739, 1962.
53. CHATO, J. C., and HERTIG, B. A.: Regulation of thermal sweating in EVA space suits. Proceedings of the Symposium on Individual Cooling. Kansas State University, 1969.
54. CHATONNET, J., and CABANAC, M.: The perception of thermal comfort. Int. J. Biometeor, 9: 183–193, 1965.
55. CHESTER, THOMAS: Comfort with summer air conditioning. ASHVE Trans. 48: 107–122, 1942.
56. CHRENKO, F. A.: Heated floors and comfort. J. Inst. of Heating and Vent. Eng. 23: 385, 1956.
57. CHRENKO, F. A.: Heated ceilings and comfort. Journ. of the Inst. of Heating and Ventilating Engineers, 20: 375–396, and 21: 145–154, 1953.
58. CHRENKO, F. A.: The assessment of subjective reactions in heating and ventilation research. Journ. of Institution of Heat. and Vent. Eng. 23: 281–300, 1955.
59. CHURCHMAN, A. T.: An approach to environmental research. JIHVE, 37: 184–190, 1969.
60. COLIN, JEAN, and HOUDAS, YVON: Experimental determination of coefficient of heat exchanges by convection of human body. J. Appl. Physiol. 22: 31–38, 1967.
61. DATTA, S. R., and RAMANATHAN, N. L.: Energy expenditure in work predicted from heart rate and pulmonary ventilation. Journ. of Applied Physiology, 26: 297–302, 1969.
62. DAVID, H. G., and MACPHERSON, R. K.: The buffering action of hygroscopic clothing. Textile Res. J. 34: 814, 1964.
63. DEIGHTON, T.: Physical factors in body temperature maintenance and heat elimination. Physiol. Rev. 13: 427, 1933.
64. DISA: The low velocity anemometer. DISA Information No. 7: 32–35, Jan. 1969.
65. DOEBELIN, ERNEST, O.: Measurement Systems. McGraw-Hill, New York, 1966.
66. DORNO, C.: Die Abkühlungsgrösse in Verschiedenen Klimaten nach Dauerregistrierungen Mittels des Davoser Frigorimeters. Met. Z. 45: 401, 1928.
67. DRYSDALE, I. W.: A short study of the effects of summer conditions on human beings made during 1950. Climate and Design of Buildings. Physiological Study No. 2, Duplicated Document No. 32, Commonwealth Experimental Building Station, Sydney, 1950.

68. DUFTON, A. F.: The Eupatheostat. J. Sci. Instr. 6: 249, 1929.
69. DUFTON, A. F.: The equivalent temperature of a room and its measurement. Dept. of Sci. and Industrial Research. Building Research Technical Paper No. 13, London, 1932.
70. DUFTON, A. F.: The use of kata-thermometers for the measurement of equivalent temperature. J. Hyg. Camb. 33: 349, 1933.
71. DUKES-DOBOS, FRANCIS N.; HENSCHEL, AUSTIN; HUMPHREYS, CLARK; KRONOVETER, KENNETH J.; BENNER, MARSHALL, and CARLSON, WALTER S.: Industrial Heat Stress – Southern Phase. U.S. Department of Health, Education and Welfare. Public Health Service, Division of Occupational Health. Cincinnati, RR-5, 1966.
72. DUNKLE, R. V.: Configuration factors for radiant heat transfer calculations involving people. Journ. of Heat Transfer, 83: 71–76, 1963.
73. EICHNA, L. W.; PARK, C. R.; NELSON, N; HORVATH, S. M., and PALMES, E. D.: Thermal regulation during acclimatization in a hot, dry (desert type) environment. Amer. J. Physiol. 163: 585–597, 1950.
74. ELLIS, F. P.: Thermal comfort in warm, humid atmospheres. Observations in a warship in the tropics. J. Hyg. 50: 415, 1952.
75. ELLIS, F. P.: Thermal comfort in warm and humid atmospheres. Observations on groups and individuals in Singapore. J. Hyg. 51: 386, 1953.
76. FAHNESTOCK, M. K.; BOYS, FLOYD E.; SARGENT II, FREDERICK, and SPRINGER, WAYNE E.: Comfort and physiological responses to work in an environment of 75 F and 45 per cent relative humidity. ASHRAE Trans. 69: 13–23, 1963.
77. FAHNESTOCK, M. K.; BOYS, FLOYD E.; SARGENT II, FREDERICK, and SILER, L. D.: Energy costs, comfort, and physiological responses to physical work in 95 F – 50% rh and 75 F – 45% environments. ASHRAE Trans. 73, part 1, 1967.
78. FANGER, P. O.: Termiske luftstrømninger langs vinduer og kolde vægge (Free convection air currents along windows and cold walls). Ingeniøren, 73: 580–584, 1964.
79. FANGER, P. O.: Calculation of thermal comfort: Introduction of a basic comfort equation. ASHRAE Trans. 73, II, 1967.
80. FANGER, P. O.; MCNALL, P. E., and NEVINS, R. G.: Predicted and measured heat losses and thermal comfort conditions for human beings. Symp. on Thermal Problems in Biotechnology, ASME, 1968.
81. FANGER, P. O.: Conditions for thermal comfort. Introduction of a general comfort equation. In J. D. HARDY: Physiological and Behavioral Temperature Regulation. Charles C. Thomas, Illinois, 1970.
82. FINNEY, D. J.: Probit Analysis. The University Press, Cambridge, 1947.
83. FLEISCH, A.: Le métabolisme basal standard et sa détermination au moyen du "Metabocalculator". Helvet. med. acta, 18: 23–44, 1951.
84. FRANK, WALTHER: Fusswärmeuntersuchungen am bekleideten Fuss. Ges. Ing. 80: 193–201, 1959.
85. FRANK, WALTHER: Die Wärmeabgabe des bekleideten und unbekleideten Fusses. Ges. Ing. 81: 333–336, 1960.
86. FRANK, WALTHER: Die Erfassung des Raumklimas mit Hilfe richtungsempfindlicher Frigorimeter. Gesundheits-Ingenieur, 89: 301–308, 1968.
87. FRANKENHÄUSER, F.: Die klimatischen Faktoren in ärztlicher Betrachtung. Medizinische Klinik, 22: 855–857, 1911.
88. GAGGE, A. P.; HERRINGTON, L. P., and WINSLOW, C.-E. A.: Thermal interchanges between the human body and its atmospheric environment. Amer. J. of Hyg., 26: 84–102, 1937.
89. GAGGE, A. P.: A new physiological variable associated with sensible and insensible perspiration. Am. J. Physiol. 120: 277–287, 1937.

90. GAGGE, A. P.; WINSLOW, C.-E. A., and HERRINGTON, L. P.: The influence of clothing on physiological reactions of the human body to varying environmental temperatures. Amer. J. Physiol. 124: 30–50, 1938.

91. GAGGE, A. P.: Standard operative temperature, generalized temperature scale applicable to direct and partitional calorimetry. Amer. J. Physiol. 131: 93, 1940.

92. GAGGE, A. P.; BURTON, A. C., and BAZETT, H. C.: A practical system of units for the description of the heat exchange of man with his environment. Science, 94: 428–430, 1941.

93. GAGGE, A. P.; RAPP, G. M., and HARDY, J. D.: Mean radiant and operative temperature for high temperature sources of radiant heat. ASHRAE Trans. 70: 419–424, 1964.

94. GAGGE, A. P.; STOLWIJK, J. A. J., and HARDY, J. D.: A novel approach to measurement of man's heat exchange with a complex radiant environment. Aerospace Med. 36: 431–435, 1965.

95. GAGGE, A. P.; HARDY, J. D., and RAPP, G. M.: Exploratory study of comfort for high temperature sources of radiant heat. ASHRAE Trans. 71, II: 19–26, 1965.

96. GAGGE, A. P.; STOLWIJK, J. A. J., and HARDY, J. D.: Comfort and thermal sensations and associated physiological responses at various ambient temperatures. Environmental Research, 1: 1–20, 1967.

97. GAGGE, A. P.; RAPP, G. M., and HARDY, J. D.: The effective radiant field and operative temperature necessary for comfort with radiant heating. ASHRAE Journ. 9: 63–66, 1967.

98. GAGGE, A. P.; RAPP, G. M., and HARDY, J. D.: The effective radiant field and operative temperature necessary for comfort with radiant heating. ASHRAE Trans. 73, part I: I, 2, 1, 1967.

99. GAGGE, A. P.; GRAICHEN, H.; STOLWIJK, J. A. J.; RAPP, G. M., and HARDY, J. D.: ASHRAE-sponsored research project RP-41 produces R-meter. ASHRAE Journ. p. 77–81, June, 1968.

100. GAGGE, A. P.; STOLWIJK, J. A. J., and NISHI, Y.: The prediction of thermal comfort when thermal equilibrium is maintained by sweating. ASHRAE Trans. 75, part 2, 1969.

101. GAGGE, A. P.; STOLWIJK, J. A. J., and SALTIN, B.: Comfort and thermal sensations and associated physiological responses during exercise at various ambient temperatures. Environmental Research, 3: 209–229, 1969.

102. GAGGE, A. P.: The effective radiant flux. An independent variable that describes the physical effect of thermal radiation on man. In J. D. Hardy: Physiological and behavioral temperature regulation, Charles C. Thomas, Illinois, 1970.

103. GARLIND, T.; GOLDBERG, L.; GRAF, K.; PERMAN, E. S.; STRANDELL, T., and STRØM, G.: Effect of ethanol on circulatory, metabolic and neurohormonal function during muscular work in men. Acta Pharmacol. et Toxicol. 17: 106–114, 1960.

104. GEBHART, BENJAMIN: Heat Transfer, McGraw-Hill, New York, 1961.

105. GIVONI, B.: The influence of work and environmental conditions on the physiological responses and thermal equilibrium of man. Proceedings of a UNESCO Symposium on Arid Zone Physiology and Psychology. Lucknow, India, 1962.

106. GIVONI, B.: Estimation of the effect of climate on man: Development of a new thermal index. Research report to UNESCO, Building Research Station, Technion, Haifa, 1963.

107. GIVONI, B.: Man, Climate and Architecture. Elsevier, Amsterdam, 1969.

108. GLICKMAN, NATHANIEL; INOUYE, TOHRU; TELSER, STANLEY E.; KEETON, ROBERT W.; HICK, FORD K., and FAHNESTOCK, MAURICE K.: Physiological adjustments of human beings to sudden change in environment. ASHVE Trans. 53: 327–356, 1947.

109. GLICKMAN, N.; INOUYE, TOHRU; KEETON, R. W.; CALLEN, I. W.; HICK, F. K., and FAHNESTOCK, M. K.: Physiological adjustment of normal subjects and cardiac patients to sudden changes in environment. ASHVE Trans. 55: 27, 1949.
110. GOROMOSOV, M. S.: Mikroklimat zilisc i ego gigieniceskoe izucenie (the microclimate of dwellings and its hygienic study). Gig. i Sanit. Nr. 8: 3–11, 1951.
111. GOROMOSOV, M. S.: The physiological basis of health standards for dwellings. Public Health Papers No. 33. World Health Organization, Geneva, 1968.
112. GRAMBERG, A.: Technische Messungen. Springer, Berlin, 1956.
113. GRANDJEAN, E.: Die physiologische Gestaltung des Raumklimas. VDI-Berichte, nr. 106, 1966.
114. GROCOTT, J. F. L.: Comfort cooling in the tropics. Journal of the Institution of Heating and Ventilating Engineers, 16: 36, 1948.
115. GUBAREFF, C. G.; JANSSEN, J. E., and TORBORG, R. H.: Thermal Radiation Properties Survey, 2. edition, Honeywell, Minneapolis, 1960.
116. GUIBERT, ARMAND, and TAYLOR, CRAIG L.: Radiation area of the human body. J. Appl. Physiol. 5: 24–37, 1952.
117. GUNST, E. VAN; ERKELEŃS, P. J., and COERDERS, W. P. J.: Some results of investigations regarding the supply of cooled air in a test room. 4e Congrès International du Chauffage et de la Climatisation, Paris, 1967.
118. HAGENAU, DIETER: Raumtemperaturregelung und Behaglichkeit. Heizung, Lüftung und Haustechnik, 21: 157–160, 1970.
119. HALE, FRANK C.; WESTLAND, RONALD A., and TAYLOR, CRAIG L.: Barometric and vapour pressure influence on insensible weight loss. J. Appl. Physiol. 12(1): 20–28, 1958.
120. HALL, J. F., and KLEMM, F. K.: Thermoregulatory responses in disparate thermal environments. J. Appl. Physiol. 23: 540–544, 1967.
121. HAMILTON, D. C., and MORGAN, W. R.: Radiant interchange configuration factors. NACA TN 2836, 1952.
122. HARDY, J. D., and MUSCHENHEIM, C.: The radiation of heat from the human body, IV. The emission, reflection and transmission of infra red radiation by the human skin. J. Clin. Invest. 13: 817, 1934.
123. HARDY, J. D., and DUBOIS, E. F.: Basal metabolism, radiation, convection and vaporization at temperatures of 22 to 35°C. J. Nutrition, 15: 477, 1938.
124. HARDY, J. D.: Control of heat loss and heat production in physiologic temperature regulation. The Harvey Lectures, 49: 242–270, 1953–54.
125. HARDY, J. D.; HAMMEL, H. T., and MURGATROYD, D.: Spectral transmittance and reflectance of excised human skin. J. Appl. Physiol. 9: 257–264, 1956.
126. HARDY, J. D.: Physiological effects of high intensity infrared heating. ASHRAE Journ. 4: 36, Nov. 1962.
127. HARDY, J. D., and STOLWIJK, J. A. J.: Partitional calorimetric studies of man during exposures to thermal transients. J. Appl. Physiol. 21: 1799–1806, 1966.
128. HARDY, J. D.: Dependence of thermal comfort on skin temperature. Physiological and behavioral temperature regulation. Charles Thomas, Illinois, 1970.
129. HARNETT, J. P.; ECKERT, E. R. G., and BIRKEBAK, R.: The emissivity and absorptivity of parachute fabrics. ASME Trans. J. Heat Transfer, Series C, 81: 195–201, 1959.
130. HEIDTKAMP, G.: Messgerät für Wärmestrahlung aus einem Raumwinkel von 180°. Ges. Ing. 74: 129–133, 1957.
131. HELLON, R. F., and CROCKFORD, G. W.: Improvements to the globe thermometer. J. Appl. Physiol. 14: 649, 1959.
132. HERRINGTON, L. P.: Basic procedure in the calculation of the heat exchange of the clothed human body. Yale Jour. Biol. and Med. 19: March, 1947.

133. HERZFELD, CHARLES M.: Temperature, its measurement and control in science and industry. Reinhold, New York, 1962–63.

134. HEY, E. N.: Small globe thermometers. Journ. of Scientific Instruments (Journ. of Physics E), Series 2, 1: 955–957, 1968.

135. HICK, F. K.; INOUYE, TOHRU; KEETON, R. W.; GLICKMANN, NATHANIEL, and FAHNESTOCK, M. K.: Physiological adjustments of clothed human beings to sudden change in environment – first hot moist and later comfortable conditions. ASHVE Trans. 58: 189–198, 1952.

136. HICKISH, D. E.: Thermal sensations of workers in light industry in summer. A field study in southern England. The Journal of Hygiene, 53: 112–123, 1955.

137. HILL, L.; VERNON, H. M., and HARGOOD, D.: The kata-thermometer as a measure of ventilation. Proc. Roy. Soc. Series B, 93: 198, 1922.

138. HILL, L.: The kata-thermometer in studies of body heat and efficiency. Med. Res. Counc. Spec. Rep. No. 73, 1928. H. M. S. O.

139. HINDMARSH, MARGARET E., and MACPHERSON, R. K.: Thermal comfort in Australia. The Australian Journ. of Science, 24: 335–339, 1962.

140. HOUGHTEN, F. C.; GUTBERLET, CARL, and QUALLEY, R. W.: Summer cooling requirements of 275 workers in an air conditioned office. ASHVE Trans. 44: 337, 1938.

141. HOUGHTEN, F. C.; NEWTON, A. B.; QUALLEY, R. W., and WITKOWSKI, EDWARD: General reactions of 274 office workers to summer cooling and air conditioning. ASHVE Trans. 44: 591, 1938.

142. HOUGHTEN, F. C., and YAGLOU, C. P.: Determining lines of equal comfort. ASHVE Trans. 29: 163, 1923.

143. HOUGHTEN, F. C., and YAGLOU, C. P.: Determination of the comfort zone. ASHVE Trans. 29: 361, 1923.

144. HOUGHTEN, F. C., and YAGLOU, C. P.: Cooling effect on human beings produced by various air velocities. ASHVE Trans. 30: 193–212, 1924.

145. HOUGHTEN, F. C.; GIESECKE, F. E.; TASKER, C., and GUTBERLET, CARL: Cooling requirements for summer comfort air conditioning. ASHVE Trans. 43: 145–185, 1937.

146. HOUGHTEN, F. C.: Draft temperatures and velocities in relation to skin temperature and feeling of warmth. ASHVE Trans. 44: 289, 1938.

147. HOUGHTEN, F. C., and COOK, W. LEIGH: Air conditioning requirements of an operating room and recovery ward. Heating, Piping and Air Conditioning, 11: 381–387, 1939.

148. HOUGHTEN, F. C.; GUTBERLET, CARL, and ROSENBERG, A. A.: Summer cooling requirements in Washington, D.C., and other metropolitan districts. ASHVE Trans. 45: 577, 1939.

149. HOUGHTEN, F. C.; OLSON, H. T., and SUCIU, JOHN, JR.: Sensation of warmth as affected by the color of the environment. Journ. of Heating, Piping and Air Conditioning, 12: 678–681, 1940.

150. HOUGHTEN, J. T., and BREWER, A. W.: A new radiometer. Journ. Sci. Instr. 31: 184–187, 1954.

151. HOUSSAY, BERNARDO A.: Human Physiology. McGraw-Hill, New York, 1955.

152. HUMPHREYS, CLARK M.; HENSCHEL, AUSTIN, and LEE, DOUGLAS H. K.: Sensible and latent heat losses from occupants of survival shelters. U.S. Department of Health, Education and Welfare. Public Health Service, Division of Occupational Health. Cincinnati, TR-29, 1965.

153. IBAMOTO, KANI-ICHIRO, and NISHI, YASUNOBU: Thermal sensation analysis and its application to air-conditioning. Bulletin of the Faculty of Engineering, Hokkaido University, No. 46, 1968.

154. INOUYE, TOHRU; HICK, F. K.; KEETON, R. W.; LOSCH, J., and GLICKMANN, NA- THANIEL: A comparison of physiological adjustment of clothed women and men to sudden changes in environment. ASHVE Trans. 59: 35–48, 1953.

155. INOUYE, TOHRU; HICK, F. K.; TELSER, S. E., and KEETON, R. W.: Effect of relative humidity on heat loss of men exposed to environments of 80, 76 and 72 F. ASHVE Trans. 59: 329–346, 1953.

156. INOUYE, TOHRU; HICK, F. K.; KEETON, R. W., and BERNSTEIN, LIONEL: Physiolog- ical responses to sudden changes in atmospheric environment. ASHVE Trans. 60: 315–328, 1954.

157. IONIDES, MARGARET; PLUMMER, J., and SIPLE, P. A.: Office of the quartermaster general (U.S.). Report from Climatology and Environmental Protection Section. Sept. 17, 1945.

158. JENNINGS, B. H., and GIVONI, BARUCH: Environment reactions in the 80 to 105 F zone. ASHRAE Trans. 65: 115–136, 1959.

159. JOKL, MILOSLAV: Zulässige Verringerung und Erhöhung der optimalen resultieren- den Temperatur des Kugelthermometers im Bereich der Füsse – in Höhe der Fussknöchel. Ges.-Ing. 90: 327–329, 1969.

160. KANDROR, I. S.: Maintenance of the energy balance of the body as the basis of the process of adaption. In: Experimental investigation of the regulation of physiological functions. Moscow, vol. 5: 73, 1961.

161. KELLOG, R. H.: Critical factors in minimal air cooling of living quarters. Project X-205. Naval Medical Research Institute, Bethesda, Washington, 1946.

162. KLAUER, H., und SCHMIEDER, F.: Messung der Wärmehaltung von Textilien. Meil- liand Textilber. 44: 33, 1963.

163. KOCH, W.; JENNINGS, B. H., and HUMPHREYS, C. M.: Environmental study II – sensation responses to temperature and humidity under still air conditions in the comfort range. ASHRAE Trans. 66: 264, 1960.

164. KOESTEL, ALFRED; HERMANN, PHILIP, and TUVE, G. L.: Comparative study of ven- tilation jets from various types of outlets. ASHVE Trans. 56: 459, 1950.

165. KOESTEL, ALFRED, and TUVE, G. L.: Performance and evaluation of room air dis- tribution systems. ASHAE Trans. 61: 533, 1955.

166. KOLLMAR, A.: Welche Deckentemperatur ist bei der Strahlungsheizung zulässig? Ges.-Ing. 75: 22–29, 1954.

167. KOLLMAR, A., and LIESE, W.: Die Strahlungsheizung. R. Oldenburg, München, 1957.

168. KOLLMAR, A.: Die wärmephysiologische Bewertung der zulässigen Kühlstärke der Luft (Katawert). Gesundheits-Ingenieur, 89: 1–4 und 33–39, 1968.

169. KOLLMAR, A.: Zur Klimatisierung von Hörsaal und Theater. Gesundheits-Ingenieur, 89: 226–232 und 334–337, 1968.

170. KOLLMAR, A.: Wärmephysiologische Abschirmung des Fensters und der Aussen- wand. Heizung, Lüftung und Haustechnik. 21: 16–19, 1970.

171. KONZ, S., and DUNCAN, J.: Cooling with a water cooled hood. Proceedings of the Symposium on Individual Cooling. Kansas State University, 1969.

172. KORSGAARD, VAGN: Undersøgelser over det termiske strålingsfelt i rum med reflek- terende vægge (Studies of the thermal radiant field in rooms with specular walls). Meddelelse XII, Lab. for Opvarmning og Ventilation, Gad, København, 1945.

173. KORSGAARD, VAGN: Necessity of using a directional mean radiant temperature to describe the thermal conditions in rooms. Heat. Pip. Air Condit. 21: 117, 1949.

174. KORSGAARD, VAGN: A new radiometer measuring directional mean radiant tem- perature. Heat Pip. Air Condit. 21: 129, 1949.

175. KORSGAARD, VAGN, og LUND MADSEN, TH.: En mannequin til bestemmelse af indendørsklimaets termiske virkninger på mennesket (A thermal manikin to study the effect of indoor climate on man). VVS, 3: 407–412, 1967.

176. KRANZ, P.: Calculating human comfort. ASHRAE Journ. 6: 68, 1964.
177. KRAUSE, B.: Ein Einfaches Globusthermometer. Gesundheits-Ingenieur, 81: 129, 1960.
178. KRAUSE, B.: Ein Richtungsempfindliches Globusthermometer. Gesundheits-Ingenieur. 81: 353, 1960.
179. KROGH, AUGUST: Måling af textilers varmeisolerende egenskaber (The heat insulating properties of textiles). Boligopvarmningsudvalgets meddelelse nr. 6, København, 1948.
180. LADELL, S. S.: Thermal comfort in temperate climates. The Practitioner, 163: 141–149, 1949.
181. LARSON, R. E.; RUST, L. W.; KYDD, A. R., and GAUVIN, G. A.: Investigations of heat and mass (water vapor and liquid) movement through clothing systems. U.S. Army, Natick Lab., Technical Report. 69-31-CM, 1968.
182. LEE, E. S.; FAN, L. T.; HWANG, C. L., and SHAIKH, M. A.: Simulation and feasibility study of a thermal comfort equation. Institute for Systems Design and Optimization, rep. nr. 3, KSU, Manhattan, Kansas, 1968.
183. LEE, E. S.; FAN, L. T.; HWANG, C. L., and SHAIKH, M. A.: Simulation and feasibility study of a thermal comfort equation. ASHRAE Journ., aug. 1968, p. 54–58.
184. LEE, D. H. K., and HENSCHEL, AUSTIN: Evaluation of thermal environment in shelters. U.S. Department of Health, Education, and Welfare, Public Health Service, Division of Occupational Health, Cincinnati, TR-8, 1963.
185. LEHMANN, G.: Praktische Arbeitsphysiologie. Thieme, Stuttgart, 1953.
186. LEITHEAD, C. S., and LIND, A. R.: Heat stress and heat disorders. Cassell, London, 1964.
187. LIDDELL, F. D. K.: Estimation of energy expenditure from expired air. J. Appl. Physiol. 18, I: 25–29, 1963.
188. LIDWELL, O. M., and WYON, D. P.: A rapid response radiometer for the estimation of mean radiant temperature in environmental studies. Journ. of Scientific Instruments. Series 2, 1: 534–538, 1968.
189. LIESE, WALTHER: Behaglichkeit – hygienische Bedeutung und klimatechnisches Normativ, Ges. Ing. 91: 94–100, 1970.
190. LIND, A. R.; HELLON, R. F.; JONES, R. M., WEINER, and FRASER, D. C.: Reactions of Mines-rescue personnel to work in hot environments. Med. Res. Bull. No. 1. London, 1957.
191. LIND, A. R., and BASS, D. E.: The optimal exposure time for the development of acclimatization to heat. Fed. Proc. 22: 704, 1963.
192. LINKE, W.: Die Luftführung in Versammlungsräumen mit festem Gestühl. VDI-Berichte Nr. 106: 37–49, 1966.
193. LUEDER, HOLGER: Gegenwärtiger Entwicklungsstand der Raum- und Bauklimatik. Schw. Bl. Heizung + Lüftung, 34: 67–78, 1967.
194. LUSTINEC, K.: Hodnoceni pracovne klimaticke zateze (The evaluation of the work and heat load). Dissertation, Charles University, Hygienic Faculty, Prague, 1965.
195. LUSTINEC, K.: The working microclimate and its classification. 15th Int. Congress on Occupational Health, IV: 549, 1966.
196. LUSTINEC, K.: The working microclimate and its evaluation. Informational News from the Branch of Industrial Hygiene and Occupational Diseases and Radiation Hygiene. Suppl. 2, 13. Inst. of Ind. Hyg. Occup. Dis., Prague, 1967.
197. LÖFSTEDT, B. E.: Human heat tolerance. University of Lund, Diss., 1966.
198. LÖFSTEDT, B. E.: Methods for measuring and expressing the permeability of clothing materials for wind, heat and humidity. Biometeorology 2. Pergamon Press, Oxford, 1966.
199. MACKWORTH, N. H.: Researches on the measurement of human performance. Med. Res. Counc. Spec. Rep. No. 268, London, 1950, H. M. S. O.

233

200. MACPHERSON, R. K.: Physiological responses to hot environments. Med. Res. Counc. Spec. Rep. Ser. No. 298. London, 1960, H. M. S. O.

201. MAES, C. M.: A computer program for calculating environmental thermal comfort. The Boeing Company, Clearinghouse. AD 693321. U.S. Department of Commerce, Springfield, Virginia, 1969.

202. MCARDLE, B.; DUNHAM, W.; HOLLING, H. E.; LADELL, W. S. S.; SCOTT, J. W.; THOMSON, M. L., and WEINER, J. S.: The prediction of the physiological effects of warm and hot environments. Med. Res. Counc. Rep. No. 47-391, 1947, H. M. S. O.

203. MCCONNELL, W. J., and SPIEGELMAN, M.: Reactions of 745 clerks to summer air conditioning. Heat., Pip. and Air Condit. 12: 318-322, 1940.

204. MCCUTCHAN, J. W., and TAYLOR, C. L.: Respiratory heat exchange with varying temperatures and humidity of inspired air. J. Appl. Physiol. 4: 121-135, 1951.

205. MCNALL JR., P. E., and SCHLEGEL, J. C.: The relative effects of convection and radiation heat transfer on thermal comfort (thermal neutrality) for sedentary and active human subjects. ASHRAE Trans. Vol. 74, part II: 131-143, 1968.

206. MCNALL JR., P. E.; JAAX, J.; ROHLES, F. H.; NEVINS, R. G., and SPRINGER, W.: Thermal comfort (thermally neutral) conditions for three levels of activity. ASHRAE Trans. 73, I, 1967.

207. MCNALL, P. E.; RYAN, P., and JAAX, J.: Seasonal variation in comfort conditions for college-age persons in the middle west. ASHRAE Trans. 74, I, 1968.

208. MCNALL, P. E.; RYAN, P. W.; ROHLES, F. H.; NEVINS, R. G., and SPRINGER, W. E.: Metabolic rates at four activity levels and their relationship to thermal comfort. ASHRAE Trans. 74, part I: IV. 3. 1., 1968.

209. MCNALL JR., P. E., and BIDDISON, R. E.: Thermal and comfort sensations of sedentary persons exposed to asymmetric radiant fields. ASHRAE Trans. 76, part 1, 1970.

210. MEREDITH, R., and HEARLE, J. W. S.: Physical methods of investigating textiles. Textile Book Publisher Inc., New York, 1959, p. 285.

211. MIDGLEY, REES A., and JAFFE, ROBERT B.: Human luteinizing hormone in serum during the menstrual cycle: Determination by radioimmunoassay. Journ. of Clinical Endocrinology. 26: 1375-1381, 1966.

212. MILLER, P. L., and NEVINS, R. G.: Room air distribution with an air distributing ceiling – Part II. ASHRAE Trans. 75, part 1, 1969.

213. MILLER, P. L., and NEVINS, R. G.: Room air distribution performance of ventilating ceilings and cone-type circular ceiling diffusers. ASHRAE Trans. 76, part 1, 1970.

214. MILLS, CLARENCE A.: Reflective radiant conditioning can provide more comfort at less cost. Refrigerating engineering, 63: 48-51, 1955.

215. MIN, T. C.; SCHUTRUM, L. F.; PARMELEE, G. V., and VOURIS, J. D.: Natural convection and radiation in a panel-heated room. ASHAE Trans. 62: 337-358, 1956.

216. MISSENARD, A.: Théorie Simplifié du Thermometre Résultant. Chauffage et Ventilation, 12: 347, 1935.

217. MISSENARD, A.: Chauffage par rayonnement Température limite du sol. Chaleur et Industrie, 155: 37, 1955.

218. MISSENARD, A.: Mise au point sur les exchanges thermiques entre le corp humain et l'ambiance; coefficient de charge thermique dans les ambiances chaudes. Ind. Thermiques. 3: 735-752, 1957.

219. MISSENARD, F. ANDRÉ: Le Chauffage et le Rafraichissement par Rayonnement. Eyrolles, Paris, 1959.

220. MITCHELL, DUNCAN: Measurement of the thermal emissivity of human skin in vivo. In J. D. HARDY: Physiological and behavioral temperature regulation. Charles C. Thomas, Illinois, 1970.

221. MOLL, W. J. H.: A thermopile for measuring radiation. Proc. Phys. Soc. 5: 257–260, 1923.

222. MOM, C. P.; WIESEBRON, J. A.; COURTICE, R., and KIP, C. G.: The application of the effective temperature scheme to the comfort zone in the Netherlands Indies. Chronica Natural, 103: 19, 1947.

223. MOM, C. P.; WIESEBRON, J. A.; COURTICE, R., and KIP, C. G.: The determination of the influence of air velocity on the feelings of comfort of men. Chronica Natural, 103: 147, 1947.

224. MORGENSEN, M. F., and ENGLISH, H. B.: The apparent warmth of colors. Amer. J. Psychol. 37: 427–428, 1926.

225. MOREHOUSE, L. E., and MILLER, A. T.: Physiology of Exercise, 1959.

226. MORSE, R. N., and KOWALCZEWSKI, J. J.: Rational basis for human thermal comfort. ASHRAE Journ. 9: 72, 1967.

227. MOSER, K.: Raum- und fertigungsklimatische Forderungen an lüftungstechnische Anlagen. Gesundheits-Ingenieur, 90: 104–111, 1969.

228. MUNCEY, R. W., and Hutson, J. M.: The effect of the floor on foot temperature. Austr. J. Appl. Sci. 4: 395, 1953.

229. MUNCEY, R. W.: The temperature of the foot and its thermal comfort. Austr. J. Appl. Sci. 5: 36, 1954.

230. MUNRO, A. F., and CHRENKO, F. A.: The effects of air temperature and velocity and of various flooring materials on the skin temperature of the feet. J. Hygiene, 46: 451, 1948.

231. NEVINS, R. G., and FLINNER, ARTHUR O.: Effect of heated-floor temperatures on comfort. Heating, Piping and Air Conditioning, 29: 149–153, 1957.

232. NEVINS, R. G.; MICHAELS, K. B., and FEYERHERM, A. M.: The effect of floor surface temperature on comfort. Part I, college-age males. ASHRAE Trans. 70: 29, 1964.

233. NEVINS, R. G.; MICHAELS, K. B., and FEYERHERM, A. M.: The effect of floor surface temperatures on comfort, Part II, college-age females. ASHRAE Trans. 70: 37, 1964.

234. NEVINS, R. G.; ROHLES, F. H.; SPRINGER, W., and FEYERHERM, A. M.: A temperature-humidity chart for thermal comfort of seated persons. ASHRAE Trans. 72. I: 283–291, 1966.

235. NEVINS, R. G., and FEYERHERM, A. M.: The effect of floor surface temperatures on comfort, Part IV, cold floors. ASHRAE Trans. 73, Part 2: III. 2. 1., 1967.

236. NEVINS, R. G., and WARD, E. D.: Room air distribution with an air distributing ceiling. ASHRAE Trans. 74, Part 1, 1968.

237. NEWBURGH, L. H.: Physiology of heat regulation and the science of clothing. W. B. Saunders Co., Philadelphia, 1949.

238. NEWLING, P. S. B.: The measurement of mean radiant temperature and the determination of the amount of radiant heat gained by a man. Med. Res. Counc. Spec. Rep. No. 54. London, 1954. H. M. S. O.

239. NEWTON, A. B.; HOUGHTEN, F. C.; GUTBERLET, CARL; QUALLEY, R. W., and TOMLINSON, C. W.: Shock experiences of 275 workers after entering and leaving cooled and air conditioned offices. ASHVE Trans. 44: 571–590, 1938.

240. NIELSEN, BODIL: Thermoregulation in rest and exercise. Copenhagen Univ. Diss., 1969.

241. NIELSEN, MARIUS: Undersøgelser over relationen mellem behagelighedsfornemmelser, opvarmningstilstand og fysiologiske reaktioner ved stillesiddende arbejde. (Studies on the relation between sensations of comfort, degree of heating and physiological reactions). Boligopvarmningsudvalgets meddelelse nr. 3, København, 1947.

242. NIELSEN, MARIUS: Undersøgelser over betydningen af gulvopvarmning for behage-lighedsfornemmelser og fodtemperaturer (On the importance of heating of floors for the sensation of comfort and the temperatures of the lower extremities). Boligopvarmningsudvalgets meddelelse, nr. 4, København, 1948.

243. NIELSEN, MARIUS, and PEDERSEN, LORENTS: Studies on the heat loss by radiation and convection from the clothed human body. Acta Physiol. Scand. 27: 272, 1952.

244. NIELSEN, MARIUS, og PEDERSEN, LORENTS: Menneskets varmeafgivelse ved konvek-tion og stråling (Man's heat loss by convection and radiation). Varme, 18: 1–12 og 18: 17–27, 1953.

245. NISHI, Y., and IBAMOTO, K.: Model skin temperature – an index of thermal sensa-tion in cold, warm and humid environments. ASHRAE Trans. 75, part 2, 1969.

246. NISHI, Y., and GAGGE, A. P.: Moisture permeation of clothing – a factor governing thermal equilibrium and comfort. ASHRAE Trans. 76, 1970.

247. NORBÄCK, PER: Experimentell undersökning av dragproblem vid indblåsning av ventilationsluft (Experimental investigation of draft problems). Tidsskrift för värme-, ventilations- och sanitetsteknik, 17: 100–105, 1946.

248. NOTTAGE, H. B.; SLABY, J. G., and GOJSZA, W. P.: Isothermal ventilation – Jet fundamentals. ASHVE Trans. 58: 107, 1952.

249. NOTTAGE, H. B.; SLABY, J. G., and GOJSZA, W. P.: Outlet turbulence intensity as a factor in isothermal – Jet flow. ASHVE Trans. 58–343, 1952.

250. OLINGSBERG, R.: Vad är drag? (What is draught?). Svensk VVS, 38: 135–141, 1967.

251. OUDEN, H. PH. L. DEN: The measurement of air velocities. I. G.-T. N. O. Report No. 27, Delft, 1958.

252. PARTRIDGE, RUTH C., and MacLEAN, D. L.: Determination of the comfort zone for school children. Journ. of Industrial Hygiene, 17: 66–71, 1935.

253. PASSMORE, R., and DURNIN, J. V. G. A.: Energy, work and leisure. Heinemann, London, 1967.

254. PASSMORE, R., and ROBSON, J. S.: A companion to medical studies. Vol. 1, Black-well, Oxford, 1968.

255. PEDERSEN, LORENTS: Varmeafgivelse ved stråling og konvektion fra et påklædt men-neske (Heat loss by radiation and convection from a clothed man). Boligop-varmningsudvalgets meddelelse nr. 10, København, 1948.

256. PEDERSEN, LORENTS: Varmestrålingsundersøgelser (Studies of thermal radiation). Dissertation, Københavns Universitet, 1948.

257. PEIRCE, F. T., and REES, W. H.: The transmission of heat through textile fabrics. Part II. J. Textile Inst. 37: 181, 1946.

258. PEPLER, R. D.: Performance and well-being in heat. Temperature, its measurement and control in science and industry, 3. part. 3: 319. New York, 1963.

259. PEPLER, R. D.: Psychological effects of heat. Chap. 12 in LEITHEAD, C. S., and LIND, A. R.: Heat stress and heat disorders. Cassell, London, 1964.

260. PFLEIDERER, H., and BÜTTNER: Bioklimatologie. Lehrbuch der Bäder- und Klima-heilkunde. H. Vogt, Springer. Berlin, 1940.

261. PFLEIDERER, H.: Die Bedeutung der Trifrigorigraphie für die bioklimatische For-schung. Bioklimatische Beiblätter. 10: 123–124, 1943.

262. PLUMMER, J. H.; IONIDES, MARGARET, and SIPLE, P. A.: Thermal balance of the human body and its application as an index of climate stress. Office of the Quartermaster General (U.S.). Report from Climatology and Environmental Protection Section. Aug. 20. 1945.

263. RABER, B. F., and HUTCHINSON, F. W.: Optimum surface distribution in panel heating and cooling systems. ASHVE Trans. 48: 231–265, 1944.

264. RABER, B. F., and HUTCHINSON, F. W.: Panel heating and cooling analysis. John Wiley & Sons, Inc., New York, 1947.

236

265. RAO, M. N.: Comfort range in tropical Calcutta. A preliminary experiment. Ind. J. Med. Res. 40: 45, 1952.

266. RAPP, G. M., and GAGGE, A. P.: Configuration factors and comfort design in radiant beam heating of man by high temperature infrared sources. ASHRAE Trans. 73, part 2, 1967.

267. RAPP, G. M., and GAGGE, A. P.: High intensity radiant heating. ASHRAE guide and data book: Systems. Chapter 17, 1970.

268. REES, W. H.: The transmission of heat through textile fabrics. J. Textile Inst. 32: 149, 1941.

269. REES, W. H.: The protective value of clothing. J. Textile Inst. 37: 132, 1946.

270. REES, W. H., and OGDEN, L. W.: Some observations upon the effect of colour on the absorption and emission of radiation by a textile fabric. Textile Institute Journal, 37: 113, 1946.

271. REINMAN, J. J.; KOESTEL, ALFRED, and TUVE, G. L.: Evaluation of three room air distribution systems for summer cooling. ASHRAE Trans. 65: 717, 1959.

272. RICHARDS, C. H.; STOLL, A. M., and HARDY, J. D.: The panradiometer: An absolute measuring instrument for environmental radiation. Rev. Sci. Inst. 22: 925, 1951.

273. RIEDEL, G.: Messung und Regelung des Klimazustandes durch eine die Erträglichkeit für den Menschen anzeigende Klimasonde. Forschungsberichte des Wirtschafts- und Verkehrsministeriums Nordrhein-Westfalen, no. 529. Westdeutscher Verlag, Köln, 1958.

274. ROBERTSON, I. D., and REID, D. D.: Standards for the basal metabolism of normal people in Britain. Lancet, 262: 940–943, 1952.

275. ROBINSON, S.; TURRELL, E. S., and GERKING, S. D.: Physiologically equivalent conditions of air temperature and humidity. Amer. J. Physiol. 143: 21, 1945.

276. RODWELL, E. C.; RENBOURN, E. T.; GREENLAND, J., and KENCHINGTON, K. W. L.: An investigation of the physiological value of sorption heat in clothing assemblies. J. Textile Inst. 56: 524, 1965.

277. ROEDLER, F.: Wärmephysiologische und hygienische Grundlagen. Chapt. 1 in Rietschel/Raiss: Heiz- und Klimatechnik, bd. 1. Springer, Berlin, 1968.

278. ROHLES, F. H.; NEVINS, RALPH G., and SPRINGER, WAYNE E.: The physiological effects of subject crowding during exposure to high thermal stress. Human physiological responses to shelter environment. Report No. 1. Kansas State University, 1966.

279. ROHLES, F. H.: Preference for the thermal environment by the elderly. Human factors, 11 (1): 37–41, 1969.

280. ROHLES, F. H.: Thermal sensations of sedentary man in moderate temperature. Institute for Environmental Research, Special Report. Kansas State University, 1970.

281. RONGE, E. H., and LÖFSTEDT, B. E.: Radiant drafts from cold ceilings. Heat, Pip. and Air Condit. 29: 167–174, 1957.

282. ROSS, R. T.: Studies in the psychology of the theater. Psychol. Rec. 2: 127–190, 1938.

283. ROWLEY, FRANK B.; JORDAN, RICHARD C., and SNYDER, WARREN E.: Comfort reactions of workers during occupancy of air conditioned offices. ASHVE Trans. 53: 357–368, 1947.

284. RUBINSTEIN, A.: Beregning af vinkelstrålingstal på DASK (Computerized calculation of angle factors). Ingeniøren, 71: 90, 1962.

285. RUDEIKO, V. A.: Vlijanie temperatury vozducha zilisca na termoreguljaciju u ljudei preklonnogo vozrasta (The effect of the air temperature in dwellings on the thermoregulation of aged persons). Gig. Sanit, 30 (2): 25–28, 1965.

286. RUMMEL, A. J.; GIESECKE, F. E.; BADGETT, W. H., and MOSES, A. T.: Reactions of office workers to air conditioning in South Texas. ASHVE Trans. 45: 459–475, 1939.

287. RYDBERG, J.: Dragproblem i samband med indblåsning av ventilationsluft (Draught problems related to the discharge of supply air). Svensk VVS, 17: 96–99, 1946.

288. RYDBERG, J.: Luftinblåsning och drag vid ventilationsanläggningar (Air distribution and draught by air-conditioning). Svensk VVS, 17: 143–148, 1946.

289. RYDBERG, J., and NORBÄCK, PER: Air distribution and draft. ASHVE Trans. 55: 225, 1949.

290. RYDBERG, J.: Kallras vid fönster (Cold downward convection currents at windows). Svensk VVS, 34: 411–413, 1963.

291. SCHARNOW, B.: Über den Gerätewert der Katathermometer. Ges. Ing. 73: 254–256, 1952.

292. SCHLEGEL, J. C., and MCNALL, P. E.: The effect of asymmetric radiation on the thermal and comfort sensations of sedentary subjects. ASHRAE Trans. 74, II, 1968.

293. SCHLÜTER, G.: Katathermometrie auf neuer Grundlage. Ges. Ing. 83: 321–326, 1963.

294. SCHÜLE, W.: Untersuchungen über die Hauttemperatur des Fusses stehen auf verschiedenartigen Fussböden. Gesundheits-Ingenieur, 75: 380, 1954.

295. SCHÜLE, W.: Wärmetechnische Fragen bei Fussböden und Decken unter besonderer Berücksichtigung der Fusswärme. Gesundheits-Ingenieur, 78: 289–295, 1957.

296. SCHÜLE, W., und LUTZ, H.: Messgeräte für raumklimatische Messungen. Ges. Ing. 85: 266–270, 1964.

297. SEVRYUKOVA, G. A.: Gigieniceskoe obocnovanie optimalnoj temperatury vozducha v muzikalno-gimnasticeskich zalach detskich doskolnych ucrezdenij (Hygienic substantiation of optimal air temperature in gymnasiums and musichalls of preschool institutions). Gig. i Sanit. 30, 12: 36–38, 1965.

298. SIBBONS, J. L. H.: Assessment of the thermal stress from energy balance considerations. J. Appl. Physiol. 21: 1207–1217, 1966.

299. SMITH, F. E.: Indices of heat stress. Med. Res. Conc. Mem. 29. HMSO, London, 1955.

300. SNELLEN, J. W.: The optimal climate in department stores. Brit. J. Ind. Med. 19 (3): 165–170, 1962.

301. SPARROW, E. M., and CESS, R. D.: Radiation heat transfer. Wadsworth, California, 1966.

302. SPRAGUE, C. H., and MCNALL, P. E.: The effects of fluctuating temperature and relative humidity on the thermal sensation (thermal comfort) of sedentary subjects. ASHRAE Trans. Part I, 76, 1970.

303. SPRINGER, W. E.; NEVINS, R. G.; FEYERHERM, A. M., and MICHAELS, K. B.: The effect of floor surface temperatures on comfort, part III, the elderly. ASHRAE Trans. Part 1: 292, 1966.

304. STOLL, A. M., and HARDY, J. D.: A method of measuring radiant temperatures of the environment. J. Appl. Physiol. 5: 117, 1952.

305. STOLL, A. M.: A wide-range thermistor radiometer for the measurement of skin temperature and environmental radiant temperature. (Rev. Sci. Instr. 28: 184–187, 1954.

306. STOLWIJK, J. A. J., and HARDY, J. D.: Partitional calorimetric studies of responses of man to thermal transients. J. Appl. Physiol. 21: 967–977, 1966.

307. STRAUB, H. E.; GILMAN, S. F., and KONZO, S.: Distribution of air within a room for year round air conditioning, part I. University of Illinois Engineering Experiment Station Bulletin, No. 435, 1956.

308. STRAUB, H. E., and CHEN, M. M.: Distribution of air within a room for year round air conditioning, part II. University of Illinois Engineering Experiment Station Bulletin, No. 442, 1957.
309. SUTTON, D. J., and McNALL, P. E.: A two-sphere radiometer. ASHVE Trans. 60: 297, 1954.
310. TASKER, C.: Cooling requirements for summer comfort air conditioning in Toronto. ASHVE Trans. 44: 549–558, 1938.
311. THILENIUS, R.: Die Konstruktion des Davosen Frigorimeters. Meteorologische Zeitschrift, 48: 254, 1931.
312. TREDRE, BARBARA: The physiological assessment of radiant heat in indoor environments. Dissertation, University of London, 1960.
313. TRIPP, WILSON; HWANG, CHING-LAI, and CRANK, R. E.: Radiation shape factors for plane surfaces and spheres, circles or cylinders. Kansas Engineering Experiment Station, KSU, No. 16, 1962.
314. TURNER, D.: Energy cost of some industrial operations. Brit. J. Industr. Med. 12: 237, 1955.
315. TUVE, G. L.: Air velocities in ventilating jets. ASHVE Trans. 59: 261, 1953.
316. TYGSTRUP, N.; WINKLER, K., and LUNDQUIST, F.: The mechanism of the fructose effect on the ethanol metabolism of the human liver. J. Clin. Invest. 44: 817–831, 1965.
317. TÖGEL, O.; BREZINA, E., and DURIG, A.: Über die kohlenhydratsparenden Wirkung des Alkohols. Bioch. Z. 50: 296–345, 1913.
318. ULDALL-JÖRGENSEN, SVEN: Infraröd strålning i ett rum (Infrared radiation in a room). Lund, 1966.
319. UNDERWOOD, C. R., and WARD, E. J.: The solar radiation area of man. Ergonomics, 9: 155–168, 1966.
320. VERNON, H. M.: The measurement of radiant heat in relation to human comfort. J. Physiol. 70, 15P, 1930.
321. VERNON, H. M.: The measurement of radiant heat in relation to human comfort. J. Industr. Hyg. and Toxicology, 14: 95, 1932.
322. VERNON, H. M.: The globe thermometer. Proc. Inst. of Heating and Ventilating Engineers, 39: 100, 1932.
323. VOGT, J. J., and METZ, B.: Nomogrammes de prédiction du débit fudoral requis ou de la durée-limite d'exposition en fonction des caractéristiques physiques d'une ambiance thermique. Communication au 4e Congrès de la Société d'Ergonimic de Longue Française, Marseille, 1966.
324. WEBB, C. G.: On some observations of indoor climate in Malaya. Journ. Inst. Heat Vent. Engineers, 20: 189, 1952–53.
325. WEBB, C. G.: An analysis of some observations of thermal comfort in an equatorial climate. British Journal of Industrial Medicine, 16: 297, 1959.
326. WEBB, PAUL: Bioastronautics Data Book, NASA, 1964.
327. WEEKS, W. S.: A new instrument for measuring cooling power: The coolometer. J. Industr. Hyg. 13: 261, 1931.
328. WENZEL, H.-G., und MÜLLER, E. A.: Untersuchungen der Behaglichkeit des Raumklimas bei Deckenheizung. Internat. Z. Physiol. Einschl. Arbeitsphysiol. 16: 335–355, 1957.
329. WERNER, G.: Wärme- och fukttransport genom vävnader (Heat and humidity transport through textiles). Meddelanden från Svenska Textilforskningsinstitutet, 14: 70, 1951.
330. WEXLER, ARNOLD: Humidity and moisture. Measurement and control in science and industry. Reinhold, New York, 1965.

239

331. WINSLOW, C.-E. A., and GREENBURG, L.: The thermo-integrator – a new instrument for the observation of thermal interchanges. Heat. Pip. Air-Condit. 7: 41–43, 1935.

332. WINSLOW, C.-E. A.; GAGGE, A. P.; GREENBURG, L.; MORIYAMA, I. M., and RODEE, E. J.: The calibration of the thermo-integrator. Amer. J. Hyg. 22: 137, 1935.

333. WINSLOW, C.-E. A., and GREENBURG, L.: The thermo-integrator – a new instrument for the observations of thermal interchanges. ASHVE Trans. 41: 149, 1935.

334. WINSLOW, C.-E. A.; GAGGE, A. P., and HERRINGTON, L. P.: The influence of air movement upon heat losses from the clothed human body. J. Physiol. 127: 505–518, 1939.

335. WINSLOW, C.-E. A.; HERRINGTON, L. P., and GAGGE, A. P.: Heat exchange and regulation in radiant environments above and below air temperature. Amer. J. Physiol. 131: 79, 1940.

336. WINSLOW, C.-E. A., and HERRINGTON, L. P.: Temperature and human life. Princeton University Press, Princeton, 1949.

337. WOODCOCK, A. H.: Moisture transfer in textile systems, part I. Textile Res. J. 32: 628, 1962.

338. WOODCOCK, A. H.: Moisture transfer in textile systems, part II. Textile Res. J. 32: 719, 1962.

339. WYNDHAM, C. H.: Thermal comfort in the hot humid tropics of Australia. Brit. J. Industr. Med. 20: 110, 1963.

340. WYON, D. P.; LIDWELL, O. M., and WILLIAMS, R. E. O.: Thermal comfort during surgical operations. Journ. of Hygiene, 66: 229, 1968.

341. WYON, D. P.: Physiological reactions of surgeons and operating theatre staff to their working environment. Dissertation, London University, 1968.

342. YAGLOU, C. P., and MILLER, W. E.: Effective temperature applied to industrial ventilation problems. ASHVE Trans. 30: 339–364, 1924.

343. YAGLOU, C. P., and MILLER, W. E.: Effective temperature with clothing. ASHVE Trans. 31: 89–99, 1925.

344. YAGLOU, C. P.: Temperature, humidity, and air movement in industries: The effective temperature index. Journ. of Indust. Hygiene, 9: 297–309, 1927.

345. YAGLOU, C. P., and DRINKER, PHILIP: The summer comfort zone: Climate and clothing. Journ. of Ind. Hygiene and Toxicology, 10: 350–363, 1928.

346. YAGLOU, C. P.; CARRIER, W. H.; HILL, E. V.; HOUGHTEN, F. C., and WALTER, J. H.: How to use the effective temperature index and comfort charts. ASHVE Trans. 38: 411–423, 1932.

347. YAGLOU, C. P., and MESSER, A.: The importance of clothing in air conditioning. J. Amer. med. Ass. 117: 1261, 1941.

348. YAGLOU, C. P.: A method for improving the effective temperature index. ASHVE Trans. 53: 307, 1947.

349. YAGLOU, C. P., and MINARD, D.: Control of heat casualties at military training centres. A. M. A. Arch. Industr. Health, 16: 302–316, 1957.

350. ZUILEN, D. VAN: Climatological factors in healthful housing. U. N. Publication Sales No. 1953, 8: 22–28, 1953.

351. ÅSTRAND, P. O.: The respiratory activity in man exposed to prolonged hypoxia. Acta Physiol. Scand. 30: 343–368, 1954.

INDEX

243